The New Naturalist
A SURVEY OF BRITISH NAT

NORTHUMBERLAND

The aim of this series is to interest the general reader
in the wildlife of Britain by recapturing the enquiring
spirit of the old naturalists. The editors believe that
the natural pride of the British public in the native
flora and fauna, to which must be added concern for
their conservation, is best fostered by maintaining a
high standard of accuracy combined with clarity of
exposition in presenting the results of modern
scientific research.

The New Naturalist

NORTHUMBERLAND

WITH ALSTON MOOR

Angus Lunn

With 16 colour plates and over 160 black
and white photographs and line drawings

Collins

HarperCollins*Publishers*
77–85 Fulham Palace Road
Hammersmith
London W6 8JB

Everything clicks at www.collins.co.uk

Collins is a registered trademark of HarperCollins*Publishers* Ltd.

05 07 09 10 08 06 04

2 4 6 8 10 9 7 5 3 1

First published 2004

ISBN 000 718484 0 (Hardback)
ISBN 000 718483 2 (Paperback)

Printed and bound in Thailand by Imago
Colour reproduction by Colourscan, Singapore

Contents

Editors' Preface

Northumberland is one of the most ecologically diverse of English counties, with its varied coastline of mud flats, saltings, sand dunes and cliffs; agricultural lowlands, mires, lakes, and woods of native trees; the distinctive outcrop of the Whin Sill traced by the line of the Roman Wall; and the wide and often boggy moorlands which rise along the border with Scotland into the high summit of The Cheviot. The county also has a fine tradition of natural history, with botanists William Turner, John Wallis and Nathaniel Winch, and zoologists Thomas Bewick, Prideaux John Selby, John Hancock, Abel Chapman and George Bolam as leading figures from earlier times. More recently, the literature on wildlife and physical features has blossomed, with major publications on flora, fauna, geology and geomorphology within the last 20 years. Yet, until now, with *Northumberland* added to the New Naturalist regional titles, there has been no single work that draws together information across the whole of this wide field.

Angus Lunn is eminently well placed to perform this task, from his perspective as geomorphologist and all-round natural historian, and the present volume is a tribute to his breadth of knowledge and skill in assimilating the many separate lines of information into a comprehensive whole. Geologists and soil specialists will find summaries of these subjects valuable in their own right, while students of vegetation will appreciate the drawing of connections to explain much of the basic diversity in plant communities. Climate and its influence on biological features are also examined in detail. Any modern treatment of regional natural history has to consider land use impact, and Northumberland has had its fair share of the pervasive human hand upon its once primeval surface. Newcomers to the county who had read only such earlier classics as Mack's *The Border Line* or Chapman's *The Borders and Beyond* would be perplexed to equate those descriptions of the moorland scene with what they see today. For this part of Northumberland has been extensively transformed – by the planting of vast blankets of coniferous trees. Angus Lunn deals with this dramatic change at length, looking at the balance sheet of wildlife losses and gains from re-afforestation of the uplands.

While the richness of the Northumbrian flora and fauna emerges from the accounts of the different main groups, the inevitable tally of loss through human impact, with damage and destruction of habitat, receives necessary examination. There is an assessment of conservation practice and requirements in looking to the future, in rounding off this very readable and up-to-date account of nature in this northernmost English county, which should have wide appeal. The Editors congratulate the author on his fine achievement, and welcome his book to the New Naturalist series as upholding its best traditions.

Author's Foreword

The book is about Northumberland, by which I mean the old geographical county (the modern administrative county, together with urban Tyneside north of the Tyne), but it has – geographically speaking – fuzzy edges, particularly in the west and southwest. It deliberately includes the part of Cumbria known as Alston Moor around Alston town, mainly because it consists of the upper valley of the River South Tyne – and surely the Tyne is properly a Northumberland river. Indeed, Alston Moor was attached to Cumberland, now Cumbria, in the early twelfth century only for the convenience of having revenues from the 'silver mines' (silver was a by-product of lead mining) collected for the Crown at Carlisle. However, the other part of the reason for including Alston Moor is my family connections with that area. In any case, for this book, Northumberland recaptures Cumbrian Cross Fell, the highest summit in the Pennines.

The editors of the New Naturalist series are interested in regional volumes dealing with the National Parks, and although this book deals with the entire county, with its great variety of habitat and wildlife – the coast, for example, and the North Pennines – emphasis is given to the Northumberland National Park, which covers a substantial proportion of the county's uplands. This happily accords with the author's delight in mountain and moorland environments, beyond the limits of cultivation – the crags and steep sided cleughs (or narrow valleys), bogs and flushes, heather and rough moorland grassland, and serendipitous corners of delight. The moorlands comprise by far the largest area of near natural or semi-natural habitat in the county.

The book tries to show what makes the natural history of Northumberland distinctive, and the several parts of the county distinctive from each other. In that sense it is about places, as well as their wildlife and habitats. To set the scene, Chapter 1 gives an overview and a flavour of Northumberland, concentrating on the upland landscapes and their natural history.

The uplands of Britain have rarely, over the last half-millennium, had economies based only on farming. They have had dual economies, with bye-occupations followed part time or by part of the community, and based on resources other than field crops and domestic livestock. In the North Pennines it was mining of lead and zinc. In heather areas, since the late eighteenth century, it has been grouse shooting. From the 1920s, in the Border valleys, it has been forestry – earlier in those parts it was cattle stealing, until the Union of England and Scotland in 1603. We will see how these geographically varied economic mixes have had an enduring effect in differentiating the landscape and the natural history, even within upland Northumberland.

The editors were also anxious that the book should concentrate on the more conspicuous aspects of the natural history of Northumberland, the vascular plants, vertebrates and larger insects, as well as the general landscape. The under-representation of invertebrates in the following chapters is for that reason, as well as because of my own inexpertness. Nonetheless, there exists much information on a number of invertebrate groups in the county, and mention should be made of the work of Mr M. D. Eyre (various insect groups), Dr G. N. Foster (water beetles), the late Mr R. Lowe (molluscs), Dr M. L. Luff (ground beetles), Dr J. D. Parrack (hoverflies), Dr S. P. Rushton (arachnids), and Mr G. Simpson (most organisms in Forestry Commission forests, including fungi, with many notable discoveries). In any case, a book covering such a large county is bound to be selective in its treatment, and biased towards the author's interests.

On a recent visit to Provence, I came across a book describing a part of the region, the immodest subtitle of which was *Mode d'emploi d'un fragment de paradis*. Northumberland is not paradise (although an industrial quarter along Newcastle's Scotswood Road, once a pleasant little village, is called Paradise), but it is a fragment of Britain with a marked sense of place and a distinctive history, reflected outstandingly in its habitats, its plants, its animals and other organisms.

Notes
(i) Dates for the more distant past are given, where possible, in calendar years BP (before the present, defined as 1950). Some, however, are in radiocarbon years BP (^{14}C BP) and are specified as such. Calendar years and radiocarbon years differ by varying amounts over time.
(ii) The mention of a site by name obviously does not imply that there is public access to it.

Apologies
I would like to extend my apologies to the authors of articles and books who are not specifically acknowledged in the text of this book, although I hope that all are featured in the bibliography, or can be traced through references in compilations of records. It was impossible, without cluttering the text unduly, and adding substantially to the length of the book, to do otherwise. It is ornithological writers in particular to whom this apology is addressed, numerous and prolific as they have been and remain in this part of the world. Many of their contributions are cited, for example, in Day *et al.* (1995). Nevertheless, I have tried to refer to the more significant works in the body of the text.

Acknowledgements
Given the wide scope of its subject material, this book could not have been written without much helpful advice by experts in their particular fields (which are not mine): Ian Armstrong, Peter Askew, Bill Burlton, Nick Cook, Phil Davey, Peter Davis, Alan Davison, Martin Davison, John Durkin, David Gardner-Medwin, Graham Gill, Gavin Hardy, Jim Heslop, Anne Lewis, Brian Little (who was especially helpful in regard to raptors, of which he has unparalleled local knowledge), Steve Lowe, Kevin O'Hara, David Noble-Rollin, Janet Simkin (providing information on lichens), John Steele, George Swan, Tony Tynan and John Walton. Additionally George Swan and John Richards have been sources of much botanical information over many years. Ian Armstrong, Geoffrey Chaytor, Nick Cook, Linda and John Reinecke, Janet Simkin, John Steele and Anne Wilson have generously provided photographs for reproduction, and June Holmes kindly arranged for the copy of Bewick's Chillingham bull to be included.

Special thanks are due to two of the editors of the New Naturalist series, Richard West and, particularly, Derek Ratcliffe, for their constructive help and advice.

Above all I thank my wife, Jean, for her patience and support in the writing of the book and for her meticulous and time-consuming preparation of the maps and diagrams.

Angus Lunn

1

An Overview

Preamble

Mrs Bennet, in *Pride and Prejudice*, regarded Newcastle as 'a place quite northward it seems'. A glance at an atlas shows that the 55°N line of latitude passes through Gosforth, a northern suburb of the city, and, continuing around the world, the same parallel leaves such frigid places as the southern part of Hudson Bay and the Aleutian Islands to the south. Northumberland is indeed the coldest part of England, in both summer, when sea level temperatures decline northwards, and winter, when they decline eastwards. Furthermore, near-shore North Sea surface temperatures are particularly low off our coastline, and in spring and early summer are colder here than anywhere else off Britain. This all hints at climatic limitations on the range of plant and animal life likely to be encountered in our county, at least when compared with more southern regions, and, additionally, a considerable number of British species reach their northern limits here. Of course, as the ground rises into the hills temperature decreases further, rainfall increases, and in consequence soils are nutrient deficient, acidic and peaty, so that limitations on plant growth become even severer. On the other hand, plants and animals adapted to cooler, wetter conditions can thrive, and the variety of upland habitats and species is one of the special features of Northumberland.

Topography

Northumberland consists of a lowland east and an upland west (Plate 1), although the western hills are penetrated by dales and interrupted by the Tyne Corridor, which links lowland southeast Northumberland and lowland northern Cumbria. Additionally, in the northeastern lowlands, upland ridges of modest altitude run parallel to the coast. In dimensions, the north–south span of the county is 112 kilometres and the east–west span 80 kilometres. The Cheviot is the highest summit in the geographical county at 815 metres a.s.l. (above sea level), but Cross Fell, in Cumbrian upper South Tynedale, reaches 893 metres. The uplands divide rather neatly into three, differing markedly in their geology and natural history: first the Cheviot Hills in the north, which we share with Scotland, made of granite and volcanic rocks; second the (mainly) sandstone hills and ridges in the middle, and third our part of the plateau and dale country of the North Pennines in the south, including Alston Moor, and shared with County Durham. The middle section contains two very different environments: moorland, and twentieth-century conifer plantations including the vast Kielder Forest. The lowlands divide into the coalfield in the southeast, industrialised, urbanised and including Newcastle: the triangle Amble–Tynemouth–Riding Mill; and the much larger, deeply rural, agricultural zone further north. The Tweedside area, a granary with huge farm steadings, is a world away from Tyneside and lies north of the Cheviots (part is north of the Tweed).

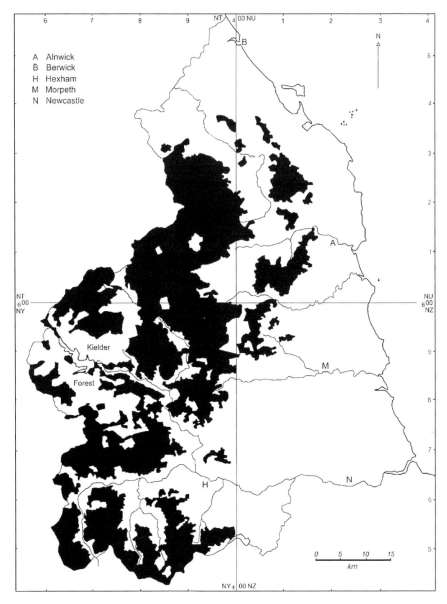

Fig. 1 Distribution of moorland (black) in Northumberland. From Lunn (1976). Virtually all of Kielder Forest and other forest blocks were planted on then moorland, and Kielder Forest has expanded somewhat to its south since the date of the map. With permission of Department of Geography, University of Newcastle upon Tyne.

Between the upland moorlands and the intensively farmed lowland is a wide intermediate zone of enclosed grassland, given over to stock raising. In fact livestock rearing is also important in much of the lowland, and 71 per cent of agricultural land in Northumberland is either permanent or temporary grassland, or rough grazing.

The 100-kilometre coastline is a separate environment, and for many naturalists is the reason for visiting Northumberland.

Moorland

About one-third of Northumberland is moorland (Fig. 1), in the broad sense of being uncultivated, substantially unenclosed, treeless upland with semi-natural vegetation. This vegetation provides rough grazing for hill sheep and cattle, and many heather-dominated moors are managed for red grouse. The proportion of the county that is moorland is similar to that for Britain as a whole.

A notable feature of Northumberland is the characteristic long views over moorland, obtained without the need to gain too much height – and in many places from the road network. According to G.M. Trevelyan in his essay *The Middle Marches* (1934):

'... Alpine or Cumbrian mountains, from their very height and the nearness of one giant to another, hide the wealth of heaven from the climber on the hill-side, who has, however, in those lands his terrestrial compensations. In fen country, the clouds are seen, but at the price of an earth of flat disillusionment. In Northumberland alone, both heaven and earth are seen; we walk all day on long ridges, high enough to give far views of moor and valley, and the sense of solitude above the world below, yet so far distant from each other, and of such equal height, that we can watch the low skirting clouds ... It is the land of the far horizons ...'

The Cheviot, in particular, is visible from modest elevations in much of the county (Plate 3b).

We will begin our moorland tour in the Cheviot Hills (Figs 2 & 3). Some valleys – the College and Harthope – are long, straight and wide, eroded by valley glaciers. Others, like that of the upper Coquet, are narrow and winding. In either case the volcanic soils on the steep valley sides carry bent–fescue grassland (dominated by bent grasses and/or sheep's fescue and red fescue), or bracken. These plant communities are interspersed with scree, and give way above, as slopes slacken, to either heather heath or acidophilous grassland, the latter dominated by mat-grass (*Nardus*), and then to blanket bog on the higher tops. (Acidophilous vegetation consists of species associated with acidic soils.) The Cheviot itself, below the blanket bog of its summit plateau, supports montane vegetation: bilberry heath, and various rill, ledge and snow-bed communities. Cheviot sheep, more demanding of good pasture than the otherwise ubiquitous Swaledales, graze the sweet bent–fescue grassland of the valley slopes and floors, and the air is full of the song of the skylark in early summer. Sheltered, bracken-covered slopes are a stronghold of the whinchat. Burn-sides inaccessible to sheep are herb rich and flowery, and in many valleys there is not a conifer plantation to be seen. The Cheviots support three herds of feral goats.

Fig. 2 Hen Hole, a glacially-excavated valley on the northern side of The Cheviot (John Steele).

Fig. 3 Alwin valley, Kidland, in the Cheviot volcanics. 1952 before afforestation (copyright Ward Philipson Group, Ltd.).

The central uplands are mainly sandstone country. East of the Cheviots are low, parallel, north–south trending ridges which are cuestas (Fig. 4) – the name given to a ridge, formed by a tilted, resistant bed of rock, which has a gentler dip slope (the surface of the bed) and a steeper scarp slope (its edge). Expanses of heather heath occur on the dip slopes (their relatively low altitude, however – some as low as 150 metres a.s.l., being reflected in the abundance of gorse), with bracken communities on the steep scarps. This low moorland tract has been particularly affected by modern agricultural reclamation, fragmenting the semi-natural vegetation. There are some notable raised bogs, including Ford and Holburn Mosses. Britain's only herd of pure park cattle, in Chillingham Park, is one of very few in the world that is completely feral, with a natural sex ratio and age distribution.

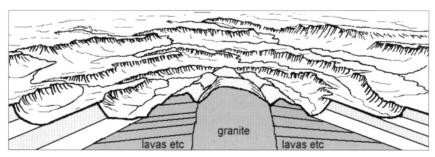

Fig. 4 Schematic diagram to show the relationship of cuestas (asymmetric ridges) to geological structure. Northumberland is depicted as if viewed from the northwest, with sedimentary strata dipping away from the Cheviot igneous massif. In reality both structure and topography are more complicated.

The sandstone cuestas become higher southwards (Fig. 5), and both north and south of the Coquet are again heather country, much of it managed for red grouse, gloriously purple and heavy with the scent of nectar in late August, alive with honeybees and bumblebees, raucous with the 'go-back, go-back' of red grouse. There is bilberry heath on rocky escarpments, and bracken again on the scarp slopes. Depressions between the cuestas contain bogs, some of them retaining a *Sphagnum* carpet. Locally, water issuing from limestones produces botanically rich, calcareous (lime- = calcium-rich) flushes, while some acidic flushes support purple moor-grass (*Molinia*)–bog myrtle communities. Sandstone slopes are in places corrugated, owing to grooves made in earlier centuries by sleds bringing grindstones cut out of outcrops down to the roads.

Fig. 5 The northward-facing escarpment of the sandstone Simonside hills, in upper Coquetdale. The sandstones are in the Fell Sandstone Group.

Further southwest, the moorlands of middle Redesdale and of its interfluve with middle North Tynedale are variously heather heaths, or *Nardus* or *Molinia* grassland, again with bogs in depressions. The Ministry of Defence's Otterburn Training Area (Fig. 6) is mainly in this tract, although part is north of the Coquet, in the Cheviot Hills. The core of the Training Area has been an artillery range since 1911, with later acquisitions, and it now extends to 23,500 hectares. The desired, open, training landscape, as well as the control of rank vegetation with a high fire risk, requires that the land is grazed, and the Training Area is divided into tenanted hill farms. Military training, however, is incompatible with more intensive agricultural management practices, and a type of moorland environment somewhat characteristic of the early part of the twentieth century has survived at Otterburn. Wildlife has benefited from low stocking rates on acidophilous grasslands, heaths and bogs, and from the survival of some ancient woodland, unimproved neutral grassland and calcareous flushes. Certainly, without the military presence, the Forestry Commission, in its mid-twentieth-century expansionist phase, would have laid claim to much of the area. Today the Otterburn Training Area provides habitat for a residual black grouse population, a remarkable concentration of breeding waders (particularly curlew: the Training Area contains between 1.3 and 1.5 per cent of the national breeding population), large heath butterfly on a number of separate bogs, and the rare plant Jacob's ladder. The Training Area is almost entirely within the National Park and occupies 23 per cent of it; despite the nature conservation benefits, now actively furthered by the MoD, military training is a very dubious land use in a National Park.

Fig. 6 Part of the MoD's Otterburn Training Area – view north, with the Cheviots in the background.

Moving still further southwestward, upper Redesdale and upper North Tynedale contain much of the Forestry Commission's Kielder Forest, which is described in Chapter 10. Above the commercial planting limit at about 520 metres a.s.l., however, large areas of magnificent blanket bog cover the plateaux and hilltops, and heather heath occupies unplanted slopes below the blanket bog. Cloudberry is spectacularly abundant, and this is a domain of the merlin, golden plover and dunlin, together with the county's other herd of feral goats. If we add Whitelee Moor farm, owned and managed by the Northumberland Wildlife Trust, to the Kielderhead Moors (Fig. 7) and other areas above the forest retained by the Forestry Commission, a more or less continuous tract of about 9,000 hectares of blanket bog and heath is under conservation management in this area. It extends from Carter Bar (where the A68 crosses the border), along the Scottish border southwestwards almost to Kielder, and then – after a short gap – along the Cumbrian boundary in the west.

Fig. 7 Black Needle (the burn), forming the Anglo-Scottish border against the
Kielderhead Moors.

In west Northumberland, in the vicinity of Hadrian's Wall, is a classic cuesta
landscape – the very best in Britain – with a west–east grain. Where moorland
vegetation has escaped afforestation its grain is similarly west–east,
characteristically with *Molinia* grassland on the south-facing dip-slopes, drier
Nardus grassland on the steeper scarp slopes and elongated bogs – many of them
high-quality *Sphagnum* bogs – occupying the inter-cuesta depressions. The
majority of bogs are best regarded as raised bogs, replacing shallow meres in
glacier-eroded basins, although some lakes survive. The bog surfaces, however,
are surmounted by the adjacent cuestas so that, oxymoronically for raised bogs,
they occupy the topographically lowest sites in their landscape. As the general
ground level rises northwards within this part of the county, and rainfall
correspondingly increases, the raised bog units tend to merge, with peat
overtopping low cuestas to form larger 'intermediate' bogs (intermediate to the
extensive blanket bogs on even higher ground). The raised and intermediate
bogs include some of the least damaged and most important bogs in Britain.
They are the national headquarters of bog-rosemary and are the habitat of
numerous populations of the large heath butterfly.

Many of the bogs occupy gaps in the southern part of Kielder Forest, difficult
ground left for planting at some later date when drainage techniques were
expected to have improved. Fortunately, Forestry Commission policy towards
nature conservation became more enlightened, and the bogs were allowed to
survive, in what became a forest–bog landscape. Many others had previously been
destroyed, and I remember ploughs ripping drains through some superb bogs
in the unenlightened 1950s and 1960s, in a largely vain attempt to grow
commercial crops of Sitka spruce and lodgepole pine on them. One of the

biggest intermediate bogs covered approximately 400 hectares north of Hindleysteel, and was drained and afforested at that time. Years later, in 1978, I noticed, on the latest edition of the Ordnance Survey 1:50,000 map, a white hole in the forest green covering the site of the bog. A visit found that the Forestry Commission had given up on the wettest part of the site, which had retained its natural vegetation, and the gap in the forest became Grain Heads Moss National Nature Reserve, now part of the Kielder Mires NNR.

Hadrian's Wall itself, in this area, follows the cuesta crest of the Whin Sill, an intrusive sheet of tough, igneous rock. Cornish (1943), in his analysis of scenery, noted how the coincidence that the Wall is presently near the boundary between improved farmland to the south and 'stern and wild' moorland to the north assisted the historical imagination in appreciating the Roman frontier environment. He remarked that it was important that the area comprised in the view should be constituted a National Park, which it subsequently was. Limestone cuestas in the same area support strips of bright green, close-grazed, sheep-dotted limestone grassland, set amidst more sombre-coloured acidophilous moorland.

Much of the upland described so far is inside the Northumberland National Park. South of the Tyne Corridor, however, are the North Pennines, not a National Park – although of the same quality – but an Area of Outstanding Natural Beauty (Figs 8 & 9). In the drier east the moorland plateaux between the dales carry heather heaths, while in the higher and wetter west the plateaux are covered by blanket bog; both habitats are managed as grouse moor, and are nationally important for golden plover and merlin. The western moorlands rise southwards to Cross Fell, with its montane vegetation. Large, ill-drained, rushy enclosures (allotments) at the moorland fringe – transitional on the sides of the dales between improved pastures and meadows below and unimproved moorland above – are habitat for England's main surviving black grouse population and for large populations of breeding waders – curlew, redshank, snipe and lapwing (Fig. 10).

Fig. 8 A North Pennine view southeastwards from Tom Smith's Stone, over Gilderdale (foreground) and the upper South Tyne valley.

Fig. 9 The valley of the Thinhope Burn, an upper South Tyne left-bank tributary.

Fig. 10 Upper South Tynedale, between Alston and Garrigill. Large, rectilinear allotments on the higher slopes.

The coast

There is a remarkable number of natural history glories along Northumberland's coastline (Fig. 11), the northern part of which is another Area of Outstanding Natural Beauty. From north to south, the Tweed estuary, at Berwick, has its gathering of non-breeding mute swans and wintering goldeneye. Holy Island (Lindisfarne) is famous for the wildfowl and waders of its intertidal sand- and mud-flats and for its dune systems. Ross Links, on the mainland opposite the southern end of Holy Island, is a peninsula with fine dune systems, and Budle Bay has more sand- and mud-flats. The Farne Islands have their grey seal colony, together with spectacular numbers and variety of nesting seabirds (Figs 12). Coquet Island has its breeding common, arctic, Sandwich and roseate terns, eiders, puffins and black-headed gulls. Near the southern end of the county is St Mary's Island, at Whitley Bay, accessible at low tide by a causeway and much visited for the seaweeds and invertebrates of its intertidal rock platform.

Fig. 11 Sandstone cliffs, Marshall Meadows Bay, north of Berwick.

Between these highlights are wide bays with sand beaches backed by dune cordons – only air and water temperatures have spared us 'Costa' development. We also have dune-covered peninsulas, which partly enclose estuaries containing salt marshes (at Alnmouth and Warkworth), and stretches of more intimate coastline consisting of successions of smaller bays, cliffed headlands, intertidal rock platforms and reefs. At intervals are the famous castles: Holy Island (Fig. 13), Bamburgh, Dunstanburgh, Warkworth, Tynemouth. Even the coalfield coast, from Amble southwards, retains sand-dune systems, and Druridge Bay, as a result of both mining subsidence and sympathetic restoration to wetland after opencast coal working, has a series of ponds and lagoons important for wildfowl and waders.

Fig. 12 Farne Islands. Brownsman Island has a building (an old lighthouse) and is separated by a narrow strait from Staple Island. The Pinnacles (sea stacks) are two-thirds of the way, from left to right, along the top of Staple Island as viewed. View from the north (Tim Gates: copyright reserved).

Fig. 13 Holy Island castle, on a whin dyke (Chapter 3).

Altogether Northumberland has about 270 hectares of salt marsh, rather little for a coastline of its length, but reflecting the scarcity of low-energy embayments and estuaries. On the other hand it has over 1,800 hectares of dune. This represents 18 per cent of England's dunes, more than any other English county, and dunes fringe about two-thirds of our coastline.

Fresh waters

The Tweed and Coquet are near-natural river systems, which are nationally rare. The Tyne, however, is far from natural – dredged, constrained and once hugely polluted in its estuary, its bed lowered by gravel extraction, the South Tyne and its tributaries contaminated with heavy metals from North Pennine mining activity, the North Tyne flow régime modified by large-scale afforestation and by the downstream effects of the huge Kielder Water reservoir. Yet the Tyne has regained its status as one of Britain's main salmon rivers. The Tweed and Coquet systems are notable for their crowfoot communities. A highlight of all the watercourses is the otter, which has made a remarkable comeback to Northumberland in the last decade or so.

As regards standing waters, Northumberland is no longer a land of lakes. The four small loughs near Hadrian's Wall in the west are the main natural lakes, but most of the very numerous meres of early post-glacial times have been infilled by peat, and their sites, as noted above, are now bogs. In contrast, the county has numerous man-made water bodies. There are about 100 ponds that are the result of coal-mining subsidence, concentrated in the southeast, and more are forming through ongoing subsidence to balance those lost by drainage or infilling. It is striking, when descending to Newcastle airport, how many ponds there are in the landscape – perhaps not surprising in the oldest commercial coalfield in the world. Landed estates created ornamental ponds and lakes, and there are still a few millponds, although many general-purpose farm ponds have been lost during agricultural intensification. The largest lakes are the water-supply reservoirs serving the urban and industrial areas. Catcleugh reservoir, near the head of Redesdale, completed in 1905, is the oldest of the large reservoirs; the Derwent reservoir, partly in County Durham, dates from 1966, and the immense Kielder Water (the largest entirely man-made lake in the UK, and an important recreational facility), from 1982. Additionally there is a system of smaller reservoirs, mainly on the upland fringe.

Other habitats

Some of our more specialised habitats are primarily of botanical interest. Lead and zinc mining in the North Pennines, although now long in the past, has left not only an important industrial archaeological heritage but also habitats contaminated with lead, zinc and other heavy metals. These metals are toxic to most organisms, but a group of plants ('metallophytes'), some uncommon, has developed tolerance to the contaminated soils. They are found on both contaminated mine dumps and river alluvium of the South Tyne and other North Pennine river systems. Particularly characteristic are spring sandwort and alpine penny-cress.

Another botanical habitat is the Whin Sill, not only where it carries Hadrian's Wall but widely as it crops out across the county. Its shallow, drought-prone but basic soils support about a dozen species and subspecies found nowhere else in Northumberland, including wild chives. A third habitat, now much reduced in area, is traditionally managed upland hay meadow, wonderfully colourful and rich in plant species.

We have a few surviving lowland mires, and Newham Fen, Ford Moss and Prestwick Carr are described in Chapter 11. The last, just outside of Newcastle, is, however, a shadow of its former glory when it was a mosaic of mere, swamp, open fen, carr and raised bog.

Northumberland, although having huge conifer forests and numerous estate plantations, has only a relatively small area of ancient semi-natural woodland. These woods are mainly on the steep valley-sides of rivers and burns, and while containing rich floras and faunas, are not notably distinctive in a British context. We do, however, have glorious bluebell woods, and the woodlands of the upland fringe support the trio of pied flycatcher, redstart and wood warbler.

What we lack

We have no limestone pavement, and although there are numerous outcrops of limestone in Northumberland, we have no really extensive areas of limestone grassland. Neither do we have chalk, apart from the waste heap at Low Prudhoe described in Chapter 11. The Magnesian Limestone, with such an impressive array of habitats and species in Durham, has only tiny outcrops in Northumberland. Most lowland heath has long ago either been reclaimed for intensive agriculture or converted to plantation. We have no canals, nor any significant coastal shingle structures.

Postamble

Suppose that our prime habitats are those which at the same time are rare at national level, well represented in Northumberland, possibly species rich and containing nationally rare and uncommon species. Maybe they should also be aesthetically pleasing, or in wild country. What then would we offer? Certainly the coastline, with its cliffs, dunes, salt marshes, intertidal flats and offshore islands – unmatched on the east coast of Britain. Certainly also the bogs of the upland west; for the quantity and quality of its bogs (and other mires) Northumberland is unsurpassed outside of the far north of Scotland. Probably also the Whin Sill, with its distinctive vegetation, and the metalliferous sites of the North Pennines, with their unusual set of plants. This is not a bad array of habitats to entice visiting naturalists.

Finally there are the naturalists themselves. Chapter 14 describes the work of a number of them, and they were a remarkable collection of individuals, whether their reputations are considered at the local, national or international level. Although they flourished particularly in the Victorian era, William Turner, John Wallis and Thomas Bewick belonged to earlier periods, and there have been and are distinguished modern naturalists living and working in North East England. Nor should we forget the contributions of Northumbrians to nature and landscape conservation, to the National Parks movement and to campaigns for access to the countryside. Charles Trevelyan, George M. Trevelyan, Edward Grey and John Dower (an adopted Northumbrian) all feature in Chapter 15.

2

Historical Introduction

Natural history is very much influenced by land-use history, and a number of themes bearing on this distinguish Northumberland's past. One is its frontier status: firstly of Rome against the natives to the north, and secondly of England against Scotland, during which time Border warfare evolved into local banditry. The survival to the present day of some relict ecosystems in the uplands may be due to the constraints upon economic development arising from the political insecurity on the Borders between the fourteenth and seventeenth centuries. The gradual emergence of a peaceful society after the Union of the Crowns in 1603, however, led eventually to a lowland agriculture of unparalleled efficiency in the late eighteenth and early nineteenth centuries. A high proportion of the land was by then held in large landed estates, the owners of which built mansions, created parks, arboreta and gardens, and, with their tenant farmers, laid out the fabric of the modern rural landscape.

From at least medieval times, mineral resources were being exploited. Newcastle became synonymous with coal, and many habitats in the coalfield are directly or indirectly connected with former coal mining. In the North Pennines, lead and zinc mining were responsible for creating the set of distinctive metalliferous habitats there. The biggest land-use change of the twentieth century, apart from general agricultural intensification, was the establishment of Kielder Forest, and other large state and private conifer plantations.

Before the Roman conquest

The first definite settlers were early Mesolithic peoples, nomadic hunters, fishers, gatherers and collectors of coastal shellfish, who arrived about 10,000 years ago. Forest had recently re-established after the last glaciation, although the landscape may have remained partly open, owing to grazing, browsing and trampling by large herbivores holding back tree establishment. Alternatively the settlers, and their later Mesolithic successors, may have used fire to open up some upland woodland, as a hunting strategy to attract game such as deer and aurochsen (wild oxen) (Simmons & Innes, 1987; Tipping, 1996). There is a rock carving of red deer, of possible Mesolithic age, under a sandstone overhang near Wooler. It may have been these more open areas that were first used for the summer grazing of domesticated stock by early Neolithic people, the first farmers, from about 4000 BC. A good case has been made by Waddington (1996) that the famous but enigmatic cup-and-ring carvings, which date from the early Neolithic and are so widespread on sandstone outcrops, demarcated transhumant grazing areas belonging to different pastoral groups (Fig. 14). The openings in the sandstone areas, however they originated, became heather heaths.

Much of the evidence as to how the environment changed during prehistoric times comes from pollen analysis, a technique explained in Chapter 6. From early Neolithic times onwards, more effectively than by Mesolithic fires, the native forests were gradually cleared for pasture, arable and other uses, although at rates which varied across the county, and with intervening periods of forest regeneration. Regeneration episodes are presumed to have been caused by population decline, owing either to social breakdown or to climate deterioration. Forest clearance was by a combination of the axe, fire and suppression of tree regeneration by domestic herbivores, and, in the uplands, fire was used for moorland vegetation management.

Fig. 14. Early Neolithic cup-and-ring carvings in sandstone, Roughtinglinn.

Neolithic woodland clearance took place particularly in the areas of dense settlement in north Northumberland, including in the Cheviots, and locally resulted in soil erosion. And some time early in the Neolithic, by about 3350 BC (Parker *et al.*, 2002), the forests lost a high proportion of their elms in the so-called 'elm-decline', a feature prominent in pollen diagrams from across northwestern Europe and perhaps due to a disease parallel to the modern elm disease. There may also, however, have been deliberate elm clearance for agriculture on the better soils.

The Bronze Age (approximately 2000–800 BC) saw continued forest clearance in both the lowlands and the hills, accompanied by further expansion of settlement, for example in the eastern Cheviots and the northern sandstone uplands. Clearance continued into Iron Age and Romano–British times, particularly on the fertile volcanic soils of the lower slopes of the Cheviot Hills. It seems that the main landscape transition in the north of the county, from more or less closed forest to open country, occurred between about 3,000 and 1,000 BC. Further south, although there were episodes of small-scale and temporary clearance during the Bronze Age (Davies & Turner, 1979; Dumayne & Barber, 1994), widespread and long-term clearance was probably later, between 500 BC and 500 AD. In some areas, indeed, there is little sign from pollen diagrams of human impact on the environment until Roman times, when there was large-scale clearance. However, on higher ground in the North Pennines, woodland was substantially lost during the first millennium BC, owing to blanket bog spread under a deteriorating climate, browsing by domestic animals and direct clearance (Turner, 1978). Much of our modern moorland owes its origin to prehistoric forest clearance.

There are rather extensive areas of ridging – a result of former ploughing – in the Cheviots and elsewhere, which are above the altitudinal limit of modern arable farming and are now extensively bracken-covered. While the broader ridges are mainly medieval, narrower so-called cord rig, which occurs up to 450 metres a.s.l., dates from the pre-Roman Iron Age onwards. On steeper slopes are cultivation terraces (lynchets), dating from the Bronze Age onwards, again conspicuous on otherwise smooth Cheviot slopes. Other widespread prehistoric landscape features in the Cheviots are settlement sites, field boundaries and clearance cairns (of boulders from the surface of glacial drift) (Topping, 1989). In fact the lower Cheviots are regarded as preserving, in moorland mainly above about 250 metres a.s.l., one of the finest fossilised Bronze Age to Romano-British landscapes in Europe. Milfield Plain, at the foot of the hills, also has a plethora of prehistoric features, and the area from the eastern Cheviots to the north Northumberland coast was clearly of great political, religious and economic importance in much of prehistory (and, as we shall see, in early medieval times), just as the Tyne Corridor was to be during the Roman period.

In the later Iron Age, the local population was at times living in more or less undefended farmsteads, but the numerous and spectacular Iron Age hill forts in the lower Cheviots and on the sandstone cuestas of north Northumberland – dating from the first millennium BC – denote earlier times of insecurity. They usually consist of multiple ramparts of piled boulders on hilltops or spurs (Fig. 15). The huge fort on the summit of Yeavering Bell was a tribal capital and was occupied for several hundred years.

Fig. 15 Rampart of Brough Law Iron Age hill fort, Breamish valley, Cheviots.

The Roman period

The Roman armies, after a brief incursion into what is now Scotland in the first century AD, had withdrawn to the narrow Solway–Tyne isthmus by about 100 AD. It was here, north of the existing, strategic, west–east Roman road, the Stanegate, that Hadrian had his wall constructed, as a permanent, linear frontier, mainly between 122 AD and 128 AD. It is the most important monument built by Romans in Britain and is the most complex and best-preserved frontier in the whole Roman Empire. For much of the next three centuries Hadrian's Wall was Rome's northwestern frontier. It consisted finally of a stone wall from Wallsend, on the north bank of the Tyne east of Newcastle, to Bowness-on-Solway in Cumbria – a distance of 117 kilometres. It was about 4.6 metres high, probably with a walkway on top protected by an additional 1.5-metre parapet. On the northern side was a ditch, except where the crags of the Whin Sill made it superfluous. A short distance to the south was the Vallum – two parallel earth mounds with a deep intervening ditch and itself a colossal earth-moving enterprise. Its function is uncertain, but Woolliscroft (1999) suggests that its primary purpose may have been as a general deterrent to mounted raiders from the north seeking to penetrate Wall gates, or to thieves from the south, but that it had secondary administrative and fiscal roles.

Forts (Housesteads is the most famous) were set every few miles along the Wall, milecastles (guardposts at wall-gates) every Roman mile and two turrets (watchtowers) between each pair of milecastles. Vindolanda was a fort and civilian settlement on the Stanegate, dating originally from before the Wall was built, as was also the fort at Corbridge at the junction of the Stanegate and Dere Street. Corbridge later grew into a substantial Roman military town. Dere Street, named later for Deira, the southern part of Anglo-Saxon Northumbria, was the main north–south road from York and London, entering modern Scotland at the remote Chew Green, a fort-complex at the head of the River Coquet. The Roman name of Chew Green is given as *Ad Fines*, roughly translating as *The Pits* (in token of its remoteness), but this was an eighteenth-century literary hoax (Woodward, 1866; the same hoax lastingly christened the *Pennines*). Outpost forts, north of the Wall, effectively extended Roman power beyond the present Scottish border.

Radiocarbon-dated pollen diagrams from sites near the Wall, including from soils or deposits sealed by structures of known Roman date, have still not completely clarified whether extensive woodland clearance had already taken place in this part of Northumberland before the Romans arrived, or whether it was the Romans who carried it out (Huntley, 1999). The situation probably varied along the Wall, with, in the Tyne valley west of Newcastle, a well-developed farmed landscape greeting the Romans when they arrived (Tolan-Smith, 1997*b*). Similarly, around Vindolanda in west Northumberland there was already open grassland (Manning *et al*, 1997) – damp and scrubby if the numerous black grouse bones from the site are anything to go by. The Romans were also eating red grouse, denoting heather moorland, judging by remains at Corbridge. In contrast, in the upland environment around Fozy Moss, adjacent to the Wall a few kilometres northeast of Housesteads, there had been relatively little human impact on the vegetation until large-scale clearance at the beginning of the Roman occupation (Dumayne & Barber, 1994). It is generally assumed that a swathe of woodland was cleared in front of the Wall for strategic reasons, and fort building also required much timber.

For most of the time under Roman rule the *Pax Romana* prevailed, the local economy was stimulated, population increased, more land was brought under cultivation (partly to feed the garrisons) and yet more natural woodland cleared. It is difficult however, despite the huge contribution of the Romans to the archaeological heritage of Northumberland (Higham, 1986, estimated that 85,000–120,000 hectares were confiscated by the military for the Wall–Vallum frontier), to point to present-day habitats, other than those associated with the structures themselves, which are different because the Romans were here. They hastened woodland clearance, but this would have happened anyway. The Romans probably introduced some plants, including weed species. Their wall fort at *Pons Aelius* (Hadrian's family name) later developed into Newcastle and may be a reason why the city is where it is. At a local level, yellow bands of flowering gorse, which readily establishes on disturbed ground, mark the Vallum and Wall ditch for long stretches.

There was a cosmopolitan military mix on the Wall frontier, but:

'Over the heather the wet wind blows,
I've lice in my tunic and a cold in my nose;
The rain comes pattering out of the sky,
I'm a Wall soldier, I don't know why.'
WH Auden: *Roman Wall blues*

Medieval and early modern periods

The Romans withdrew in 411 AD. The numerous bogs in the Hadrian's Wall area have afforded one of the densest concentrations of pollen sequences for the Roman and post-Roman period in the British Isles, providing detailed information on vegetation change. Dark & Dark (1996) have argued strongly for a general abandonment of land, with widespread woodland regeneration, in that area in the immediate post-Roman period. Dark (1996) further argued that in this respect the Wall area was strikingly different from much of the remainder of Britain. This was due to the loss of markets in the Roman garrison and, presumably, reduced security. However, the landscape remained at least partly open (Dumayne-Peaty, 1999), and the subsequent forest clearance indicated by pollen diagrams perhaps occurred during the relatively peaceful and settled conditions of the seventh and eighth centuries. The Wall itself, and associated forts and buildings, became a quarry for ready dressed stone, for castles, churches, houses and field walls, until the emergence of antiquarian concerns in the nineteenth century.

Little is known historically about the period immediately following the withdrawal of the Roman army. Britain was segmented into Celtic kingdoms, and then, from the mid-sixth century, Anglian invaders began to settle in the region. The early Anglian kingdom of Bernicia (Northumberland and Durham up to and including the Scottish Lothians) united in about 600 AD with its southern neighbour Deira to form the larger kingdom of Northumbria. At the height of its power the latter encompassed all the land between the Forth and the Humber, together with western areas including modern Cumbria. Royal capitals included Bamburgh, Yeavering and Maelmin (= Milfield). The golden age of Northumbrian art and learning – when the region was of major European cultural importance – was from the mid-seventh to the mid-eighth centuries. Monasteries were established at Lindisfarne and Hexham in Northumberland, and Jarrow and

Monkwearmouth in Durham. Bede was pursuing his scholarship and writing, and Cuthbert (ca. 634–687 AD) was Bishop of Lindisfarne, where the Lindisfarne Gospels were soon to be created. By the late eighth century, however, Viking raids were affecting the coastal region, although there was minimal actual Viking settlement in North East England (hence the distinctive non-Scandinavian dialect, dominance of Anglian and scarcity of Scandinavian place names). The kingdom of Northumbria was subsumed into England in the mid-tenth century, and at about the same time the boundary with Scotland was established more or less on its present line, except for Berwick, then still in Scotland.

After the Norman Conquest, Northumberland assumed its role as a Border county, and many of its famous castles date, at least in their origins, from the Norman period – on estates held from the Crown by feudal barons in return for defence against the Scots. The most powerful of these by the late fourteenth century, and the most powerful by far thereafter, was the Percy Earl of Northumberland.

Relative peace from the mid-twelfth century saw the establishment of further monasteries on both sides of the Border; Cistercian Newminster, near Morpeth, acquired extensive grazing lands in the Cheviots right up to the Border line. There was population growth, continued woodland clearance, and the expansion of settlement high up the hill valleys. Royal hunting forests (later becoming baronial) were established, collectively occupying vast tracts of the uplands – Rothbury, Gilderdale, Knarsdale, East and West Allendale, Cheviot, Kidland, Chatton, Redesdale, Chirdon, Lowes (named for the west Northumberland loughs) – and, on a smaller scale, parks, including Hulne Park at Alnwick. The hunting forests, for a time, preserved woodland, and red and roe deer; there was still a herd of red deer in Knarsdale – by then largely reduced to moorland – at the end of the eighteenth century. The parks were stocked with fallow deer, which had been introduced to Britain by the Normans; unlike the territorial, woodland roe deer it is a herd dwelling, mainly grazing animal, suited to its park environment. Chillingham Park was enclosed by the thirteenth century and the white park cattle may have been there then, but are first mentioned in 1646. As regards the amount of woodland left in the landscape, by analogy with other parts of England the proportion in the lowlands at the end of the thirteenth century may not have been too dissimilar from that at the beginning of the twentieth century. In time, the remoter moorlands, including the former hunting forests, became 'shieling grounds', to which cattle were driven in summer and herded from shielings – summer dwellings whose sites have been found scattered over the uplands.

All changed with the outbreak of the Scottish wars at the end of the thirteenth century, and more than three centuries of misery and destruction of civilisation ensued. Disruption, and insecurity of life and property, prevailed. A powerful brake was put on agricultural progress, and settlement and cultivation retreated from the hills. Castles were strengthened or, like Dunstanburgh, built from scratch. Towns built or strengthened their walls. The Borders, on both sides, were organised into Marches for defence. There was periodic official or semi-official warfare, raiding and reprisal between England and Scotland, culminating in 1513 in the Battle of Flodden, 4 kilometres southeast of Cornhill-on-Tweed, at which the Scots were defeated.

Concurrently, in the dales on either side of the Border, there developed during these anarchic times a lawless, clan-based way of life based upon predatory cattle rustling (reiving) to supplement subsistence agriculture. In their sixteenth-century heyday, farmer-thieves, grouped under surnames – on the English side Charlton, Milburn, Hall, Robson, Dodd, Crozier, etc. – raided on horseback both each other, and Scottish and English farms and settlements beyond their Border homelands. In Northumberland, these were upper North Tynedale and Redesdale, and on the Scottish side Liddesdale was notorious. By the seventeenth century the bandits were known as 'mosstroopers', after the numerous soft bogs (mosses) – now mainly nature reserves – of west Northumberland. They, with local knowledge, were able to navigate among them without becoming bogged down when driving home livestock stolen on raids south of the Wall. The valleys nearest to the Border were abandoned for permanent settlement, although pasturing of cattle on the summer shieling grounds continued except in the worst years of trouble. In this respect a land-use practice that had been widespread in the British uplands in medieval times survived late in the Borders (Winchester, 2000). Harrying penetrated deep into Northumberland and was ruinous to agriculture, so that by the end of the sixteenth century the county was in a piteous condition. The activities of the thieving and feuding clans gave rise to many of the atmospheric Border ballads, reflecting events played out variously on the Scottish or the English sides – and contemporary with Shakespeare's England.

There is a classic 1541 description of Kidland, in the Cheviots, by the border commissioners Bowes and Ellerker. It:

> '... lieth so open on the north side towards Scotland and upon the south-west part towards the country of Redesdale. And ... the said valleys or hopes of Kidland lieth so distant and divided by mountains one from another that such as inhabit in one of those hopes, valleys or graines can not hear the fray, outcry or exclamation of such as dwell in another hope or valley upon the other side of the said mountain nor come nor assemble to their assistance in time of necessity. Wherefore we cannot find any of the neighbours thereabouts willing continually to inhabit or plenish within the said ground of Kidland ... although they might have stone houses builded thereupon for their defence ... the dangers afore recited be so great and manifest.'

The passage refers to stone houses, and thieves, honest farmers and landowners alike built defensible homes for safe sanctuary: the county bristled with defensive buildings. The more affluent could afford towers (pele towers) and the humbler just defensible farmhouses – the bastle houses that were and are so numerous in Northumberland, as far away from the Border as the North Pennines.

Although the Union of the Crowns theoretically converted Northumberland from a Border county to a 'middle shire', old habits died hard, reiving was only reluctantly given up in the Border dales and the seventeenth-century English Civil War saw Northumberland again occupied by Scottish armies.

Pollen diagrams from the uplands north of the Tyne Corridor (for example, Davies & Turner, 1979) indicate extensive secondary regeneration of woodland and scrub – especially of birch, alder and hazel – on previously cleared ground from about the fourteenth century, although there are dating uncertainties in the pollen record. The abandonment of land in the uplands, or reduced stocking levels, would allow tree regeneration, although the climatic deterioration of the Little Ice Age of ca. 1350–1850 may have contributed to agricultural regression.

It is likely that the centuries of political, social and economic insecurity had a profound effect on upland ecosystems. Natural and semi-natural habitats would survive, or re-establish, which would not otherwise have done so – wetland as well as woodland – and we will explore in Chapter 8 how ecosystems that survived until the seventeenth century could have further persisted to the present. Ground predators survived later here than was the case in more peaceful areas, Northumberland being the last English county to lose the wild cat, in the 1850s (Yalden, 1999).

Modern times
The countryside
By the later seventeenth century Northumberland was re-emerging to civilisation. The agricultural essayist, John Grey of Dilston, claimed (1841) that the peasant farming population had been so weakened by the centuries of warfare, raiding and destruction, and therefore unable to resist change, that once the brakes were released, agricultural reform, though starting late, was carried further in Northumberland than anywhere else in Britain. Certainly by the middle of the nineteenth-century landscape and society had been transformed. Enclosure of the lowlands had been completed – much of it, on the better land, taking place by private agreement by the mid-eighteenth century, before the period of Parliamentary enclosures. The lowlands were laid out anew in large rectangular fields. (In very modern times there has been less impulsion to clear away hedgerows than in parts of the country where fields were not already as large as in Northumberland, and the stock-rearing tradition also justifies hedged fields.) Most of the moorlands – where, in the seventeenth century, shieling grounds had become tenanted hill farms – were also enclosed, with farms gradually consolidating and becoming increasingly market oriented, especially on good sheep land in the Cheviots (Fig. 16).

Fig. 16 Whiteburnshank, a former hill farm in Kidland (in the Cheviots), before afforestation (copyright Ward Philipson Group Ltd).

Upland enclosure involved dividing the lower moorlands, with more readily improvable soils, both into fields and, at slightly higher altitudes, rectangular allotments of up to a few tens of hectares in area. Many of the allotments were, over time, partially improved. The parts of holdings in the remoter and wilder moorlands were simply surrounded by boundary walls or fences. Compared with neighbouring counties in northern England, Northumberland was left with relatively little common land, only about 10,000 hectares now being registered, mainly in the North Pennines. Stone sheep folds (stells) were constructed in their thousands on the moorlands (Fig. 17). Lime for soil improvement and mortar was supplied by hundreds of lime kilns, in both uplands and lowlands, exploiting local limestone and coal. They ranged in size from field kilns to large commercial sets. Peat, as in earlier times, was dug from upland bogs for domestic fuel, a practice that continued on remote farms until the mid-twentieth century.

Fig. 17 Contour-adapted sheep stell in the valley of the Bateinghope Burn, upper Redesdale.

Farms, which for security reasons had been crammed into villages, were dispersed into their fields, many, with their cottages, becoming substantial farm-hamlets. Tenant farmers were offered long leases on large farms as an incentive to maximise output (and rent). Landowners, employing knowledgeable and powerful agents, further attracted progressive tenants by providing for them substantial farm steadings in a great rebuilding – mainly in sandstone – dating from about 1780 to 1850. The tenants emulated each other in innovative cropping and stock breeding, and both the Border Leicester and Cheviot breeds of sheep were developed in north Northumberland. Droving of cattle across the Border hills from Scotland to English markets resumed on a large scale, along medieval routes – the 'streets' of the O.S. maps. By 1841 Grey was able to write that Northumberland exhibited an agriculture 'approaching probably as near to perfection as any that this country at present exhibits'. 'Perfection', of course, in the sense of productive, progressive, profitable. Inevitably much wildlife habitat was lost, particularly in the lowlands.

Perhaps because of previous Border military need, a larger proportion of Northumberland was held in large estates by the end of the nineteenth century than was the case in any other English county. Fifty per cent of the county, excluding 'waste', was in estates of more than 10,000 acres and another 21 per cent in estates of 3,000–10,000 acres (Thompson, 1963). Greatest of the landowners was still the Duke of Northumberland, but many estates came into the hands of families whose wealth was founded on coal or industry. Grand (or modest, according to income) country houses, mainly in classical styles, were built amidst parks, some descended from medieval hunting parks. Lakes and ponds, for amenity and fishing, and arboreta were created. One of the most dramatic houses is Cragside, at Rothbury, with extensive wooded grounds, built for the Victorian engineer-entrepreneur W.G. (later Lord) Armstrong, whose enormous shipbuilding, armaments and engineering works stretched along the Tyne above Newcastle. Still today, Northumberland has the highest percentage of rented land in England, as well as the largest average farm holding size.

Hunting foxes replaced hunting deer as the preferred lifestyle of the better off, so kennels were built, fox (and pheasant) coverts planted, while the new hawthorn hedges of the enclosed fields added to the excitements of pursuit. Numerous plantations, many of conifers (Norway spruce, Scots pine and, especially, European larch) were established in the lowlands for estate timber, and also on the lower moorlands for stock shelter. In the uplands, sporting estates were developed, based on the heather-dominated moorlands with their red grouse populations. The opening up of numerous large and small quarries for building stone and limestone created new habitats, including quarry ponds. There were clay pits (for bricks and tiles) and sand and gravel workings.

Systematic game management, including control of 'vermin', was practised by the end of the eighteenth century. There was intensive persecution by gamekeepers, armed with more effective guns, of virtually all predatory birds and mammals threatening, or considered to threaten, game bags. Among birds of prey, red kite (formerly widespread, but latterly confined to upland woods), buzzard and golden eagle (which had nested in the Cheviot corries) were extinct in Northumberland by the 1840s, marsh harrier (once at Newham Fen and on the western moors) followed, hen harrier became very uncommon, and raven, jay and inland populations of cormorant (a perceived threat to game fishing) were also targeted, as were inland colonies of lesser black-backed gull. Even kestrel was regarded as a pest. Mammals that were slaughtered were polecat (lost from Northumberland by 1915), pine marten (which had very desirable fur as well as being a predator) and wild cat. However, as both Rossiter (1998, 1999) and Yalden (1999) have pointed out, reductions of the populations of species regarded as pests had not begun with game preservation by private estates. At parish level churchwardens had been offering bounties for the purpose since the seventeenth century. Of course, the populations of game birds increased, black grouse even being provided with plots of corn. Drainage of fens led to the loss of the bittern as a breeding species.

Industry

Equally profound changes were occurring away from the land. There is an arresting Impressionist painting by Monet, *Waterloo Bridge, effect of sun with smoke*, painted in 1903, which says it all. The smoke was, in effect, shipped from the Tyne, which had been exporting coal to London and elsewhere from medieval times. Gray, in his *Chorographia* (1649), said that Newcastle (meaning North East England) had been justly famous on four occasions. Firstly, when it was the outermost limit of the Roman Empire; secondly, when the monasteries of the region were influential throughout Europe; thirdly, when it formed a bulwark against the Scots; and fourthly, for its present trade in coal, salt and grindstones. With British population growth and the Industrial Revolution, the demand for coal – for shipping along the coast and abroad, and for local industrial use – exploded. Mines were sunk across the Northumberland and Durham coalfield and to coal seams in rural areas – in 1914 there were over 130 collieries in Northumberland alone (Figs 18 & 19). At first they were within horse-drawn waggonway reach of navigable water, particularly the Tyne, but later, with the perfection of the railway locomotive here in Northumberland by George Stephenson, this transport limitation was removed (railways were born of the North Eastern coal trade). The availability of abundant, cheap coal, generated industry on Tyneside and in southeast Northumberland: shipbuilding and repairing (with all the ancillary industries), chemicals, iron manufacture, engineering, glass making and armaments. Thus arose industrial Tyneside during the eighteenth and nineteenth centuries, one of the very first truly industrial societies.

Fig. 18 A relict of a once-familiar sight in southeast Northumberland – the pithead gear at Woodhorn colliery, now a museum (David Noble-Rollin).

Fig. 19 The site of Fordmoss colliery village, abandoned in about 1914. The chimney served the colliery engine-house.

Numerous new habitats were created, not least along the railways in ballast and track-sides, and in the marshalling yards and station precincts. There were also, along the Tyne and elsewhere, the ballast hills constructed from ships' ballast, as colliers returned without cargo. The once diverse array of ballast plants, introduced from many parts of the world, is covered in Chapter 7. Nowadays we tend to forget the pit-heaps themselves, less than half a century ago so dominant in the southeast Northumberland landscape. All have been removed or genteelly landscaped.

No canals were ever constructed in Northumberland, but the much dredged lower Tyne bisected the heart of the coalfield, and, together with the coalfield ports of Seaton Sluice, Blyth and Amble, adequately served maritime trade via the waggonway and railway network. On the Tyne, coal was shipped down the river in keels, shallow-draughted vessels into which waggons tipped coal from staiths (wooden jetties), for transfer to sea-going colliers. (Reivers, displaced by pacification of the Border dales, found employment in the pits, industry and transport. The Charltons, Milburns, Robsons, etc. became keelmen and pitmen – and descendants, some of them, footballers.)

Pollution was on an epic scale. Celia Fiennes, already in 1698, observed that 'this country all about is full of this Coale the sulphur of it taints the aire and it smells strongly to strangers; upon a high hill 2 mile from Newcastle I could see all about the country which was full of coale pits' (Morris, 1947). The lower

Tyne was killed by an unspeakable broth of raw sewage and chemical effluent. Trees, especially conifers, succumbed to sulphur dioxide and soot, as did lichens and bryophytes. There were even soot-covered redstarts in the Newcastle area.

Contemporary with all this development based upon coal was a substantial mining industry in the North Pennines, based on lead, and later zinc, ores. Iron ores, fluorite, barytes and witherite have also been mined on a considerable scale. Galena (the lead ore) almost always bears silver, and this was extracted as a by-product, and on an important scale, from at least as early as the twelfth century. Large-scale lead mining began in the early seventeenth century, with peak production in the mid-nineteenth century. Zinc was mined mainly from 1880 to 1920. Small settlements – for example Nenthead, on Alston Moor – expanded to house the new population. Many miners, however, were part-time farmers, living in houses built amidst the fields. There were hundreds of mines, large and small, together with washing plants and smelters (Fig. 20). Flues from the latter, carrying poisonous fumes, ended in chimneys on nearby hilltops – some still standing. New roads, amongst the highest in Britain, were built over the moorlands to link the dales, and are locations from which to appreciate Trevelyan's long views. Railways later penetrated to the heart of the dales. By the end of the nineteenth century, however, the North Pennine mines, from having been the principal base metal producers in Britain over the previous 150 years (at peak production the area was one of the most productive orefields in the world), were in rapid decline owing to exhaustion and competition. The industry, however, has left not only an industrial archaeological heritage, but, like coal, has influenced present-day land use and ecology in ways some of which are discussed in the following chapters.

Fig. 20 Mid Level, Rotherhope Fell Mine, Alston Moor. The mine produced mainly lead ore and fluorite.

The flourishing industrial economy of Tyneside and southeast Northumberland, up to the outbreak of the First World War, brought about the growth of residential suburbs for the growing middle-class population, and market towns and villages within commuting range of Tyneside similarly expanded. Gardens provided new habitat, greatly enlarged again with twentieth-century greenfield housing estate development. And, despite the enormous changes wrought to the environment and landscape of Tyneside, and the wider coalfield area, by eighteenth- and nineteenth-century industry, a surprising amount was transient. Mines and pit heaps have all but gone, industrial sites have become country parks or nature reserves, whole pit villages have been erased, railways and waggonways are now pleasant walkways, the Tyne is once again a salmon river. The surviving heavy industries along the Tyne have been supplemented by modern factory and warehouse estates, and business parks, dispersed through the county.

3

Pre-Quaternary Geology

Rocks make habitats by their influence on soil and on slope (hard rocks can support crags), and local climate is determined by the altitude to which they have been uplifted. Rocks also make the general landscape, which is the stage for our natural history. This chapter describes Northumberland's varied rock types, relating their distribution to that of our main habitats. Much further information on Northumberland's geology is to be found in Johnson (1995).

Plate 2 is a map of the 'solid geology'. This means that the rock groups shown are those that would crop out at the surface if the superficial Quaternary-age 'drift' was removed. (There are separate published drift maps, dividing this generally looser material into glacial till, alluvium, peat, etc.) It will be seen that the Cheviot Hills, in the northwest of the county, consist of igneous rocks, derived as magma from the Earth's interior, and that they are of Devonian age (418–362 million years old). Almost the whole of the rest of Northumberland's solid land surface consists of sedimentary rocks of Carboniferous age (362–290 million years). These rocks were deposited in stratified form on river beds or in the sea, or, in the case of coal seams, formed from fossilised wetland vegetation. The sedimentary strata dip generally away from the Cheviots, towards the east, southeast and south, such that successively younger beds crop out in broad arcs further and further away from the Cheviots, as shown diagrammatically in Figure 4. While the Cheviot igneous rocks in general form high ground, there is no particular correlation between individual sedimentary strata and elevation; for example, the bed of limestone known as the Great Limestone occurs at 700 metres near Cross Fell and at sea level on the north Northumberland coast. However, within each part of the county, more resistant strata form higher ground, and the thick sandstones of the Fell Sandstone Group almost invariably form uplands.

Cheviot Hills

The Cheviot igneous massif, part of which is in Scotland, is the eroded remains of a volcano, later intruded from below by a granite and seamed with dykes (vertical sheets of igneous rocks injected as magma into fissures: the dykes are picked out on the ground as blocky lineaments). The granite forms The Cheviot itself and adjacent hills including Hedgehope. Soils derived from granite, because of its mineral composition – high in quartz and low in compounds yielding bases and major plant nutrients – are sandy, acidic and infertile. The surrounding lower hills of the Cheviots – among the more prominent are Yeavering Bell, Newton Tors, Cushat Law, Windy Gyle and Thirl Moor – are volcanic (Plates 5a, 5b; Figs 21, 22 & 23). They consist mainly of sequences of lava, but include also some pyroclastic rocks, composed of particles explosively ejected from volcanoes; these latter vary from rocks made up of coarse fragments (agglomerates) to finer-grained rocks (ashes). Although some of these volcanic rocks, the rhyolites, have a similar chemical make-up to the granite and yield similar soils, most of them are andesites. These are richer in minerals which contain bases, including calcium, and nutrients, and so – at least in lower rainfall areas with less leaching (loss of soluble compounds by percolating water) – produce less acidic and more fertile soils. This is reflected in their flora, and basiphilous (base-loving) plants such as hairy rock-cress, maiden pink, common rock-rose and burnet saxifrage occur on rock outcrops near the valley floors.

Fig. 21 The Border ridge in the Cheviots, from Windy Gyle towards The Cheviot. Foreground Cheviot volcanics, higher ground granite (John Steele).

Fig. 22 Yeavering Bell, in the Cheviot volcanics and iconic in Northumberland. There is a large Iron Age fort on the summit, and an ancient, semi-natural woodland, with oak and alder, on its lower slopes (copyright Allan Potts).

Fig. 23 The valley of the Allerhope Burn, upper Coquetdale – in the Cheviot volcanics (John Steele).

The intrusion of the granite magma into the roots of the earlier volcano strongly heated, and recrystallised, the volcanic rocks in a zone about a kilometre wide around the granite. This is now apparent at the ground surface as a metamorphic aureole, with much tougher rocks than is typical of the volcanics. That is why they are able to support crags, otherwise rather scarce in the Cheviots, notably in The Bizzle and Hen Hole – corries on the northern side of The Cheviot. On these crags, and in other habitats within the aureole, are the only examples Northumberland has to offer of a basiphilous montane flora, although there are related habitats on limestone high on Cross Fell in Cumbria.

The volcanic rocks do not provide easily shaped building stones, but were used for domestic buildings and field walls in the Cheviots.

Topographically, individual Cheviot Hills are either conical or plateau-like, depending on the distance apart of the mainly narrow, steep-sided valleys that dissect the granite and volcanics. The higher, flatter hills have blanket bog on their summits.

On the southwestern fringe of the Cheviot Hills, in uppermost Coquetdale and Redesdale, is an outcrop of Silurian-age sedimentary strata consisting of tightly folded shales (some metamorphosed to slates) and greywackes (sandstones composed of quartz and feldspar). Judging by plants growing on these rocks, at least some of them are calcareous. The main road over Carter Bar into Scotland follows this outcrop in Redesdale. Such older rocks otherwise are the basement for the overlying Carboniferous rocks that form the surface (under the drift) of most of the rest of Northumberland.

Carboniferous Northumberland

The Carboniferous age sedimentary rocks consist of limestones and (composed of respectively increasing particle sizes) mudstones and shales, siltstones, and sandstones, together with coal seams. These rocks have long been classified informally into groups according to their relative importance in each group. From oldest to youngest they are: the Cementstone Group (cementstones are muddy limestones), Fell Sandstone Group, Scremerston Coal Group, Lower Limestone Group, Middle Limestone Group, Millstone Grit (subsuming the Upper Limestone Group) and Lower and Middle Coal Measures. All these groups, except the Coal Measures, crop out in both the uplands and the lowlands, as indicated on Plate 2. Their outcrop patterns, however, are different north and south of the Tyne Corridor.

North of the Tyne Corridor

Where, as is the case in much of this area, there is a sequence of alternating weak and resistant strata with a significant dip, the typical landform is the cuesta (Fig. 4). Because each rock group crops out as a broad arc, half-encircling the Cheviots, the cuestas (made of the hard strata within each group) also arc around the Cheviots, with their scarps facing inwards. Resistant thick strata, particularly the sandstones, form major cuestas while thinner beds form minor ones, perhaps only a few metres high. Upland Northumberland, north of the Tyne Corridor, is classic cuesta country, and many of the long views are from the crests of cuestas (Fig. 24). Between are belts of lower ground, varying in width from a few tens of metres to one or more kilometres.

Fig. 24 Cuesta landscape, looking eastwards from near Greenhead.

As is apparent from Plate 2, the oldest Carboniferous rocks crop out nearest to the Cheviots. They belong to the Cementstone Group, whose strata consist mainly of weak mudstones and shales, forming low, farmed country south and east of the Cheviots, which rise abruptly from it. Next, away from the Cheviots, are the prominent single or multiple cuestas consisting of the thick, resistant sandstones of the Fell Sandstone Group (Fig. 25). The sandstones, or glacial drift derived from them, produce sandy soils, readily leached, typically carrying upland heather heath, managed as grouse moor. Individual hills such as Simonside (429 metres) and Tosson (440 metres) are conspicuous on the horizon from the outskirts of Newcastle. Further west, in upper Redesdale and upper North Tynedale, the Fell Sandstone hills are bulkier and, rather than making cuestas, are tabular in form; they include Carter Fell (579 metres), Peel Fell (602 metres), Deadwater Fell (569 metres) and Glendhu Hill (514 metres), and are much afforested.

Fig. 25 Key Heugh. Fell Sandstone cuesta crags above the Grasslees valley, amidst upland heather heath.

The Scremerston Coal, Lower Limestone and Middle Limestone groups, and the Millstone Grit (grits are sandstones), consist of repeated upward sequences of limestone, shale or mudstone, siltstone, sandstone and coal, the relative importance of the components being indicated by the group names (limestones, or coals, are absent in some of the groups). Coals in the Scremerston Coal Group, for example, were formerly widely mined in rural Northumberland. The sandstones and limestones make more or less prominent cuestas in the uplands. Hadrian's Wall, in the west of the county, runs through a famous landscape of east–west cuestas, separated by linear depressions (Fig. 26); streams follow these intercuesta depressions. The limestones in these groups account for a broad zone across the centre of the county within which occur linear patches of calcareous soil on the outcrops, and numerous flushes where base-rich water emerges, having passed through limestone or calcareous shales. Most of the limestones are only a few metres thick, and comprise only a relatively small proportion of the total thickness of strata in each group, but one bed, the Great Limestone, is thicker – up to 20 metres. It has the widest outcrop and is the most extensively quarried. Thicker sandstones in the Lower Limestone Group make the cuestas of the Ottercops and the Wanneys, heather-covered like the Fell Sandstones (Fig. 27).

Fig. 26 A minor cuesta formed by a thin sandstone, adjacent to the Wark section of Kielder Forest.

Fig. 27 Hangingstone Crag, in the Bewcastle Fells of northeast Cumbria. A Fell Sandstone sandstone with upland heather heath.

In the lowlands of the east of the county the cuesta forms are subdued, or lost under thick drift; there are still, however, local limestone influences at outcrop or in flushes. In southeast Northumberland crop out the Coal Measures, with their thick, productive coal seams. They were the basis of industry and urbanisation, and the indirect cause, as noted in Chapter 2, of many important habitats. Not least of these are the innumerable wetlands resulting from coal-mining subsidence. There is now only a single large colliery, Ellington, in this once great coalfield, but much opencast coal excavation. Thick Coal Measure sandstones make the low hills on the northwestern outskirts of Newcastle, from where there are such long views to the hills, and several of the coalfield villages are sited on sandstone knolls protruding through the drift. There is also a string of outliers of the Coal Measures west of Hexham, in and near the South Tyne valley, where coal was mined. Much of the drift which covers so much of the lowlands is a clayey glacial till derived largely by erosion of the shales and mudstones of the Carboniferous sequence, with the important consequence that the resulting soils are heavy and characterised by impeded drainage.

South of the Tyne Corridor
Here are the North Pennines, which in terms of geological structure is the Alston Block. Carboniferous sedimentary rocks again underlie most of the landscape – the Limestone groups and the Millstone Grit – but in this area they lie more or less horizontally (although tilted slightly away from a structural dome centred in the Cross Fell area) and therefore do not form cuestas. Instead there is plateau-benchland-dale topography. The main rivers have eroded dales, separated by wide – some very flat – plateaux, and the dale-sides are benched, or stepped, owing to resistant and weak rocks cropping out successively one above the other; the tough rocks, limestones and sandstones, form the benches (Fig. 28). Plantations were typically established on the risers of the benches (too steep, or with soils too shallow, for a hay crop), while meadows and pastures are on the treads of the staircase. The plateaux are developed on Millstone Grit sandstones, while the lower slopes and floors of the dales are in the underlying Limestone Groups. The elevation of the plateaux declines gradually from the west (overlooking the Vale of Eden in Cumbria) to the lower moorlands around the upper Derwent in the east. In the wetter west, and at the dale-heads, the plateaux, and even the higher valley-side benches, have developed blanket bog. The plateaux further east are drier, both because of a rain-shadow effect and because they are lower, and carry either heather heath (managed as grouse moor) or acidophilous grasslands.

Fig. 28 Benched dale-side, Ayle Common, North Pennines.

Cross Fell and its neighbours, Great (848 metres) and Little Dun Fells (842 metres) – all in Cumbria – are isolated residuals of even higher sandstones in the Millstone Grit sequence. In Northumberland the highest Pennine summits are on the southern and southwestern county boundary and include Killhope Law (673 metres – doubling as the highest summit in County Durham), Grey Nag (656 metres) and Tom Smith's Stone (631 metres).

The thicker sandstones and limestones locally form crags on the sides of dales, and, more commonly, where rivers and burns have cut gorges through them. Altogether, upland Northumberland has very numerous sandstone crags, including cuesta crags north of the Tyne Corridor, and some of these, with their pure air, support important lichen communities.

Throughout Northumberland, the sandstones have been used as building stones for houses, castles and public buildings and for field and moorland walls.

Whin Sill

This is a famous North East England rock formation and topographic feature, and provides important and distinctive habitats (Chapter 11). The Great Whin Sill is a somewhat complex set of sheets of igneous rock, with associated dykes, squeezed as magma between pre-existing sedimentary rocks near the end of the Carboniferous period. The main sheet is up to 70 metres or so thick. The normal rock of the sill is quartz-dolerite, blue-grey in colour, and in chemical composition is near to basalt. Early literature in fact refers to the rock as basalt; whinstone is a local name for any very hard, dark rock. The sill normally occurs at various horizons within the Limestone groups, although in the north, in the Kyloe Hills, it is intrusive into the Fell Sandstone Group. Because the sill is normally concordant with the strata into which it is intruded, its effect on the topography is analogous to that of other tough strata. North of the Tyne Corridor, therefore, owing to its thickness and extreme hardness, it makes a prominent cuesta, often with sheer crags on the scarp slope (Fig. 29). The crags show rough columnar jointing.

The whin cuesta begins near to Greenhead in the west of the county, carries the most spectacular section of Hadrian's Wall on its crest (with crags facing

Fig. 29 Cuestas near Crag Lough (mid-left, ice-covered). The most prominent cuesta is that of the Whin Sill, along the crest of which runs Hadrian's Wall.

defensively northwards; Plate 4b), then trends northeast across the county to reach the coast at Cullernose Point, which headland it forms (Fig. 30). Northwards from there its dip slope shelves gently into the North Sea until Dunstanburgh Castle is reached (Fig. 31). Offshore it forms, and through its resistance is responsible for the existence of, the Farne Islands, each island being a piece of cuesta with landward-facing sea cliffs and stacks (most famously The Pinnacles on Staple Island) and eastward shelving dip slopes. It returns to the mainland to underlie Bamburgh Castle, skirts Budle Bay and ends up in the Kyloe Hills. A whin dyke forms the hillock on Holy Island known as The Heugh and another that on which Holy Island Castle sits. The commanding and defensive opportunities offered by the Whin Sill have always been exploited.

Fig. 30 The Whin Sill at Cullernose Point (in distance), its dip slope shelving into the North Sea. Carboniferous sedimentary rocks in foreground.

Fig. 31 Dunstanburgh: the castle on an outcrop of the Whin Sill. The whin dips gently into the sea, except where the bay in the foreground, eroded behind the outcrop, has allowed cliff development on the cuesta scarp (Tim Gates: copyright reserved).

In the North Pennines the sill makes a pronounced dale-side bench, and there are gorges, below waterfalls, where rivers and burns flow over the edge of its outcrop. The best examples in our area are on Alston Moor, at Tyne Force and Cash Force (Fig. 32).

Fig. 32 Cash Force and gorge, where the Cash Burn pours over the Whin Sill on Alston Moor.

The Whin Sill is probably the most sampled igneous body in the world, and is the archetypal sill of geological science, although perversely it is now regarded as transgressing and jumping through the succession too much to be a bona fide sill. It was extensively quarried for paving sets, and is now a source of road aggregate. The rock is too tough to be shaped as a building stone, but was nonetheless used as the material to hand, for example at Craster.

Coastline

As the Carboniferous sedimentary strata, and the Whin Sill, sequentially intersect the coast in their broad arcs around the Cheviots, they make a sequence of cliffed headlands, bays and reefs. Thick sandstones form most of the headlands, although at Tynemouth, under the castle and priory, Permian-age Magnesian Limestone (otherwise a feature of the Durham coast) forms the upper part of the headland above a Coal Measure sandstone. At Cullernose Point and Castle Point, Dunstanburgh, the Whin Sill is responsible. Thinner sandstones, and limestones, form reefs – running out to sea or parallel with the shore. Weak rocks have been eroded to form bays. Glacial drift backs the longer bays: Seaton Sluice–Blyth, Druridge, Warkworth–Alnmouth, Beadnell; and shales are responsible for the smaller bays characteristic of the north Northumberland coast (Fig. 33).

Fig. 33 The coast at Howick, where the alternation of resistant and weak rocks makes for an indented coastline.

The natural history of the islands is described in Chapter 13. Holy Island is a large, low, farmed island, the main part of which is a square roughly 2x2 kilometres, separated from the mainland by tidal flats. It is underlain by strata in the Middle Limestone Group, including limestones formerly quarried for lime-burning (and by the prominent whin dykes previously mentioned), and has a widespread cover of glacial till. Blown sand is extensive to the north, and on the long western peninsula known as The Snook, and even the interior soils developed on till have a veneer of blown sand.

Northern Pennine Orefield

The Alston Block lies within the Northern Pennine Orefield, introduced in Chapter 2 (the Orefield also includes the Yorkshire Dales further south). Lead was produced mainly from galena ore, zinc from sphalerite and secondary ores, and iron from various ores. Cadmium and copper are also present, in low but ecologically significant concentrations, the former in solid solution in sphalerite and the latter in chalcopyrite (copper was produced very locally). Mineralisation occurred in the Upper Permian. The landscape of the upper dales – of the Derwent, East Allen, West Allen, South Tyne, Nent – is dominated by evidence of former mining activity. From our point of view, the industry caused many new habitats to be created, including plantations, reservoirs and a specialised agricultural landscape of smallholdings reclaimed from the moorland to remarkably high altitudes. Most distinctive, however, are habitats with waters or soils contaminated by heavy metals – lead, zinc, cadmium, copper – which are toxic to most organisms when present above critical concentrations.

One set of metalliferous habitats includes the mines themselves – their spoil dumps and dressing floors – together with the smelt mills and transport routes. Most of the productive oreshoots, both veins (where the mineralising fluids precipitated the ores in more or less vertical fissures in the rocks) and replacement flats (where limestone was chemically replaced by the minerals), occur within the Great Limestone. Its outcrop, on both the dale-sides and high on the fells, therefore localised many of the mines.

Secondly there is river alluvium. Particles of heavy metal ore, derived from mining and processing operations, were transported and redeposited on flood plains and channel beds. Such metalliferous alluvium is a distinctive soil of the South Tyne/Tyne system, and is found – now mainly on low, gravel terraces (Chapter 6) – both in and far beyond the Orefield, reaching to Newburn below the tidal limit. The contaminated alluvium is still being reworked through the river system.

The special, heavy metal-tolerant flora of these toxic soils is described in Chapter 11. There is a small outlier of the Orefield in the Tyne Corridor west and north of Haydon Bridge and eastwards to Fallowfield, which also contains metalliferous habitats.

Magnificent mineral specimens, especially of fluorspar, were collected from some of the mines, where they grew in cavities within the orebodies; they are found as windowsill decorations in North Pennine households, as well as in museums around the world.

4

The Ice Ages

About 20,000 years BP all or most of Northumberland was buried beneath a vast northern British ice sheet. As recently as 12,000 years ago there may still have been active glaciers in the Cheviots. Geologically these events are extremely recent. At 20,000 years ago modern humans *Homo sapiens* were already living in Europe south of the great ice sheets, and by 10,000 years ago farming communities were established in the Middle East. The period of the ice ages is the Quaternary sub-era – spanning approximately the last 2.6 million years of geological time. The Quaternary is characterised by a markedly fluctuating climate, with a long series of glacial and interglacial (temperate) stages. Glaciation was variously by ice sheets – like the one that reached its maximum in Britain about 20,000 years BP – or only by valley and other small upland glaciers. (For details see Lunn, 1995.)

Northumberland's topography and superficial geology, and therefore its habitats, were quite profoundly altered by glacial processes. This is partly because glaciation has been so recent that the landforms and deposits produced are still relatively fresh and unmodified. It is also because the geological work of glacier ice, glacial meltwater and prolonged frost is very effective. However, Northumberland's glacial landscape is very obviously not like the classic glacial landscapes of the Lake District or western Scottish Highlands. In the latter areas the effects of erosion by valley and corrie glaciers dominate the landscape. In Northumberland, with the exception of some parts of the Cheviots and North Pennines, glaciation was entirely by ice sheets, the effects of which, while considerable, are generally less spectacular (Fig. 34).

Fig. 34 Grooves eroded into the surface of the Whin Sill on Staple Island (Farnes) by the last ice sheet. The grassy bank is the edge of a till sheet.

The most recent cold climate stage is known in Britain as the Devensian (ca. 112,000–11,500 BP: it contains the latest widespread glaciation of the region), and the present temperate stage is the Flandrian (synonyms are Holocene, Post-glacial). In Northumberland, although earlier ice sheets affected the county, virtually all glacial deposits so far described are believed to belong to the Devensian, the last cold stage. In temperate stages of the Quaternary, Britain experienced climates similar to that of the present, with forest vegetation re-establishing on each occasion. These interglacial forests contained more, and more exotic or extinct, tree species the earlier they occurred in the Quaternary.

The latter part of the Devensian cold stage is known as the Dimlington Stadial (a stadial is a cold sub-stage). It was then, between about 26,000 and 15,000 years BP, that the major ice sheet referred to above advanced and retreated – at its maximum it extended southwards as far as north Norfolk. The Stadial was followed, in what is known as the Late-glacial period, by the mild Windermere Interstadial (ca. 14,600–12,900 years BP) and then by a brief, very cold episode, the Loch Lomond Stadial (the Younger Dryas of the Continent; ca. 12,900–11,500 years BP). During the Loch Lomond Stadial a large ice cap reformed in the western Scottish Highlands, and it is likely that the northern Cheviot valleys – The Bizzle and Hen Hole – contained small corrie glaciers at this time, as perhaps did the short valleys on the Pennine escarpment, west of Cross Fell. (The Bizzle has a typical, amphitheatre-like, corrie shape, but the Hen Hole valley is less well defined as a corrie (Fig. 35).)

Fig. 35 The Bizzle, a corrie on the northern flank of The Cheviot. The crags are in the metamorphic aureole and support a basiphilous montane flora. (Copyright Allan Potts.)

Dimlington Stadial ice sheet

Figure 36 shows ice sheet flow lines as they may have been late in the last glacial maximum. Most of Northumberland was glaciated by ice originating externally to the north and west, in the Tweed basin, Galloway and the Lake District, but flow was strongly influenced by local topography. As source areas varied in their dominance with the progress of glaciation, so the confluent ice masses jockeyed in a complex manner, particularly in the lowland areas. The southward deflection of Cheviot and Tweed valley ice along the coastal belt was most likely caused by the presence of a Scandinavian ice sheet off the present coast, confluent with British ice.

The external ice, on the evidence of erratics (boulders and stones carried from identifiable source outcrops), failed to override both the higher parts of the

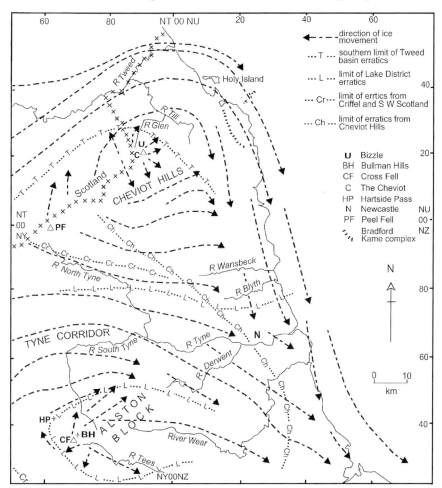

Fig. 36 Ice sheet flow lines late in the last glacial maximum (Dimlington Stadial). Slightly modified from Lunn (1995). With permission of Natural History Society of Northumbria.

North Pennines and of the Cheviot Hills; Lake District ice, for example, appears not to have crossed the Pennine escarpment much south of Hartside Pass. It is still uncertain whether the locally generated glaciers in these uplands were complete ice caps, or alternatively formed less extensive glacier networks, leaving the summits, such as Cross Fell, and high divides free of ice (as nunataks) at least during the Dimlington Stadial glaciation. In either case the local glaciers were confluent with the external ice. Limits of some main erratic suites are shown in Figure 36.

Whilst most erratics are of boulder or smaller size, some consist of extensive rafts of rock strata, detached from their beds and dragged forward by the ice sheet. Most of these giant erratics in our area are completely or partly buried by glacial drift, but the Bullman Hills, in the North Pennines, are exposed as landforms. These limestone knolls, at about 615 metres a.s.l., rise abruptly some 20 metres above the surrounding plateau, are up to 200 metres in diameter and consist of several displaced masses of the Great Limestone, which have been transported by ice about 1 kilometre northwards or northeastwards from an outcrop below the summit of Cross Fell. Their bright green limestone grassland contrasts sharply with the dull hues of the surrounding blanket bog, and calcicole (lime-loving) plants such as mossy saxifrage and mountain everlasting grow in the sheep-cropped turf (Fig. 37). On a smaller scale, the Kielder Stone is a lichen-draped block of sandstone, the size of a double-decker bus. A landmark in Border balladry, it sits isolated on the Scottish border line in a remote cleugh amidst blanket bog, and has been shifted an unknown distance by ice (Fig. 38).

Fig. 37 The Bullman Hills, near Cross Fell in the North Pennines. They are rafted giant erratics of the Great Limestone.

Fig. 38 The Kielder Stone, a huge sandstone erratic on the Scottish border line, Kielderhead
Moors. (V. Blankenburgs, with kind permission of Forest Enterprise and Northumberland
Archives Services: 2722-01-0186)

Till

Much of Northumberland is underlain by sheets of glacial drift, from less than
a metre up to about 10 metres or more thick, and covering the rocks described
in Chapter 3. Drift was the parent material of the present soils, and therefore
strongly influences present vegetation and land use. It underlies much of
agricultural lowland Northumberland, of inbye land in the uplands, and
substantial areas of moorland and forest. The drift was deposited largely by, or
in association with, the Dimlington Stadial ice sheet, and consists either of till
(boulder clay), derived directly from the glacier ice or by deformation of
underlying material, or of various water-laid sediments. The latter were deposited
by meltwater from the decaying ice sheet, including in lakes dammed against
the retreating ice.

Till typically comprises stones set in a matrix of finer material, usually with
much clay. On the upland plateaux and cuestas it tends to be thin, and sandy or
stony, or completely absent. In North Pennine dales it is, in general, distributed
asymmetrically, with deep and extensive sheets only on the sides of the valleys
lee with respect to ice sheet flow (for example, on the western sides of upper
South Tynedale and of the Allendales). This pattern of distribution indicates
dominant erosive activity of the ice sheet on interfluves, and slopes facing up-
glacier, and complementary deposition of till on lee slopes. At the heads of the
Pennine dales, and in the Cheviots, till occurs at least up to 615 metres a.s.l..

In the lowlands, till is more or less ubiquitous except where sandstone and Whin Sill cuestas and knolls protrude through it.

Over considerable areas till, or other drift, has been moulded by the ice into drumlins. These are ellipsoidal, stream-lined hillocks, typically up to 500 metres long and 10–20 metres high, with their long axes parallel to ice flow lines. Arrays of drumlins occur on Tweedside, where they impose a strong southwest–northeast grain upon the landscape, west of the lower North Tyne valley, and in the Tyne Corridor in the west of the county. Inter-drumlin hollows, where they have proved difficult to drain, contain surviving lowland wetlands. Elsewhere, however, till forms rather featureless plains.

In The Bizzle, moundy moraine is thought to represent the limit of a small Loch Lomond Stadial glacier.

Shake holes

Thin tills, where they overlie limestone, are commonly punctured by lines of 'shake holes', a few metres in diameter, where till has subsided into solution-widened fissures in the underlying limestone (Fig. 39). There are thousands of these circular depressions, on the dip slopes of limestone cuestas north of the Tyne Corridor and on valley-side benches in the North Pennines. Their clay-lined bottoms commonly contain populations of soft-rush (and sometimes rusting farm machinery). Others contain small natural ponds, perched on the permeable limestone, habitat for aquatic invertebrates such as dragonfly larvae, and amphibians. In parts of the North Pennine dales the myriads of shake holes are confounded by the numerous mine shafts and shallow coal pits to produce a moonscape landscape.

Fig. 39 Landscape northeast of Cross Fell. In the near-distance is an array of shake holes, one containing a pool. Further away is eroding blanket peat, and beyond that the Bullman Hills, limestone giant erratics.

Glacial erosion

Erosion by successive ice sheets substantially modified the pre-glacial landscape. This alteration took various forms.

North Pennines

In our part of the North Pennines, ice sheet flow was generally across the pre-existing river valleys. The effect of this was to impose a very marked asymmetry on the dale cross-profiles. Glacial erosion steepened the slopes facing up-glacier (the 'stoss' slopes, here facing west or southwest) and at the same time picked out on these slopes the variations of the rocks in resistance to erosion. Thus the stoss sides of the dales were not only steepened but are markedly benched (as described in Chapter 3), owing to the sequential outcrop on them of resistant rocks – which form the benches – and weak shales and mudstones. The lee slopes of the dales, on the other hand, are smoother and gentler, the more so owing to selective deposition of till low on the lee slopes, as just described. All of upper South Tynedale, West Allendale, East Allendale and the Derwent valley display this cross-section asymmetry. The southwest-facing Ayle Common, on the eastern side of the South Tyne just north of Alston, has a spectacularly benched landform – especially clear in low evening sunlight (Fig. 40). Some individual hills also have a marked stoss-and-lee form, for example Park Fell, southwest of Alston, standing in the path of ice streaming over Hartside Pass from the Lake District.

Fig. 40 Benching on the up-glacier (ice sheet) face of Ayle Common, upper South Tynedale.

Limestone pavement would normally be expected to occur in glaciated limestone uplands, as is the case further south in the Yorkshire Dales, but there is none in this part of the North Pennines. This is because the individual limestone beds here are thinner than further south, and the sandstones and shales correspondingly thicker, so contributing more material to the till which was deposited over limestone outcrops.

The Tyne Corridor

The thick ice streaming eastwards (within the broader ice sheet) along this pre-glacial through-valley selectively eroded its bed, converting the valley into a glacial trough. This is followed by the A69 trunk road and the railway between Newcastle and Carlisle. The trough is partly infilled with drift, without which the lower Tyne valley would be well below present sea level at least as far upstream as Wylam. Even now, the river is tidal almost to there. The lowermost Tyne valley is therefore a virtual fjord – a drowned glacial trough – famously bridged at Newcastle. The colonies of kittiwakes nesting on buildings and structures by the lower Tyne add to the fjord-like perception.

The erosional deepening of the South Tyne/Tyne valley with respect to adjacent uplands is at least partly responsible for the deep incision of tributary rivers as they descend to it, although long-term uplift of the North Pennines to the south probably also contributed. Notable among these incised tributaries is the River Allen, falling to the South Tyne through spectacular incised meanders, whose steep slopes are clothed by ancient, semi-natural woodland.

Cuestas
Between the Tyne Corridor and the southern margin of the Cheviot Hills the ice was flowing eastwards, more or less parallel with the west–east strike of rock outcrop. Ice sheet erosion was therefore able to emphasise and accentuate the cuesta forms – most clearly in the vicinity of Hadrian's Wall. The ice scoured and lowered the weak rocks of the inter-cuesta depressions, leaving these with numerous closed basins (Plate 6a). Most of the meres that formerly occupied these basins have been infilled by peat accumulation and are now represented by the raised and intermediate bogs.

Cheviot Hills
The parts of the Cheviots exposed to external ice show stoss-and-lee forms similar to those in the North Pennines. Because valleys tend to be closer spaced, however, it is the interfluves that are perceived as asymmetrical rather than the valleys. The ridges lying athwart ice flow directions are steepened and roughened on their western sides (facing up-glacier) and gentler and smoother to the east. This landform is particularly clear when viewing the volcanic Cheviots from the upper Coquetdale road west of Alwinton.

As noted, during the Loch Lomond Stadial there may have been small glaciers occupying the two corries (The Bizzle and Hen Hole) on the northern flanks of The Cheviot. Numerous other phases of local mountain glaciation (less extensive than ice sheet glaciation) occurred during the Quaternary, and it is likely that in some of these phases there developed in the Cheviots not just corrie glaciers, but also valley glaciers. These would also be present during the build-up phases to ice sheet glaciation, and erosion by such valley glaciers is a likely explanation of the trough shapes of the College valley and the long, straight valley of the Harthope Burn.

Lowland Northumberland
Although, in most of the lowlands, glacial erosional landforms are buried by drift, south-flowing ice created crag-and-tail features at outcrops of the Whin Sill in the coastal plain south of Budle Bay. Long tails of drift, or weaker rocks, trail southwards behind the protective whin knolls, for example at Spindlestone.

Mapping of rockhead under the drift in southeast Northumberland shows that the solid rock surface is dissected by a number of buried valleys. These have long been a subject of concern in North East England, because they cut out coal seams and presented a mining flood hazard where their deposits are pervious. Some underlie surface valleys, while others are without surface expression. They descend to at least 20 metres below present sea level where they cross the present coastline. Beyond the fact that they must be at least of pre-Late Devensian origin, their age is unknown; they may reasonably be inferred to relate to low relative sea levels of Quaternary cold stages, when much water was locked up on land as ice. They contain the greatest drift thicknesses in the county, with up to 60 metres, predominantly of water-laid sediments.

Deposition by glacial meltwaters

The deposits and landforms associated with the deglaciation at the end of the Dimlington Stadial are particularly clear and fresh. The ice sheet was retreating rapidly through Northumberland at about 17,000–16,000 years BP. Copious meltwater streams deposited water-sorted sands and gravels under, on, in, against and in front of the retreating and thinning ice sheet, which, at least towards its margins, was by now stagnant. Finer material – silt and clay – was carried directly into the sea or deposited in lakes. Some of the lakes occupied depressions in the newly exposed land surface, while others, where sectors of the ice sheet were retreating down-slope, were temporarily dammed up against the ice front.

The water-laid glacial deposits in Northumberland occur in three main contexts:

1. **In a north–south zone a few kilometres inland from the coast**. This probably represents the zone of confluence between ice of western and of northern origin. Meltwater would be concentrated here during ice wastage, both when the two components of the ice sheet were still confluent and immediately after they separated. Sediments were laid down in a variety of ice-contact and proglacial (in front of the ice sheet) environments, including in a series of lakes trapped between the western and northern ice. Laminated silts and clays were deposited in these lakes, forming impervious soil parent materials.

In the north is the Bradford kame complex (Fig. 36: a kame is a ridge or mound of meltwater sands and gravels). It includes a long, sinuous esker consisting of earthy gravels, stretching from Spindlestone southwards to Fallodon, and adjacent bulky mounds of finer sands and silts. The esker probably represents the deposits of a subglacial stream.

2. **In large topographic basins, where the free escape of meltwater was impeded**. Examples are Milfield plain and the Wooperton area, respectively north and south of Wooler. Here too deposition occurred in both ice-contact and proglacial environments. In the Wooperton area a lobe of the northwestward retreating ice sheet stagnated in the basin between the Cheviot Hills to the west and the Fell Sandstone cuesta to the east. There is now a strange, choppy landscape of sand and gravel hillocks with intervening depressions, probably arising as sediments originally deposited on the surface of the decaying ice were let down chaotically as the ice melted. The depressions are kettle holes and dead-ice hollows, representing respectively smaller and larger masses of melted-out ice.

On further retreat, the ice margin came to stand at about Etal, north of Wooler, impounding a large lake in Milfield plain. Meltwater from the west, flowing through the valley now occupied by the River Glen, built a large sand and gravel delta into the lake. The delta surface is the wide, level terrace occupying the western half of the plain; it was described as being a wilderness of broom in the eighteenth century, before enclosure. Agricultural improvers later established the numerous plantations on the delta surface, to reduce wind speed and prevent the sandy soils blowing from their fields. Under the eastern part of Milfield plain, where the ice-dammed lake was not encroached by the delta, are thick deposits of lacustrine clays and silts, their surface a few metres below that of the delta, although they are now largely overlain by more recent river alluvium. This lower ground, pasture rather than arable, is conspicuously less well drained.

Probably at a stage in ice retreat roughly contemporary with the existence of Milfield Lake, sands and gravels were being deposited amongst decaying ice on low ground between Cornhill and Etal. They now form eskers and kames with intervening wetland hollows. Part of Flodden battlefield lay in the southern part of this belt of sand and gravel.

3. **In the major river valleys of the Tyne and the Tweed**. In both cases huge volumes of meltwater passed through the margins of the retreating ice sheets, from vast up-glacier catchments. In the case of the Tyne the catchment at one stage included much of the northern Lake District and parts of southwest Scotland. Probably the ice was still actively flowing while its front retreated, but in the terminal zone – perhaps a few kilometres wide – it was stagnant. In this marginal, stagnant zone, sands and gravels deposited on, under or against the decaying ice are now represented by a moundy topography of kames, eskers and intervening hollows, for example in the floor of the South Tyne valley west of Hexham and extending to Gilsland. In front of the ice margin, in the case of both the Tyne and the Tweed, outwash valley trains of cobbles and gravels extended far down-valley. The modern rivers have cut down through these deposits, leaving the former meltwater river beds as wide, flanking terraces. These are conspicuous by the Tweed in the Carham–Wark–Coldstream area and along much of the length of the South Tyne/Tyne. Many villages are sited upon them.

Numerous quarries, some very large, have worked the thicker sand and gravel, and laminated clay/silt, deposits. The latter provided the raw material for brick making, from Roman times through to the great coal-based Victorian industrial expansion of the North East.

Meltwater channels

Meltwater streams, in torrential parts of their courses, eroded into drift or bedrock. Many steep-sided valleys occur in positions where modern streams could not possibly have eroded them, and are glacial meltwater channels. The relative contributions of meltwater erosion and of normal stream erosion in the cases of other, similar, channels that do contain modern streams is unclear. However, it is likely that the valleys of many modern rivers or burns were initiated as part of a glacial meltwater drainage system.

Much of this meltwater drainage is considered to have been subglacial, with streams flowing in tunnels at the base of the ice sheet. A large-scale example of such a subglacial channel is Beldon Cleugh in the North Pennines, cut some 50 metres into rock and with a markedly sinuous course where it crosses the watershed from the Devils Water to the Beldon Burn (Fig. 41). Another large example is the Butt Hill channel, which cuts right through the main North Pennine watershed in the wild country between Hartside Pass and Cold Fell. On both the northern and southern flanks of the eastern Cheviots are other large channels, cut into rock, many severing the ends of spurs from the main mass of the hills. All these large subglacial channels are aligned in the direction of former ice flow, that is, of the ice surface gradient. This is because the latter largely determined, and was reflected by, the hydrological gradient within the ice, which drives subglacial meltwater flow.

Fig. 41 Beldon Cleugh, a glacial meltwater channel in the North Pennines.

There are many thousands of glacial meltwater channels in Northumberland, from major to minor. Some, aligned along the contour, probably formed when streams descending already ice-free hillsides encountered residual ice in the valleys and coursed along its margins. The steep sides of meltwater channels in the uplands normally carry a drier variant of moorland vegetation – heather heath, acidophilous grassland or bracken – set within blanket mire or some other type of wet moorland. The channels provide shelter for sheep in hard weather, and tend to be well grazed.

In the lowlands, the gorge-like tracts of some of the east-flowing rivers probably also originated as subglacial meltwater channels, as did the many narrow, deeply incised valleys that are drained by relatively small streams and are the wooded denes of Chapter 9. The gorges and denes interrupt the till-covered coastal plain, and are cut down into the Carboniferous sedimentary rocks. In the north of Northumberland the winding gorge of the lower River Till was largely eroded by meltwater.

Periglacial landforms and deposits

During cold but non-glacial times of the Late-glacial period, Northumberland experienced a periglacial climate and environment, dominated by frost-processes. One such episode was during the Loch Lomond Stadial, when frost-riving of exposed, jointed rocks caused widespread scree formation. There are block screes below the crags of both the Whin Sill and the thicker sandstones (Fig. 42), but the closely jointed volcanic rocks of the Cheviots, which are highly frost-susceptible, disintegrated to form the widespread fine to medium-coarse scree aprons – partly vegetated – of the steep, lower hill slopes.

Fig. 42 The Screes, below the summit of Cross Fell – sandstone block scree.

Drift deposits are prone to mass movement down slope, both immediately after glacier ice has melted (before vegetation has stabilised the ground) and in periglacial environments, and much general smoothing of slopes occurred. In the Cheviots, weathered granite, frost-disintegrated volcanics and till were all affected, and sheets of stony-loamy sediment now form smooth, sloping terraces on the lower valley sides, terminating in bluffs above the rivers and burns (Harrison, 2002). Major landslip scars, usually where sandstone failed where overlying weak shale, toed by moraine-like rubble, may also be of Late-glacial age; an example is the feature called Upper Stony Holes, near Peel Fell.

Above about 615 metres in the north Pennines there are blockfields (carrs) on more or less level ground, and also patterned ground, both being frost-produced forms, relict from Late-glacial times. The patterns include sorted stone polygons and stripes, in each case approximately 1–2 metres in separation; they are readily observed on Cross Fell and Great and Little Dun Fells, where the polygons are traversed by Pennine Way walkers (Fig. 43).

Fig. 43 Fossil stone polygons on Cross Fell summit.

In the Cheviot Hills conspicuous bosses of rock, similar to the tors on Dartmoor, project 10 to 15 metres above otherwise relatively featureless surfaces. Bellyside Crag (Fig. 44) and Braydon Crag on The Cheviot are examples, as is the feature on Great Standrop, north of the headwaters of the River Breamish. They are indeed tors, landmarks for walkers and shepherds. There are about a dozen of them, situated at 395 to 660 metres above sea level, and consisting of granite or of metamorphosed lava. One theory of tor formation is that they developed as a result of disintegration of bedrock by frost processes to an irregular buried weathering front. The sound bosses on this front were then exhumed as tors by stripping of the enveloping loose material. The erosion was accomplished either by gravitational mass movement or by glacial erosion. The alternative theory is that the rotting of bedrock (prior to stripping) occurred in a pre-Quaternary, subtropical environment.

Fig. 44 A Cheviot tor, Bellyside Crag, in granite.

5

Climate and Soils

Climate

Much information on climate in Northumberland has been provided by Manley (1946) and the Northumbrian River Authority (1973), and the climate section of this chapter is largely based on these sources.

Temperature

We have already noted that Northumberland is the coldest part of England, and that near-shore North Sea surface temperatures are also low. Sea temperatures are particularly low in spring and early summer, when east winds prevail and we all shiver. July sea level temperatures on land are about 14.5–15.0°C (averages of daily mean temperature), with sea-surface temperatures offshore about 13°C; in southeastern England both are about 2°C higher. In January, sea level temperatures on land are about 3.0–3.5°C and sea-surface temperatures about 5.5°C. However, in the vicinity of the coast, winter temperatures are a degree or two higher than inland, and summer temperatures lower, owing to the ameliorating effect of the sea.

Temperatures on land in Britain decrease with height at a lapse rate of about 0.6–0.7°C per 100 metres. This represents an extreme sensitivity of climate to altitude and largely explains the huge environmental differences between the lowlands and the upland moorlands. For example, the July mean temperature at 600 metres a.s.l. (approximately 2,000 feet) is about 11°C and at 750 metres a.s.l. (almost 2,500 feet) 10°C. Gordon Manley, who wrote the volume in this series *Climate and the British scene* (1952) used to tell the story of taking a visiting Scandinavian professor up to Great Dun Fell, breasting the scarp crest and finding spread out before them the immense, eastward panorama of the North Pennine moorlands between Teesdale and Weardale. The professor exclaimed: 'This is the tundra', as he at once recognised a cold, northern scene.

Precipitation

By British standards, lowland Northumberland is rather dry, owing to a rain-shadow effect of the uplands to the west and southwest, from which direction come the main moisture-bearing winds. However, within the county, precipitation increases both westwards and with altitude, and moderately heavy precipitation falls on the western uplands. Figure 45 shows average annual precipitation. The wettest part of Northumberland is in the North Pennines – on the main watershed between the Tyne and the Eden drainage – with in places more than 1,525 millimetres, and the driest is the mouth of the Tweed with as little as 610 millimetres – about the same as Palermo, in Sicily. Most of the coastal plain and of lowland north Northumberland receive less than 700 millimetres. The hills from Carter Bar southwestwards to the head of the River Irthing receive more than 1,270 millimetres. This is sufficient, when combined with low temperatures, to promote extensive peat accumulation in the blanket bogs that dominate the landscape of these hills and of the higher plateaux of the North Pennines. The Cheviots, owing to their easterly location, experience an enhanced rain-shadow effect, so that The Cheviot itself, at 815 metres a.s.l., receives little over 1,145 millimetres, whereas similar altitudes in the Cross Fell area receive more than 1,780 millimetres. Nonetheless, this is still wet enough for blanket bog to have formed on The Cheviot and on the main Cheviot summit ridges.

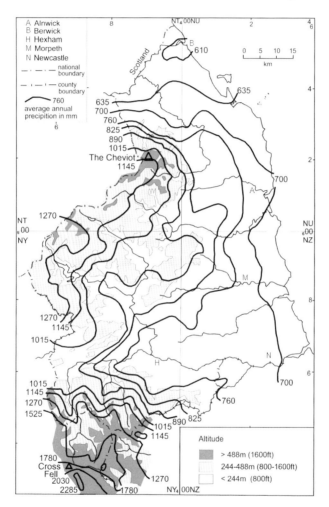

Fig. 45 Precipitation. Average annual precipitation (mm). After Northumbrian River Authority (1973), with permission of Environment Agency.

The boundary between improved farmland and moorland (the 'moorland edge'), although not closely correlated with rainfall, is in many areas close to the 890-millimeter isohyet (line of equal rainfall). Simply, more rainfall means poorer soils, as explained in the section on soils (p.75), which are therefore unable to repay or sustain intensive management and are left unreclaimed, as moorland. In broad terms precipitation reflects the contour map, with the rather dry Tyne Corridor conspicuous. On average, precipitation in the summer and winter half-years is similar, but July and August are the wettest months, and March and April the driest. Cloudiness increases with altitude, and Great Dun Fell expects morning fog on two days out of three.

Snowfall is normally brought to Northumberland with northerly and easterly polar air masses, and the altitude effect causes the Cheviots, and the eastern slopes of the North Pennines, to experience the heaviest falls (usually between December and March), the deepest snow and the longest snow-lie. On the coast there are fewer than ten days on average with snow lying (very seldom at Holy Island), Kielder has 33 days, but snow lies on more than 100 days on The Cheviot and Great Dun Fell. In some years there has been snow on The Cheviot and on Cross Fell until July. North East England is the region of most frequent snowfall in England and Wales. Of course these snowfall figures are long-term averages, and have not been reflected in recent warmer winters.

The main effect of precipitation on plants is indirect, via its effects on the soil. Soils in high rainfall areas tend to be acidic and nutrient-deficient (because heavily leached), or waterlogged. In particular, as explained in Chapter 8, more or less permanently waterlogged soils accumulate peat – the only partly decayed remains of vegetation. Comparing Figure 45 and the map showing the distribution of peat (Fig. 62), it seems that something like 1,145–1,270 millimetres, or on gentle slopes 1,000 millimetres, are required for blanket bog development. More precisely, according to Lindsay *et al.* (1988) the climatic requirements for blanket bog formation are first a minimum annual rainfall of 1,000 millimetres; second a minimum of 160 'wet days' (with 1 millimetre or more precipitation within 24 hours) per year; and third a cool climate with mean temperature less than 15°C for the warmest month. The second condition is just met by the parts of Northumberland with blanket bog and the third is comfortably met in the uplands.

Haar

A particularly bleak feature of the climate of the northeast coast of England, as it is elsewhere on the east coast, in late spring and early summer – especially May and June – is the persistent presence of haar or sea fret. This is either very low stratus cloud, or fog, accompanied by low temperatures and intermittent drizzle, brought in on easterly winds chilled to saturation by the still cold North Sea. At this time of the year the coldest western North Sea waters lie off the local coast. The haar penetrates varying distances inland and is partly responsible for lowland Northumberland's low mean summer temperatures. Other areas of Britain are typically bathed in sunshine when the sea fret shrouds our coastal zone, and on the west coast at the same latitude mean daily maximum temperatures in May are 3°C higher than on the Northumberland coast. It is often said that there is no spring in Northumberland, and on Holy Island May is very often the worst month of the twelve. At other seasons, however, including the remainder of the summer, the coastal zone experiences the highest numbers of hours of sunshine in the county.

Two ferns (a group many of whose members avoid exposed, dry conditions) become locally frequent on mortared walls very near to the coast. These are wall-rue and maidenhair spleenwort, probably owing to the beneficial effects (shading, humidity) of the sea frets. Cool, afternoon, summer sea breezes also favour these ferns. The cool climate of the coastal zone also conserves soil humidity, promoting rapid growth there of introduced western North American coniferous trees. Fortunately coal smoke no longer turns fog into smog.

The North Pennines

The high altitude to which the dual lead mining and farming economy pushed the moorland edge, by land reclamation in the dales, was mentioned in Chapter 3. Baker (1868) was greatly impressed by this, noting that, just over the Durham boundary from Alston Moor, the Grasshill farmhouse lay at the extraordinary altitude of 610 metres (2,000 feet) a.s.l. In Northumberland, the small settlement of Coalcleugh in West Allendale is at 533 metres. At Grasshill, admittedly in the shelter of an old limekiln, the farmer grew rhubarb, potatoes and turnips. In the Allendales, oats were grown at 488 metres, barley at 290 metres, and plum, raspberry, red- and blackcurrants, cabbage, onion and other garden plants at 503 metres. Since many of the houses are still inhabited (although few as full-time farms), we can still find many of the garden and orchard species growing high up the valleys today, despite the severe North Pennine climate.

Plants and animals reaching their northern British limits in Northumberland
The distributions of all plants and animals are affected by climate. In Britain, where moisture shortage is not limiting for most species, some aspect of temperature determines broad distributions for many. There are species that are southern, or northern, or upland, or have some other type of distribution pattern. For invertebrates the effect may be indirect, via a food plant. Although the temperature effect can operate in many detailed ways – through late frost incidence, winter cold, summer warmth, for example – it is likely that, for many organisms, what is called accumulated temperature is critical. This is a measure of the total amount of heat energy (heat sums) available during the growing or active season. There are various ways of calculating it. One measure of heat sums is of accumulated temperature above 0°C for January to June (i.e. summing the number of daily mean temperature degrees above 0°C for every day in that period). A map is reproduced as Figure 46, and it can be seen that accumulated temperature (so calculated) varies from more than 1,350 day-degrees on the coast to only 850 days on Cross Fell – the coldest place in England.

Provided that its particular heat threshold is surpassed a plant, or an animal, whose range is controlled in this way, can survive (if it can get there and if the rest of the habitat conditions are right). This means that many British species have summer-temperature-controlled northern limits to their distributions, and since Northumberland extends over 100 kilometres from south to north (equivalent to 0.5°C temperature difference) it is to be expected that a number of plants and animals will reach their northern limits in Britain in the county. Of course, species that have southern limits in Northumberland (there are many fewer) must be responding to different aspects of temperature (or to other factors entirely). As regards heat sums, however, it is one thing to show a correlation between a species' geographical limit and a particular sum, or to define a species' climate space using other data, and quite another to work out

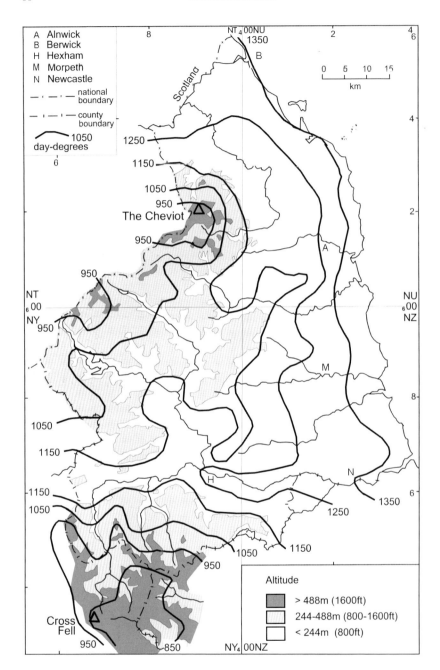

Fig. 46 Mean accumulated temperature above 0°C (day-degrees), January to June.
Reproduced from National Soil Resources Institute: Jarvis *et al.* (1984). Copyright Cranfield
University 2004. No part of this publication may be reproduced without the express written
permission of Cranfield University.

what particular aspect of the climate is the controlling factor, and how it works physiologically.

A Northumberland plant for which this has been done is a tree, the small-leaved lime. The critical event is fertilisation of the ovum by the pollen, which requires mean daily maximum temperatures at flowering (in July–August) of at least 19°C, achieved today only some 200 kilometres south of Northumberland (Pigott & Huntley, 1981; Pigott, 1991). Yet the lime occurs, although infrequently, as a probably native species at least as far north as the Tyne valley, presumably as vegetatively surviving trees from lime woods that became established in the warmer conditions of the mid-Holocene. Lime can sprout and root from fallen trunks.

There are, of course, reasons other than climate that might explain organisms having northern limits in Northumberland. Limestone habitats, although not extensive here, are even less so further north in Scotland. Slow-dispersing species may only have reached this far north, on recolonisation of England following the last glaciation. For invertebrates, the host plants might be missing, or for plants the mycorrhizae (symbiotic root fungi). There are hosts of possibilities for an organism not occurring somewhere, but some aspect of temperature will often be the cause.

Plants
The following is a list of full species, but including one subspecies (the spleenwort), of native vascular plants, excluding hybrids, which reach their northern British limits in the county, based on records from 1970s onwards in the distribution maps of Preston *et al.* (2002). (For some species there are a few earlier records from localities further north.) Some of the species have Scottish records, in Berwickshire or in southwest Scotland, but from localities no further north than the Northumberland ones.

> lobed maidenhair spleenwort
> mousetail (native status uncertain)
> sea-purslane
> shiny glasswort
> upright chickweed
> tasteless water-pepper
> golden dock
> common sea-lavender
> musk mallow
> early dog-violet
> white bryony
> * bird's-eye primrose
> creeping jenny
> field rose
> small-flowered sweet briar
> smooth tare
> slender trefoil
> dyer's greenweed
> whorled water-milfoil
> sea-buckthorn
> spurge laurel
> square-stalked willowherb
> field maple

greater burnet saxifrage
fine-leaved water dropwort
wild celery
lesser centaury
yellow-wort
* Jacob's ladder
wild privet
saw-wort
hawkweed oxtongue
blue fleabane (now known as a probable native on Mull)
hoary ragwort
frogbit
opposite-leaved pondweed
lords and ladies
divided sedge
dune fescue
curved hard-grass
tor grass
sea couch
chives
daffodil
green-flowered helleborine
bee orchid

Additionally, sea-holly is at its northernmost east-coast locality in Northumberland. Small-leaved lime has not been included in the list, although it has been regarded as reaching its northern limit in the Tyne valley, because its status in Scotland is uncertain. Bee orchid has spread northwards into the county in recent years and yellow-wort has expanded its distribution rapidly.

The 44 species listed (after excluding the two species marked with an asterisk, as being mid-British in their distribution) are not an excessive number to have their northern limits within the 112 kilometre length of the county. Let us assume, for the sake of argument, that species belonging to the Southern-temperate and Mediterranean geographical elements of the British flora (pp 93–94) might be expected to have northern limits somewhere in Britain, plus say half of the Temperate element. These sum to 696 species, and since Northumberland accounts for about 10 per cent of the north–south length of Britain, other things being equal and with a uniform north–south temperature gradient, about 70 species would, pro rata, be expected to reach their limits here – rather more than the 44 in the list.

A few other species, common enough further south in England and still abundant in south Northumberland, tail off rapidly in the north of the county and have only a few localities in Scotland. These include great burnet, spindle and betony. Great burnet has a remarkably abrupt – almost linear – northern limit to its main distribution at the River Coquet, which is difficult to explain. It is characteristic of upland meadows so the cause in this case is unlikely to be directly related to temperature.

Animals
Some more conspicuous animals that are believed to reach their northern limits in Northumberland, or almost so, are:

BUTTERFLIES
small skipper
white-letter hairstreak
wall (possibly in Berwickshire)

REPTILES AND AMPHIBIANS
grass snake
The grass snake's northern distribution limit is probably temperature controlled, since like all our reptiles and amphibians it relies on external heat sources for its metabolism and activities. There are reliable twentieth-century records for Northumberland, but none recently of which I am certain.

BREEDING BIRDS
Birds are mobile, and occasional breeding occurrences blur range boundaries; also proof of breeding can be difficult. The following list should be read with those qualifications:
hobby
little ringed plover (an irregular breeder in Scotland)
turtle dove (not a regular breeder here or in Scotland)
little owl (just gets into Scotland)
nightjar (just gets into Scotland)
lesser spotted woodpecker (a very rare breeder)
reed warbler (limited breeding in Scotland)
bearded tit (a very rare breeder)
willow tit (a very few localities further north)
nuthatch (a few localities in the Scottish Borders, and spreading north still)

MAMMALS
dormouse
Dormice, no longer known in Scotland, are thought to be sensitive to cold, wet summers, which adversely affect survival and reproductive success (Bright, 1996). Brandt's and noctule bats are here probably near their northern limits.

Plants and animals reaching their southern limits in Northumberland
Compared with the 46 species reaching their northern limit here, only four vascular plant species reach their southern limits in Northumberland:
        Issler's clubmoss
        small cranberry
        slender-leaved pondweed
        curved sedge
  Another four coastal species reach their southern east-coast limits:
        early orache
        Scots lovage
        seaside centaury
        spring squill
  Additionally the upland species, dwarf cornel, has only a couple of records further south, and dwarf birch only one.
  The low number of plant species reaching southern limits here reflects the well-known fact that for many groups species-richness declines northwards in Britain, but is also due to montane species finding suitable habitats south of

Northumberland, in the Lake District and North Wales.

The eider duck reaches its southernmost east-coast breeding limit on Coquet Island.

The natural tree line

In mountain regions of the world there is a well-recognised altitudinal limit to tree growth – the tree line – although this is often a zone rather than a sharp boundary. There has been much discussion as to which climatic factor, or factors, determine this limit (it does not seem to matter too much which tree species are at the tree line in a particular region).

Most recently, Körner (1998, 1999) has reviewed the subject. He concluded that the most likely, worldwide, limiting factor is some critical minimum temperature threshold for investment by the tree in tissue development and growth (rather than any limitation of photosynthesis by temperature: i.e. there is not a shortage of materials, rather a low-temperature inhibition on their use). There is a requirement, according to Körner, for a minimal mean growing season air temperature of 5.5–7.5°C, which applies at all latitudes. (He rejects the minimum-temperature-for-the-warmest-month alternative.) However, he also accepts that this overall thermal limitation is modulated by other, regional factors, and wind is likely to be an important depressing factor at the higher levels of the oceanic uplands of northern Britain – as, indeed, has long been widely accepted (Grace, 1997). Applying Körner's temperature threshold in northern England, with a lapse rate of 0.6–0.7°C per 100 metres and assuming a five-month growing season at higher altitudes, leads to the prediction of a temperature-controlled natural tree line here in the order of 1,000 metres a.s.l. or somewhat higher – that is, above the altitudes of the highest summits in the Cheviots, North Pennines and Lake District.

In Britain, where most natural woodland has long disappeared, the only natural altitudinal tree line is considered to be in the Cairngorms, at Creag Fhiaclach, with Scots pine growing up to an altitude normally given as about 640 metres a.s.l. (recent large-scale maps indicate that it is nearer 600 metres), but it is likely that in more sheltered spots it could, in the absence of grazing, reach somewhat higher. Recently, the removal of red deer from another Cairngorm mountainside, in Glenmore, has seen Scots pine establish up to about 700 metres a.s.l., albeit as krummholz (stunted trees) (D. Jardine, pers. comm.). Since Northumberland is some 200 kilometres further south, the local tree line (other factors being equal) might be expected to be slightly higher again. Individual trees recorded in the Scottish Highlands are downy birch at 760 metres a.s.l. and rowan at 975 metres, with seedlings higher still, while Wilson (1956) gives 870 metres for rowan in the Lake District, on Helvellyn. However, exceptionally favourable microhabitats can be expected to distort the general patterns.

In our area, Ashgill plantation on Alston Moor, dating from the mid-nineteenth century, ascends to a ridge crest at 614 metres, where stunted Norway spruce and European larch now survive to just below the summit, although only in the shelter of a stone dyke about 2 metres high, which they have scarcely overtopped. Those furthest from its shelter have died. The larch has grown stout trunks with a prostrate habit, while the spruce is vertical but dwarfed (Figs 47 & 48). The plantation was described by Lewis (1904), who noted that the spruce, which was then still alive at the summit itself, had a dense shrubby growth to about 1 metre high. Nearby, on the Durham side of Killhope Law, an experimental Forestry Commission plantation of several provenances of Sitka spruce and lodgepole pine, now restored to moorland, had its upper planted limit, with krummholz, at 655 metres. Also, as an experiment by interested naturalists (D. Phillips pers. comm.), a small group of Sitka spruce was planted in 1977 high on Cross Fell at about 700m a.s.l., inside a small walled enclosure. Surviving trees are now about 3 metres tall, overtopping the walls (Fig. 49). The difficulties trees are having, at all these exposed Pennine sites, indicates significant regional modulation by wind damage or stress of any temperature-controlled tree line. In Britain mean wind speeds at 600 metres a.s.l. are 20–30 kilometres per hour, on Great Dun Fell at 848 metres they are 37 kilometres per hour, and there are frequent gales. A gust of 214 kilometres per hour was recorded on Great Dun Fell, and gusts of over 180 kilometres per hour occur every few years. No doubt wind-blast by snow or hail above a snow cover is particularly lethal, or the effect of wind on heavy rime, but it is now accepted that wind depresses growth rates directly by mechanically induced physiological effects (Telewski, 1995). Wind also cools plant tissues.

Fig. 47 Ashgill plantation, Alston Moor, just below the 614-metre a.s.l. ridge crest. Stunted Norway spruce and dead skeletons.

Fig. 48 Ashgill plantation, view west from below ridge crest. Prostrate European larch.

Fig. 49 Three metre tall Sitka spruce, planted in 1977 in an enclosure at Greg's Hut at about 700 metres a.s.l. below Cross Fell. Photograph 2003.

In the light of all these considerations, in the normal absence of shelter and under present climatic conditions, a natural tree line for Northumberland at 600–700 metres a.s.l. is suggested, but varying very considerably depending on wind exposure. Aspect, with respect to solar radiation, will also have an effect. The former tree line would tongue up sheltered valleys and be depressed on spurs. Such a tree line at 600–700 metres a.s.l. leaves only a very small area above the forest limit: the high divides of Alston Moor and the highest Cheviots. Millar (1964) described several high-altitude conifer plantations on Alston Moor, and noted that there appeared to be a sudden increase in the exposure factor at about 450–520 metres, above which stunting and deformation increased rapidly.

Even at much lower altitudes, Kielder Forest is a wind-dominated forest, the risk of wind-throw severely constraining management despite deep ditching to lower the water table and so aid root penetration (Chapter 10).

But temperature and wind are not the only factors that determine upper tree limits. No native trees will normally grow on acidic, nutrient-deficient peat with a high water table, although birch and Scots pine can invade if the water table is lowered by natural or human causes, and browsing by native herbivores may also have helped to keep bogs clear of trees. The extensive blanket bogs would therefore have precluded woodland on the higher plateaux and summits (as did other bogs at lower elevations), and woodland would ascend, on mineral soils, only to the lower edge of the peat blanket, which is now commonly as low as 350–400 metres. A much greater area of natural Northumberland would therefore have been treeless for this reason (parts of the area shown as bog on Figure 62) than for those just discussed. However, the extent of blanket and other peat some 6,000 years ago, before the beginning of significant impact of man on the forest is not known (it has certainly spread considerably since then). Peat now covers about 9–10 per cent of the county, blanket peat was accumulating by 8,000 years BP and if we hazard a guess that only one-third of the 9–10 per cent existed 6,000 years ago, and add a small area for mineral soils above the climatic tree line, and other habitats too stressful or unstable for trees – coastal dunes, salt marsh, scree, river alluvium and river banks, rock outcrops and the wettest flushes – perhaps 4 to 5 per cent of the county was not able to support forest at the last moment when there was a natural vegetation cover. The possibility, however, that not all the potential forest land was actually tree-covered is discussed in Chapter 6.

Above the natural tree line
Larger-scale periglacial features inherited from Late-glacial times were described in Chapter 4, but on the highest ground in the North Pennines and Cheviots, above about 685 metres a.s.l., there is still a frost-dominated climate, producing various small-scale periglacial landforms. For example, 'ploughing blocks' are scattered beside the Pennine Way on the northern approach to Cross Fell; sandstone boulders are moving downhill faster than the finer material in which they are set, producing a bow-wave in the turf in front and leaving a furrow behind. In fact, the high summits today provide us with our nearest experience of an ice age world (Fig. 50), and a fall in July temperature of only about 3°C might suffice to bring permanent snow and small glaciers back to Cross Fell and the Cheviot corries. Global warming, however, seems a much more certain prospect for future centuries, with a bleak future for the plants and animals adapted to life at high altitudes. There is no higher ground here for them to retreat to in a warming world.

Fig. 50 'The glaciers on Cheviot', 14 May 1915. The illustration (a drawing from a photograph) is from Abel Chapman's *The Borders and beyond*. Chapman, following heavy March and May snowfalls, encountered a 'seven-foot sheer wall of green ice', beyond the head of The Bizzle at 730 metres a.s.l. It would not really be ice, but a stage in the transformation of snow to ice, nevertheless indicating the near-glacial conditions on the high summits. Presumably the artist added the feral goat and the peregrine for effect.

Holocene climate change

Even during the 11,500 years of post-glacial time climate has changed, and in the mid-Holocene conditions were warmer than in recent centuries (Briffa & Atkinson, 1997). This allowed trees to ascend higher than today, as indicated by timber buried in Pennine peat up to almost 800 metres a.s.l., and pollen analysis of peat also indicates former higher tree lines. Turner (1984) considered that there was open birch scrub on the flat summit of Cross Fell (893 metres) at the highest altitude possible in North East England. However, the survival on the summit from Late-glacial times of periglacial stone polygons, which may be disturbed by root activity, perhaps makes it more likely that the woodland was just off the summit. Subsequently the climate deteriorated and the Cross Fell woodland broke down and disappeared. A marked change towards cooler and wetter conditions occurred during the first millennium BC, leading to further blanket bog spread. Blanket bog development was also facilitated by forest clearance, which both allowed more rain to reach the ground and reduced transpiration.

One way in which this post-glacial climatic variation has been studied is through peat stratigraphy – the changes in plant fossil composition and in degree of peat humification at different levels in bogs. Dominance of the remains of species characteristic of wetter microhabitats, together with less humified peat, indicate wetter bog surfaces, and vice versa, the changes presumably caused by varying climate. Recently, another indicator of bog wetness has been found to be the particular types of testate amoebae preserved as microfossils in the peat (Charman *et al.* 1999). These creatures are protists with a test (hard outer covering), and, as each type has a particular peat wetness requirement, the assemblage present indicates the mean annual level of the contemporary water table, at or below the bog surface.

The first detailed peat stratigraphical work in the region was on Bolton Fell Moss, in eastern Cumbria (Barber, 1981; Barber *et al.*,1994), but has been extended to Butterburn Flow (on the Cumbrian side of the county boundary), and into Northumberland at Felecia Moss, Coom Rigg Moss and The Wou (for example, Hendon *et al.* 2001). There turns out to be a good correlation between periods with wettest bog surfaces and independent evidence of changing climate. For example, the Little Ice Age, the cool, wet period of the fourteenth to nineteenth centuries AD, showed rapid peat growth under the influence of a high water table. There were also earlier wet shifts, judging from peat stratigraphy (Hughes *et al.*, 2000), and the general deterioration of climate in the first millennium BC was evident.

Soils

Of the various factors determining the type of soil at a locality, two of the most important are climate and parent material. The amount of rainfall affects both the movement of soluble compounds and fine particles (clay and humus) downwards through light-textured (more sandy, freely draining) soils, and the propensity to waterlogging in heavy (clayey) soils. Soil parent material is the raw material, and is either weathered bedrock or drift. Parent material determines soil texture (for example, how sandy, clayey the soil is) and also its chemical composition (for example, how calcareous it is). It follows that in the uplands, with high rainfall, soils tend either to be acidic, with low pH, and infertile (because soluble bases and nutrients have been leached out), or waterlogged, with a consequent tendency for peat to accumulate. It also follows that soils developed on sandstones, or drift with a sandy texture, will be leached, while clayey soils will tend to have impeded drainage. Soils developed directly on limestone will be calcareous, and basic in reaction – with a high pH.

These considerations suggest a simple model for Northumberland's soils (Table 1).

Table 1 Main soil types.

	higher precipitation (uplands)	lower precipitation (lowlands)
freely draining (sandy)	leached, acidic, nutrient-deficient **podzolic soils**	less leached, less acidic, less nutrient-deficient **brown soils**
impeded drainage (clayey)	waterlogged for much of year, accumulation of surface layer of acidic raw humus **stagnohumic gley soils**	seasonally waterlogged, **stagnogley soils**

Podzol and *gley* are from Russian words meaning respectively *ash-grey soil*, referring to the colour of the upper horizon of podzols, and *clarty*, denoting the wetness of gleys.

Additionally, very high, year-round rainfall leads to more or less permanent waterlogging and the accumulation of peat, resulting in one type of peat soil. Immature soils over little altered parent materials include rankers, on non-calcareous materials, and rendzinas, on limestones. And, where waterlogging is caused by fluctuating ground water from below rather than impedance of surface water, the soils are ground-water gleys (the stagnogleys and stagnohumic gleys are surface-water gleys).

These are the soil types whose broad distributions are shown in Figure 51. Of course the detail is much more complex; there are intermediate soil types and variations within the main types, and many localities whose soils produce interesting habitats do not appear on a map at this scale. This is true of all the limestone outcrops (with rendzinas and related soils) and of the Whin Sill. The very thin but basic soils developed on the whin are regarded as rankers where there is no drift present, or as brown soils where there is thin, stony drift.

In the lowlands, stagnogley soils predominate, on the widespread glacial tills. However, with artificial underground drainage they make (together with the brown soils) fertile farmland. In the uplands, podzolic soils, stagnohumic gleys and peats predominate – collectively very infertile and supporting mainly moorland vegetation or conifer forests.

The following sections go into a little more detail about the main soil types, relating their distribution to the geology.

Stagnogley soils
These are seasonally waterlogged, normally grey or grey-brown in colour (owing to anaerobic, reducing conditions) but with ochreous mottles along root channels and other partings. They are developed on clayey or otherwise fine-textured parent materials in the lowlands, mainly the widespread, heavy, glacial tills. Before agricultural drainage, damp habitats of great variety would have occurred on these soils, and survive in some lowland woods and sparsely in farmland. Otherwise stagnogleys have been drastically modified for agriculture, by ploughing, drainage, manuring and fertiliser application. Efficient drainage, beginning gradually in the eighteenth century, must have been one of the most significant adverse influences on formerly widespread, wetland plants and animals, and losses have continued to the present day. However, the field-drains fed into a ditch network, which was a new habitat. Stagnogleys also typically

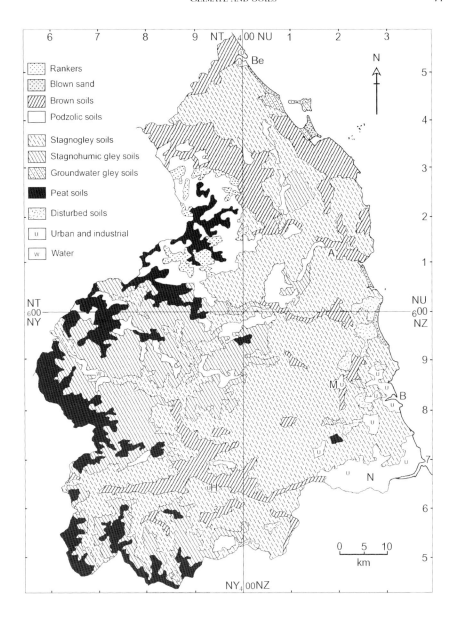

Fig. 51 Soils. The distributions of soil types are generalised and are as implied by the distribution of the soil associations which they dominate. Reproduced from National Soil Resources Institute: *Soil Survey of England and Wales* (1983). Copyright Cranfield University and for the Controller of HMSO, 2004. No part of this publication may be reproduced without the express written permission of Cranfield University.
A: Alnwick, B: Blyth, Be: Berwick, H: Hexham, M: Morpeth, N: Newcastle

underlie marginal land on either side of the moorland edge, where rushes, especially soft-rush and compact rush, are conspicuous. Many North Pennine allotments, so important for black grouse and breeding waders, are notably rushy. The stagnogleys were commonly, and over a long period, worked into rig and-furrow, and this pattern remains prominent on some higher farmland under permanent pasture, not subjected to modern ploughing.

A subgroup of stagnogleys is the pelo-stagnogley, dominant in the coalfield area of southeast Northumberland and with a higher than typical clay content and therefore an even greater drainage impedance. The causes of the high clay content are probably the high proportion of local Coal Measure shale material in the till, together with the local presence of glacial lake clays. These coalfield pelo-stagnogleys, when combined with widespread coal-mining subsidence, account for severe agricultural drainage problems in this area, associated with which is the survival, on awkward-to-manage sites, of old, neutral grassland with a rich flora, described in Chapter 11. Since the 1940s over one-third of the coalfield area has been, or is currently being, worked for opencast coal. When opencasting is finished the land is restored mainly to agriculture, and the resulting clay-rich soils (often former pelo-stagnogleys), compacted by heavy machinery, commonly also have severe drainage impedance and are immature gleys.

Stagnohumic gley soils
Also called peaty gleys. Unlike the stagnogleys, these have a peaty topsoil up to 40 centimetres thick. They are waterlogged for long periods and are particularly widespread in the uplands owing to higher precipitation: they are generally very acidic. Like the stagnogleys they occur mainly on tills. Such soils are found on cuesta dip slopes, and also widely in the North Tynedale/Redesdale area and in the North Pennines. In the last two areas they typically occupy intermediate slopes of the higher hills, between blanket bog above and stagnogleys below. The moorland vegetation on these soils is normally some type of acidophilous grassland or wet heath. Both stagnogleys and stagnohumic gleys are extensive under Kielder Forest. The former were originally planted mainly with Norway spruce and the latter with Sitka spruce.

Ground-water gleys
These occur on alluvial flood plains beside rivers and streams, and in the floors of kettle holes amidst glacial meltwater deposits.

Podzolic soils
These are leached, nutrient deficient and acidic. They have pale upper horizons, because iron (and aluminium) have been translocated downwards, and are redder at depth, where the iron has been precipitated. There is a surface layer of thin peaty humus known as 'mor', acids from which accelerate the leaching process. As noted above, podzolic soils develop in higher rainfall zones in areas where soil parent materials are relatively sandy and freely draining. They are therefore associated particularly with the dip slopes of cuestas developed on rocks of the Fell Sandstone Group and on other sandstones. Many have an iron pan, a thin, impermeable layer where iron compounds have been concentrated, and which can cause waterlogging above the pan. In many areas they have probably developed only after forest clearance, the trees having previously arrested podzolisation by reducing the amount of rain reaching the ground, and

as a result of their roots recycling leached minerals; there had been a delicate balance under the forest. Podzolic soils underlie many heather heaths, as well as a variety of acidophilous grasslands. One of the most characteristic Northumbrian landscapes is heather heath, managed as grouse moor, on the podzolic soils of sandstone cuestas. A less-developed podzolic soil occurs widely on the andesites and granite of the Cheviot Hills, also carrying acidophilous grassland or heather heath.

Brown soils
These are found on similar parent materials to the podzolic soils, but in lower rainfall areas – on the upland fringes and in the lowlands. These soils are neither podzolised nor strongly gleyed, and are more fertile. In the uplands they are characteristic of loamy alluvium along the burns, where they support strips of close-grazed bent–fescue grassland – locally rushy where the ground water table is close to the surface. In the lowlands, brown soils have been much modified by cultivation.

Rankers
These are shallow, immature, non-calcareous soils. One type (humic rankers), on broken rocky ground, consists of peaty mor lying directly over bedrock, and is characteristic of sandstone cuesta scarps and steep slopes of the Cheviot granite. The vegetation is commonly a mixture of crowberry, bilberry and cowberry. Boulder ramparts of Iron Age hill forts simulate this ecosystem. The other ranker type (brown rankers) is found on steep, Cheviot andesite slopes. They are shallow, dark brown stony soils composed of relatively small scree fragments, and carry either bent–fescue grassland or bracken, with patches of bare scree.

Rendzinas
These are equivalent soils on limestone, and commonly occur alongside calcareous brown earths, developed on thin drift and transitional to brown soils. On limestone cuestas north of the Tyne Corridor, and on limestone benches on the sides of Pennine dales, rendzinas support strips of limestone grassland, smelling of wild thyme and close-grazed by sheep.

Peat soils
These soils, which develop where there is more or less permanent waterlogging, are described in Chapter 8. They are a feature of the high hills and the depressions between the cuestas, and the ecosystems they support are one of the county's glories.

In overview, the pattern of soil distribution closely follows that of rock type, but is greatly influenced by climate. Surface-water gleys preponderate – heavy soils with impeded drainage – stagnogleys in the lowlands and stagnohumic gleys in the uplands. Brown soils occur locally, mainly in the lowlands – on tills with less-impeded drainage, or on glacial and alluvial sands and gravels. In the uplands, podzolic soils characterise the sandstones and large parts of the Cheviots, as does peat the highest ground. This preponderance of very acidic and nutrient-deficient soils in the uplands perhaps predicates a poor flora, but the uplands also contain many patches of other soil types, some of which are base rich and which contribute to floristic diversity out of all proportion to their limited extents. These include soils developed on limestone, on the Whin Sill, on the more basic andesites and in a great variety of flushes.

6

Ecological History

During the many cold phases of the Quaternary, tundra landscapes supported cold-climate faunas, and nineteenth-century industrial, port and urban development in the North East, together with the use of hand tools, gave every opportunity to discover fossil remains in glacial and other sediments. Among large, cold-climate mammals, woolly mammoth and woolly rhinoceros have been found in County Durham, giant deer in both Northumberland and Durham, and woolly mammoth and reindeer in Berwickshire; all except reindeer are extinct. Although the specimens are undated, they probably belong to a period either just preceding the advance of the Dimlington Stadial ice sheet, or just after its retreat. Perhaps these animals ranged over Northumberland during at least parts of the Late-glacial period, not so very long ago.

Late Glacial times

Assuming there was a complete ice cover, the retreating ice sheet, over the millennia centred about 16,000 BP, left a landscape empty of plants and animals: all had to re-immigrate either from southern Britain or from glacial refugia perhaps far south in Europe. Evidence of the sequence of events comes mainly from fossils, including pollen and spores, preserved in sediments infilling the ponds and lakes that formed on the uneven glacial landscape, and as components of newly forming peats. The earliest vegetation was treeless, owing to both continuing cold in the vicinity of the retreating ice sheet, and to the distance from woodland refugia; the landscape was akin to tundra. At the beginning of the Windermere Interstadial (ca. 14,600 BP), however, the climate ameliorated, tree birches (different from the already present dwarf birch of the tundra) arrived and, for a time, Northumberland was at or near the northern forest limit in Britain, with an open birch woodland. The climate then deteriorated, and from about 12,900 BP, renewed intense cold characterised the Loch Lomond Stadial, with a retreat southwards of woodland.

Early post-glacial times (early Holocene)

At about 11,500 years ago the climate again rapidly ameliorated, trees were able to grow and reproduce in Northumberland, and the cool-temperate forest species with which we are familiar dispersed back from their glacial refugia. The birches, hazel and Scots pine arrived first, then the more warmth-demanding oaks, elm and small-leaved lime. The trees in the reconstituted forest altered in their relative abundances during the early post-glacial millennia, and lime was late in reaching this far north. There was a major increase in the amount of alder woodland at about 7,000 BP, probably as a result of increasing precipitation and rising soil water tables, which favoured this wetland tree.

Most of the information we have about these vegetation changes comes from the technique of pollen analysis, which, following visits by the Swedish pollen analyst G. Erdtman in the 1920s, was effectively introduced into Britain by Dr Kathleen Blackburn (Chapter 14). This was in association with the geologist Dr Arthur Raistrick, both of Armstrong College, now the University of Newcastle. Some of the first British pollen diagrams, dating from the early 1930s, were for sites in North East England. The technique relies firstly on some of the abundant pollen and spores produced by the regional and local vegetation becoming incorporated into the current year's layer of lake mud or fresh peat; and secondly on the fact that the cell walls of pollen grains or spores are preserved indefinitely, in an identifiable condition, in these oxygen-deficient environments. Cores are obtained from the deposits, and grains from successive layers identified and counted on a microscope slide. Pollen diagrams are then prepared, with each pollen type portrayed as a bar graph. The diagram therefore represents the changing local and regional vegetation during the time when the peat or lake deposits were accumulating – whether the changes were caused by natural events or human intervention.

There are several dozen published diagrams for Northumberland. That for Fozy Moss (Fig. 52), immediately north of Hadrian's Wall in the west of the county, covers approximately the last 4,000 years, by which time human influence was becoming dominant. Clearly, in this area however, there was little impact on the vegetation until the Roman occupation, when massive forest clearance allowed grasses to rise to dominance. The summary panel shows the changing balance of trees, shrubs and herbs.

Just as the vegetation changed with post-glacial warming, so did the fauna. Conditions became unsuited to the open-ground tundra mammals of the Late-glacial period, and these were replaced by forest species including the extinct aurochs, elk, red and roe deer, wild boar, wolf, brown bear, beaver and lynx. There is Northumberland or Durham fossil evidence for the presence of all these apart from beaver, which, however, is known from Yorkshire to the south and from sites in the Scottish Borders to the north, and beaver skins were exported from Newcastle in the twelfth century. The horns of aurochsen are occasionally exposed at the base of erosion gullies in blanket peat. Over the Durham boundary, near to Langdon Beck in upper Teesdale, is the Teesdale Cave system in the Great Limestone. It contained fossils of *inter alia* wolf, brown bear, lynx, wild boar and mountain hare, a typical early to mid-Holocene assemblage. Of all these mammals, only the roe and red deer, and mountain hare, survived in Britain, and only the deer are now wild in Northumberland. The aurochs, regarded as the direct ancestor of European domestic cattle, was probably extinct in England if not in Scotland, by Roman times (Yalden, 1999), while wolves survived locally until at least the thirteenth century (Mennell & Perkins, 1863–4).

The former natural vegetation

The landscape at the dawn of agriculture in these parts, about 6,000 years ago, was still – bar an unknown amount of open ground maintained by Mesolithic fires – a substantially natural one, and it is interesting to speculate about what the vegetation was like. The evidence we can use includes, primarily, pollen diagrams. Additionally we can use the distribution of surviving patches of vegetation we think are relict from the natural environment, knowledge of the ecological requirements of plant species, fossil remains, place names, and to some extent documentary evidence. There are three particular questions to which we would like answers: (1) where were the forest limits? (2) what was

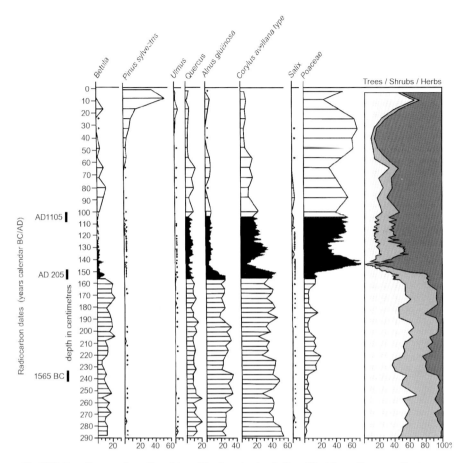

Fig. 52 Pollen diagram from Fozy Moss, Northumberland. Simplified from Dumayne-Peaty
(1999). Percentages are of the sum of the pollen and spores from plants not growing on the
mire itself. In black zone sampling was at very close intervals. Fozy Moss is immediately north
of Hadrian's Wall, in the west of the county. The calibrated radiocarbon dates show that
there was little human impact on the vegetation of the area around the mire until the
Roman occupation, when massive clearance produced a more or less deforested landscape.
Poaceae (grasses) rise to dominance. The summary panel at the right clearly shows the
changes. With permission of Blackwell Publishing Ltd.

the composition of the forest? (3) what types of vegetation occurred in the non-
forested areas? The first question was tackled in the previous chapter: broadly
the temperature and wind-controlled upper tree line was reckoned to be at about
600–700 metres a.s.l., but there were rather extensive areas of treeless bog at
lower altitudes, as well as some other treeless habitats. I suggested that perhaps
4 to 5 per cent of Northumberland consisted of environments physically
unsuitable for forest.

However, a new paradigm of what the natural, early and mid-Holocene
environment might have been like in the lowlands of western and central Europe

has been presented by the Dutch ecologist, Vera (2000). He has argued that large native herbivores, already present before the re-immigration of trees and shrubs after the last cold stage, sufficiently suppressed regeneration over quite extensive areas to have maintained a parkland landscape, and it was this, not forest, which was entered by the first farmers and pastoralists. Vera argued that oak is a light-demanding species, and that in competition with taller and shade-bearing species it would depend upon semi-open conditions to maintain the abundances shown in pollen diagrams. Similarly, the high proportions of hazel pollen would also be explained by its likely abundance as scrub in a grazed parkland landscape. In Northumberland, however, several of the main potential competitors of oak – small-leaved lime, beech, hornbeam – were either near their climatic limit (lime) or did not reach our area at all through natural dispersal, so that parkland conditions here are probably not necessary for oak's dominance. Nonetheless, Vera's arguments are interesting, and it is a very attractive, biodiverse environment that he postulates. Svenning (2002), in criticism, considered that the European lowland forests would have had significant openings only in certain environments, including flood plains and areas of acidic, nutrient-deficient soils (now heathland).

The wildwood

So what sorts of forest did we have? The main tree species were birch, pine, oak, elm and alder. Understorey trees and shrubs included hazel, rowan, aspen, juniper, bird and wild cherries, hawthorn and holly. Willows of several species grew on diverse wetlands. We had no sycamore, prominent in many semi-natural woodlands and plantations today – it was introduced to Britain possibly in the sixteenth century – nor beech or hornbeam, which had not yet expanded widely even in the south of England at this time. (Beech's absence was not due to our unfavourable climate, since it grows and reproduces well even in our hill areas.) Small-leaved lime was not prominent, and it may have occurred sparsely in woodlands in the south of the county. Ash was only locally dominant. The pollen diagrams, however, because of the wide provenance of pollen, give only a general idea of the distribution of the different forest types and normally cannot tell us whether the trees commonly occurred in mixtures or in pure stands. Something in between seems likely, judging from surviving ancient woodlands.

As much as any part of Britain, Northumberland seems to have been an oak environment (Bennett, 1989). Pedunculate oak appears to have been the predominant lowland species, probably dominant on the widespread, heavy, stagnogley soils with impeded drainage, which it tolerates. Both it and sessile oak occurred in the uplands, separated by soil type: pedunculate oak on the gley soils and sessile oak on brown and podzolic soils. However, the two native oaks freely hybridise and backcross, and distributions would have been confused. Variants of oak-dominated woodland appear to have been the norm in Northumberland, up to an altitude of ca. 500 metres a.s.l.

Wych elm was almost certainly the only native elm, and was an important component of lowland and dales woodlands, although less abundant in the uplands. It may have dominated on the more base rich of the gley and brown soils. Alder contributed very large amounts of pollen at both upland and lowland sites, probably more than can be accounted for by a local over-representation of this soil-moisture-demanding species around the wetland sites suitable for pollen analysis. The tree can be inferred to have been an important component of the general forests. Gley soils are, after all, preponderant in Northumberland and alder can be envisaged as occupying wetter sites on these soils, in a matrix of oak. It occurs in this context in semi-natural woodlands today, as well as in pure hillside alder woods. Alder would additionally have formed gallery woodland along watercourses, and occupied ground-water gleys on flood plains (alder carr characterised the Tyne flood plain at Scotswood in the late Mesolithic and early Neolithic: Passmore *et al.*, 1992). Hazel contributed abundant pollen, especially in the uplands, but its status in the structure of the forest is unclear; it tolerates heavy soils. Much lowland woodland would have consisted of oak, elm and hazel. Ash, judging by its occurrence in apparently ancient, semi-natural woodland today, was a tree of shallow, calcareous soils derived from Cheviot andesites or North Pennine limestones. It is today characteristic of cleugh woodlands in the latter area, and pollen diagrams support a former high ash presence there. Ash would also, presumably, have been a component of the diverse, lowland dene woodlands.

In the uplands, as in the lowlands, oak prevailed. However, drawing on a series of pollen diagrams from the North Pennines and supported by records of wood remains in peat, Turner & Hodgson (1983) concluded that pine increased in abundance towards the northeast of that area – the upper valley of the Derwent. They noted similarities between the climate there and the parts of northeastern Scotland formerly dominated by Scots pine – especially the low spring and early summer temperatures of North East England and the frequency of easterly winds in those seasons. The austere local climate, and prevalent podzolic soils developed on the local sandstones, favoured Scots pine, and there was evidence that some pine woods persisted through medieval times. North of the Tyne Corridor too, pine pollen remained locally significant, with pine woodlands presumably on sandstone cuestas and on the slopes of the sandstone hills at the head of Redesdale and North Tynedale. These woodlands would reasonably be in a zone above the oak and other broadleaved woodlands. Evidence of the survival of pine wood well past the end of the wildwood period comes from place names, discussed below, and the possible existence of a relict pine wood is discussed in Chapter 9.

Above the upper limit of oak or of pine it seems likely that birch scrub formed an upper belt of woodland, probably in a mosaic with various willows and with rowan. Fragments of birch woodland still occur in the remotest recesses of some hill burns, where headwater rills from the blanket bogs of the plateaux fall into cleughs. Pollen diagrams indicate that birch was also abundant in the lowlands, presumably partly on wetlands around the pollen sites. The two native tree birches, silver birch and downy birch, hybridise to an unknown extent, but of the parent species silver birch is commoner today on lighter soils and in the lowlands and downy birch on heavier, acidic and peaty soils in the uplands. This presumably reflects their distributions in the wildwood. Judging by the relatively numerous surviving populations of juniper, this species must also have been abundant in the wildwood. Its ecology suggests that it would have occurred on freely draining soils, perhaps, like birch, in a zone at the upper woodland margin, mainly as an understorey shrub. Relict populations are commonest in the North Pennines, and some are near to valley floors suggesting that it was not entirely an upper woodland margin shrub. The forest would have been increasingly open towards its upper limits, owing to constraints of climate and soil.

Place names tell us which trees caught the attention of late-prehistoric and early medieval people, but tell us little about vegetation distributions. (The names are of Old English origin unless indicated otherwise.) Oak names dominate with, for example, Acklington, Akeld and Acomb. Allerwash refers to alder, as may Celtic *verno*, perhaps giving Waren. Ashington and Eshott are ash, Embley is elm, Espley is aspen, Hazelrigg and (Old Norse) Hesleyside are hazel as possibly is Coanwood, from Celtic *collen*. Linshiels, in the upper Coquet valley, just possibly could be a lime name – there are favoured south-facing slopes nearby, on andesite lava. Hull (1936) wondered whether Abshields was derived from *aebs* (Scots pine) – the farm is near to Longhorsley Moor, a tract of lowland heath that can readily be envisaged as former pine habitat. Possibly also the first elements of Trewhitt, in Coquetdale, and Tarset, in North Tynedale, might be Scandinavian *tyri* (dry, resinous wood).

The non-forested areas

As outlined in Chapter 5, the main open (non-forested) areas before human intervention were the highest areas in the Cheviots and North Pennines, above the upper tree line, and the very much more extensive upland bogs. Along the coast, the salt marshes were treeless (no British trees will tolerate high salinity), but showing a transition to woodland now seldom, if ever, seen. The unstable seaward zones of the dune systems were also treeless, but more sheltered and stabilised landward zones would have supported scrub, as locally they do now, if not woodland: hawthorn, blackthorn, sea-buckthorn, silver birch. The Farne Islands and Coquet Island were treeless owing to gales and salt spray. Inland crags, and horizontal rock surfaces, were partly open, with trees and shrubs rooted in joints and bedding planes. Screes, apart from the most unstable, were probably wooded. Landslip scars along rivers and burns were temporary open habitats, as were low-water river beds. Most wetlands, however, apart from the bogs and lake-edge swamp communities, were at least lightly wooded with species tolerant of high water tables. Finally there were the gaps in the forest itself. Vera argued for a parkland landscape, but even if there was not the degree of herbivore grazing pressure that he assumed, both natural and Mesolithic disturbance of the forest would generate gaps – which would be maintained by herbivores. Whatever the scale of forest openings, aurochsen would have been a keystone species in maintaining glades, and poaching wet areas to provide habitats for plants of bare ground.

This list of open habitats includes many of those that support relict natural or near-natural vegetation today. The same factors that were inimical to tree growth have continued to defend them against excessive human interference.

An analysis of the habitat preferences of the county's native vascular flora (Plate 3; Chapter 7) indicates that about 16 per cent of our species are primarily woodland ones, requiring shade or other woodland attributes. This, on the face of it, leaves 84 per cent that favour non-shaded open landscapes. Subtracting the specialised montane, coastal and wetland species, and those with wide ecological tolerances (together 42 per cent), this still leaves another 42 per cent of Northumberland's native vascular plants that are entirely or mainly dry-land, open-country species. They must therefore have survived the forest stages of the early and mid-Holocene in the approximately 4 to 5 per cent of Northumberland that was not a forest environment, or have immigrated later from other parts of Britain. But since much of the 4 to 5 per cent was bog, supporting a very few species, only tiny fragments of the county were apparently the refuge for a large part of its native flora – unless Vera's parkland model holds good. Most of the species expanded as the forests were gradually cleared, as pollen diagrams indeed clearly show. It is likely, judging by the species richness of dune systems here and elsewhere, that these were a particularly important refuge, but so would be river banks and channel beds. The wide shingle beds of the North Pennine and Cheviot rivers today support an ever-changing assemblage of adventitious species from a wide variety of habitats. But perhaps this is all to misjudge the natural variety of the forest landscape.

Land use, soil erosion and rivers

The gradual change in vegetation and land use after 6,000 years ago, from a predominantly wooded environment to moorland rough grazing and intensively managed farmland, had important consequences for the hydrological cycle. Runoff, sediment transport down hill slopes and stream régimes were all affected. In the Cheviots, Tipping (1992, 1998) showed that prehistoric forest clearance led to soil erosion and, through enhanced runoff, increased flooding by the rivers, both of which led to valley floor build-up by increased deposition on river beds and flood plains. He found two major phases of prehistoric river aggradation, dating respectively from early Bronze Age and from late Iron Age/Romano-British times, which are now represented as coarse gravels forming river terraces. Conversely, woodland regeneration, bringing greater slope stability, reduced river sedimentation. However, changing climate also likely affected river activity.

In the south of the county, historic river activity in the Tyne basin is the most intensively studied in Britain, thanks to work in the Department of Geography at the University of Newcastle. Considerable changes in valley floors have occurred during the later Holocene, with alternation of aggradation and entrenchment, again probably caused by changes in both climate and land use (Macklin, 1992, Macklin *et al.*, 1992). An episodic repetition of valley floor build-up, followed by down-cutting, has produced conspicuous flights of alluvial terraces flanking the upland burns. The main impact of forest clearance on river régimes in the North Pennines seems to have been to increase the sensitivity of the landscape to climate change, particularly with respect to flood magnitude, which caused the alternation of aggradation and incision (Fig. 53).

In the North Pennine mining area, huge inputs of mine waste to the river systems led not only to the distinctive metalliferous flora to be described in Chapter 11, but also to physical changes on the valley floors. In the seventeenth and eighteenth centuries, coarse material came from the primitive, hydraulic, quarrying technique of 'hushing': the practice of releasing dammed-up water down hillsides along the outcrop of a vein (and leaving deep, dry valleys, 'hushes'). Later, discarded low-grade ore, or fine metal waste produced during preparation of the ores, dominated inputs – at first directly into the rivers and later, after preventive legislation in 1876, through erosion of stream-side spoil dumps. A result of these excessive loads was valley floor aggradation, and an accompanying switch from single-thread, meandering river channels to braided, multi-thread reaches. Following the collapse of the mining industry there was a general return to a single channel in the twentieth century, with incision leaving the former river beds and flood plains as flights of low terraces up to several metres above the modern channels, many with highly contaminated soils.

Fig. 53 Holocene alluvial terraces of the Thinhope Burn, North Pennines.

Changing sea levels

When glacier ice withdrew from the coast at the end of the last glaciation, relative sea level was probably lower than it is now on the Northumberland coast. The amount by which the local land surface had been depressed by the weight of the ice sheet was less than the amount by which the sea surface itself was lower owing to water being locked up in the world's various ice sheets. During deglaciation, global sea level rose faster than the local land rebounded, so that up to the mid-Holocene there was a general transgression of the sea over the coastal zone. Estuaries, like that of the Tyne, were flooded, and embayments created in low-lying areas. Since then there has been a gradual emergence of the land, owing to continued slow rebound after ice-sheet melting ceased. There has therefore been a marine regression on the Northumberland coast over the last few thousand years, after a mid- to late-Holocene high-stand of sea level. This high-stand has, very locally, left raised beaches a couple of metres or so above present sea level, for example beside Holy Island Castle (Plater, 2002).

Evidence for relative sea level movements in Northumberland comes from borings through coastal deposits, which show alternating layers of tidal-marsh peat and estuarine silt, indicating respectively lower and higher relative sea levels (Horton *et al.*, 1999; Shennan *et al.*, 2000; Shennan & Horton, 2002). Northumberland is near the hinge zone between present crustal rise (to the north, owing to rebound from ice-sheet loading) and compensating crustal depression to the south. Thus, over the last 4,000 years, north Northumberland has been rising relative to the sea at about 0.7 millimetre per year and south Northumberland only at 0.2 millimetre. In the twentieth century, however, global mean sea level rose at 1–2 millimetres per year, almost certainly due to global warming, reversing the long-term relative sea level trend for Northumberland.

Overall, since about 4000–3000 BP, north Northumberland has risen relative to the sea by about 2.5 metres and south Northumberland by only about 0.5 metres. A sideline to this work is that borings at Broom House farm, near Cheswick, revealed a layer of coarse sand, in peat, inland of what was then a marine embayment. This was possibly the result of a tsunami (tidal wave) generated by a major submarine landslide off the Norwegian coast at about 7,500-8,000 BP (Fig. 54).

Fig. 54 A core through peat at Broom House farm, near Cheswick. The pale layer is coarse sand, possibly deposited on the slowly accumulating peat by a tsunami some 7,500–8,000 years ago.

Dunes

As relative sea level changed, so would the position of the coastline, and coastal dunes would correspondingly shift to and fro, although dunes might also shift at times of stable sea level. There is evidence of dune movement, for example, at Druridge Bay, with compacted beds of peat, up to 1 metre thick, exposed on the foreshore. The peat had accumulated in wetlands behind the dunes, which later migrated inland across the wetland. The peat itself overlies *in situ* stumps of well-grown oak and alder rooted in till – the so-called submerged forest – dating from the period before the dune-impounded wetland developed (Fig. 55). The period of peat formation at Druridge Bay was from about 4700 to 2800 radiocarbon years BP (Innes & Frank, 1988). These dune systems, in their present positions, are therefore not more than a few thousand years old.

Fig. 55 A subfossil tree stump, rooted in till, on the foreshore at Druridge Bay – part of the 'submerged forest'.

Direct dating of dune sand by Wilson *et al.* (2001), using a technique known as optically stimulated luminescence, has surprisingly indicated that many of our Northumberland dunes are of even more recent construction, being built during the Little Ice Age of the fourteenth to nineteenth centuries AD. Possibly a combination then of storminess, more prevalent easterly winds and falling sea level (the rebound mentioned above) provided both the sand supply and accommodation space for many of the dune systems. However, whether dunes were previously less widespread on our coast than they have been since the Little Ice Age, or alternatively were periodically being destroyed and reconstructed, either on the same sites or as they migrated inland or seawards, remain open questions.

7

Flora and Fauna

This chapter provides information about the more conspicuous groups of plants and animals living in Northumberland, drawing on recent compilations about their distribution and status. These sources are Swan's *Flora of Northumberland* (1993) and its *Supplement* (2001), Day *et al.'s Atlas of breeding birds in Northumbria* [Northumberland as used here] (1995), Kerr's *Northumbrian birds* (2001), Dunn & Parrack's *The moths and butterflies of Northumberland and Durham* (1986, 1992) and the *Red Data Book for Northumberland* (1998), with 1999 supplement, edited by Kerslake. The latter lists the more uncommon taxa in a wide variety of groups. These works are testimony to the huge amount of recording activity being undertaken in the region. Additionally there are the national atlases of vascular plants (Preston *et al.*, 2002), of breeding birds (Gibbons *et al.*, 1993), of bats (Richardson, 2000) and of butterflies (Asher *et al.*, 2001).

Vascular plants
Professor Swan has recorded 782 species native to Northumberland (the geographical county) and still occurring in the wild. I have followed the interpretation of 'native' or 'introduced' of the *New atlas of the British flora*, with the exception of Scots pine which, for the reasons given on page 150, is regarded as possibly native here. The total of 782 excludes subspecies (where more than one occurs), varieties, hybrids and microspecies (critical species) of dandelion, bramble, hawkweed and eyebright. Additionally Swan recorded 714 taxa now regarded as introductions – some now extinct, others still part of the flora. He also noted about 36 native species that had become extinct since earlier *Floras*. The total of 782 native species is 51 per cent of the equivalent British Isles total, and is comparable with County Durham's 858 (Graham, 1988), once Durham species now regarded as introductions and Durham extinctions are deducted from that total. The area of Durham is only about half that of Northumberland, but that county includes the upper Teesdale habitats, the Magnesian Limestone plateau and is further south, three factors adding to the total. Cumbria's larger total of 945 extant, non-critical species (Halliday, 1997) is also to be expected owing to its greater range of habitats. The total number of vascular plant taxa recorded by Swan as occurring, or having occurred, in the county is 1,965.

Habitats
Although many plants are catholic in their habitats I have attempted to classify them according to the one in which they are most commonly found (Plate 3a). One hundred and twenty five species (16 per cent of the total) occur mainly in woodland. This is many more than the 50 species (including rarities) given in Chapter 9 as likely indicators of ancient, semi-natural woodland in Northumberland, including as it does the more readily dispersed of woodland plants, likely to find their way to more recent woods. The total, however, is similar

to the number of species expected to be found in a diverse, ancient, semi-natural woodland of reasonable size (Briarwood Banks, in the lower Allen valley is an example), suggesting that in such woods most species can be expected to be present. Presumably much of the woodland flora was relatively well distributed through the wildwood and most has survived in the larger relicts. There are no 'nationally rare' *Red Data Book* – RDB – species (Wigginton, 1999) and only four 'nationally scarce' (Stewart *et al.* 1994) plants in our woods: Scots pine (if native), downy currant, creeping lady's-tresses (if native and not introduced with pine seedlings) and wood barley. Distinctive types of woodland are not our speciality.

The Whin Sill, on the other hand, is a speciality (Chapter 11), and the 18 whin species include five that are nationally scarce: maiden pink, spignel, chives, spring cinquefoil and angular Solomon's-seal. Similarly, metalliferous habitats are a speciality with eight species, six of which are nationally rare or scarce. Bogs are another speciality, although not species rich, with only 17 species. Three of these are nationally scarce: small cranberry, tall bog-sedge and bog orchid. The latter occurs in soakways in blanket bog, and in acidic flushes (Fig. 56).

Fig. 56 Bog orchid, known from six sites in the county.

Our montane habitats are relatively poor, with only 11 species, mainly in the Cheviot corries. Of these alpine foxtail, the lady's-mantle *Alchemilla glomerulans* and the eyebright taxon *Euphrasia frigida* are nationally scarce. However, the higher ground on Cross Fell, in Cumbria, together with other parts of Alston Moor (not part of these analyses), add the rare or scarce species spring gentian, alpine forget-me-not, hoary whitlowgrass, alpine cinquefoil and hair sedge.

Coastal habitats contain 86 specialist species (11 per cent of the total), of which seven are in dune slacks, but only long-stalked orache and coralroot orchid are nationally scarce. Fifty-one species are aquatic (including 15 *Potamogeton* species), 21 mainly in flushes and another 113 in a variety of other wetland habitats; including the bogs and dune slacks this makes 209 wetland species, 26.7 per cent of the total flora – in spite of centuries of drainage of the heavy lowland soils and of moorland. Sixty-five species (8 per cent) are ruderals, plants characteristic of disturbed soils – in urban areas, arable farmland and some naturally disturbed sites. The ruderals include two out of the three Northumberland non-critical species or subspecies that are British endemics, found nowhere else in the world: white ramping-fumitory (*Fumaria capreolota* subsp. *babingtonii*) and purple ramping-fumitory. Both are very rare with us and the latter may be extinct. (The third British endemic is Young's helleborine, although its taxonomic status is under review.)

Life form
Another way of classifying plants is by their life form, the most widely accepted classification being that developed by the Danish botanist Raunkiaer. His system was based on the physical size and life cycle strategy of the plant, and especially the position of perennating, vegetative parts in relation to ground level during the unfavourable season. The relative proportions of a flora in Raunkiaer's various classes is its 'biological spectrum', and each climatic zone has its characteristic spectrum. Figure 57 (in which the terms are explained), using bar graphs, shows the biological spectrum for Northumberland compared with a standard cool temperate one for Denmark, at the same latitude across the North Sea. The spectra are remarkably similar.

Therophytes – annuals, which survive the unfavourable season, or persist despite repeated disturbance of their habitat, as seeds – account for 17 per cent of Northumberland's flora. They include coastal species of sand dunes, shingle beaches or salt marsh, and others occur on the considerable areas of disturbed ground in arable fields, where some weeds survive herbicide applications, and urban and industrial areas, including allotments and gardens. Additionally, bare silt on river channel margins, with which we are well endowed, is the natural habitat of many annuals.

Out of the 18 Whin Sill species, eight are therophytes, avoiding the summer drought of the thin soils. Rather surprisingly for such soils there are also four geophytes: spring squill, chives, field garlic and angular Solomon's-seal. Presumably the underground storage organs are located in crevices in the rock surface. The montane species understandably include no phanerophytes (trees and tall shrubs), geophytes (the need to regrow the photosynthetic apparatus is a disadvantage with a short montane growing season) or, for the same reason and with one exception – the eyebright *Euphrasia frigida* – therophytes. Rather, montane species are hemicryptophytes and chamaephytes.

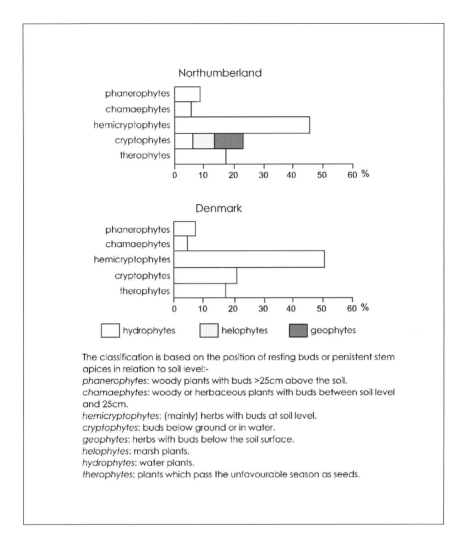

Fig. 57 Biological spectra: Northumberland and Denmark. Life-form classes for Northumberland species from Clapham *et al.* (1987). Danish data from Raunkiaer (1934).

Geographical elements

The most recent classification of the British and Irish flora into geographical elements, based on the distribution of species outside of Britain, is by Preston & Hill (1997). Table 2 compares the proportions of the Northumberland flora belonging to the various elements with those for the British Isles as a whole. The scheme is based on the distribution of species in the main latitudinal climatic belts (the major biomes), and, within these, on eastern distributional limits (in relation to the British Isles) in the Northern Hemisphere – that is, on greater or lesser restriction to western oceanic margins. Species belonging to a category have similar climatic requirements, and, presumably, dispersal histories.

	1 Ocea	2 Subocea	3 Euro	4 Eusib	5 Euras	6 Circ	Total
1 Arctic-montane	- (-)	- (-)	0.6 (2.0)	0.1 (0.4)	0.1 (0.2)	0.8 (2.8)	1.6 (5.4)
2 Boreo-arctic montane	- (0.1)	- (-)	0.6 (0.4)	- (0.1)	- (-)	1.7 (1.7)	2.3 (2.3)
3 Wide-boreal	- (-)	- (-)	- (-)	0.1 (0.1)	0.1 (0.1)	1.9 (1.2)	2.1 (1.4)
4 Boreo-montane	0.4 (0.5)	0.4 (0.3)	1.7 (1.9)	0.8 (0.6)	0.5 (0.3)	3.8 (3.4)	7.6 (7.0)
5 Boreo-temperate	0.6 (0.6)	0.6 (0.6)	4.7 (3.2)	6.5 (4.5)	3.7 (2.6)	6.8 (4.3)	22.9 (15.8)
6 Wide-temperate	- (0.1)	- (-)	0.5 (0.2)	1.0 (0.7)	0.5 (0.3)	1.7 (0.9)	3.7 (2.2)
7 Temperate	2.6 (3.2)	2.8 (1.9)	22.2 (20.0)	7.9 (8.1)	2.8 2.6)	2.6 (1.8)	40.9 (37.6)
8 Southern-temperate	0.5 (1.7)	2.8 (3.6)	5.9 (7.2)	4.1 (5.5)	1.3 (1.1)	1.3 (0.9)	15.9 (20.0)
9 Mediterranean	1.3 (4.7)	1.8 (3.2)	- (0.4)				3.1 (8.3)
Total	5.4 (10.9)	8.4 (9.6)	36.2 (35.3)	20.5 (20.0)	9.0 (7.2)	20.6 (17.0)	100.1 (100.0)

The eastern limit categories are:- 1 Oceanic; 2 Suboceanic; 3 European; 4 Eurosiberian; 5 Eurasian; 6 Circumpolar. For the Mediterranean elements: 91 denotes Mediterranean-Atlantic; 92 Submediterranean-Subatlantic; 93 Mediterranean-montane (British and Irish data from Preston & Hill, 1997.)

Table 2 Percentages of Northumberland species in geographical elements (British and Irish percentages shown in brackets)

The table shows that Northumberland is under-represented in the Arctic-montane element, lacking substantial and varied areas of high enough ground. We are also deficient in Southern-temperate and Mediterranean species. On the other hand, we are over-represented in species belonging to the Wide-boreal, Boreo-temperate and Wide-temperate elements. These contain species with, or including, northern and/or upland distributions on the Continent. None of this is surprising for a rather northern, rather upland county like Northumberland, lacking mountain extremes. We are also, as an east-side county, low on all the oceanic elements.

Distribution within Northumberland

Forty-three per cent of the vascular plant species are widespread over the county, and coastal species account for another 11 per cent. As to the remainder, there is a very clear east–west separation – many species are either markedly western or eastern – primarily reflecting the upland–lowland division of the county as it affects climate, soils and land use, and there are some notable complementary distributions. Thus spiked water-milfoil is largely in the east and alternate water-milfoil largely western – both occur in lakes, ponds and slow-flowing streams, but the latter is in peaty or otherwise acidic water. Similarly, celery-leaved buttercup is eastern and both ivy-leaved crowfoot and round-leaved crowfoot western, the latter – a suboceanic species – sometimes in pools in blocked gullies in blanket bog. A less pronounced north–south separation is accounted for firstly by the Cheviot montane species (in the north); secondly by some arable ruderals of the northern part of the county; and thirdly by species reaching or approaching their northern limits in the south of the county. There are a few metallophytes and upland limestone species that occur mainly in the southwest – spring sandwort, alpine pennycress, moonwort, alpine bistort – and a few species are found mainly in the southeast, with its warmer, drier climate; these include several of the old neutral grassland species described in Chapter 11.

About half of the pteridophytes (clubmosses, horsetails and ferns) are widespread, and the others western or southwestern, as is expected of a group many of whose members require a humid climate. Rustyback and soft shield-fern, however, are eastern, although not southeastern. In the coalfield/industrial area air pollution seems to have adversely affected ferns, and common species like polypody, wall-rue and maidenhair spleenwort are largely missing there.

Commonness/rarity
As regards rarity in Northumberland, Swan's *Flora* divides the county into 255 5x5 kilometre squares. Presence of a plant in 30 or fewer squares is arbitrarily taken here as the local criterion of uncommonness, although the fact that most coastal species, owing to geometry, are in the 30 or fewer squares class skews the arithmetic. Pro rata to Stewart *et al.*'s national criterion of 'scarcity' for plants (those occurring in 100 or fewer of the country's approximately 3,500 10x10 kilometre squares), presence in eight or fewer Northumberland squares is taken as the local criterion of scarcity. Analysing the Northumberland flora in this way, out of the 782 native species, 142 are 'uncommon' and, another 173 are 'scarce' – the 315 account for 40 per cent of the flora. Clearly, the rarer the commoner (there are more 'scarce' than just 'uncommon' species).

As regards British scarcity and rarity, 50 of our species are nationally scarce and a further eight Northumberland taxa (not all full species) qualify for the 3rd edition of the vascular plant *British Red Data Book*. The criteria for listing in the *Red Data Book* are based on decline, threat, population dynamics and distribution. The eight taxa are:

> Issler's clubmoss
> Killarney fern (we have the gametophyte only)
> lobed maidenhair spleenwort
> a lady's-mantle (*Alchemilla acutiloba*)
> a lady's-mantle (*A. micans*)
> Jacob's ladder
> northern spike-rush
> Young's helleborine

Issler's clubmoss, with a single locality high in William's Cleugh, a headwater valley of the North Tyne near the Scottish border, is noted on page 150 as a possible native pine wood relict. Killarney fern, an oceanic species, has one known locality, under northwest-facing sandstone crags in Kielder Forest. The spleenwort has a single known station on a shaded, calcareous rock wall in Hareshaw Dene. The lady's-mantle *Alchemilla acutiloba* is a Boreo-temperate species whose British distribution is centred in upper Teesdale, but with a single Northumberland locality in the upper Derwent valley. *A. micans*, another lady's-mantle, is also a Boreo-temperate species that occurs in a few localities in calcareous grassland in the lower North Tyne area; it is not otherwise now known in the British Isles and is the only British vascular plant species, in the usage of this chapter, confined to Northumberland. (A further site, the Scroggs, near Chollerford, has been destroyed by quarrying and the plant transplanted by the quarry company into translocated turf in a worked-out part of the quarry, so far successfully. It is unclear whether the *Alchemilla micans* was rooted in limestone or whin (the quarried rock).) Jacob's ladder has two localities in a damp, tall-herb community on the Cheviot volcanics of upper Coquetdale. Northern spike-rush is a fugitive species of sandy alluvium by rivers and burns and is localised in Redesdale,

North Tynedale and by the River Irthing. Young's helleborine is now known in central Scotland and in Yorkshire, but in Britain was first identified in Northumberland (Richards & Porter, 1982); it occurs at a handful of localities in woodland

Bog orchid featured in the 2nd edition of the vascular plant *British Red Data Book* (Perring & Farrell, 1983), although not in the 3rd, and the UK is believed to contain more than 25 per cent of the world population of the species. It has six known sites in the county, although it is inconspicuous and difficult to find.

The following nationally scarce and RDB plants are not only well represented in Northumberland (occurring here in more than eight squares), but the county, together with the adjacent Scottish Borders and Cumbria, holds a substantial proportion of their British populations. They are our botanical specialities:

spring sandwort	metallophyte
maiden pink	basic rocks, river shingle
alpine penny-cress	metallophyte
downy currant	woodland
hairy stonecrop	base-rich flushes, whin
pale forget-me-not	acidic flushes, rills
an eyebright (*Euphrasia rostkoviana* subsp. *montana*	meadows
northern hawk's-beard	meadows
northern spike-rush	upland river margins

Bog-rosemary might be added, although it just fails to meet the nationally scarce criterion. As can be seen, the plants belong to a variety of habitats. Pale forget-me-not is plentiful by springs and streams in the Cheviots (and at the head of Redesdale) and in the North Pennines, but oddly lacking in the extensive uplands between.

Deergrass

Professor Swan, with meticulous observation, has clarified the status of taxa within deergrass *Tricophorum cespitosum* and described a new taxon within the species, the hybrid *T. cespitosum* nothosubsp. *foersteri* (Hollingsworth & Swan, 1999; Swan, 1999, 2003).

The subspecies *germanicum* is very common and widely dominant on blanket bogs in the county and elsewhere, but there are additionally four notable Northumberland taxa.

Tricophorum cespitosum subsp. *cespitosum* is now known in Britain only from Northumberland, the Scottish Borders and the Scottish Highlands, occurring in Northumberland in the somewhat base-enriched margins of *Sphagnum* mires. *T. cespitosum* nothosubsp. *foersteri* is the characteristic deergrass of the raised and intermediate mires of west Northumberland and is a sterile hybrid between the two subspecies. The first extant British records were all from or adjacent to Northumberland, but it has now been looked for and found elsewhere. The more widespread form of *foersteri* is non-proliferous. The proliferous form, in which some of the flowers proliferate to give green plantlets, however, occurs on at least 17 local mires, and has very few other British localities (it is known only from Britain). There is also a proliferous form of *T. cespitosum* subsp. *germanicum*, known in Northumberland only from a site near Hareshaw Head. Clearly these taxa, not easy to separate, may prove to be more widespread in Britain than currently known, but Swan has made Northumberland the focus of deergrass studies. We should certainly call the hybrid, *foersteri*, 'Swan's deergrass'.

Introductions

Swan's *Flora* and *Supplement* record 714 taxa that are/were introductions, through human agency, to Northumberland, although not necessarily to Britain. There is an empirically derived 'tens rule' (see Williamson, 1996), which states that very roughly 10 per cent of imported organisms will escape into the wild, 10 per cent of these will become established (naturalised) with a self-sustaining population (the other 90 per cent are simply casual), and 10 per cent of the established species will assume pest status (in the case of plants, become weeds) – organisms that somebody wishes were not there. The problems caused can be economic, ecological (mainly through competition) or affecting public health (for example, giant hogweed). Swan divides his introduced species into 'colonists' (unintentional invaders), and 'hortals' (intentionally introduced, often as garden plants), and both are classified into either 'casual' or 'naturalised', in much the same sense as in the tens rule, so it is interesting to see whether the rule is followed in Northumberland.

There are 242 'naturalised' taxa, which is 36 per cent of the 673 which were recognised as introductions at the time of Swan's *Flora* (the 714 given at the beginning of this section takes account of more recent interpretations of native/introduced status), and which, according to the tens rule, is many too many. Admittedly a number of the naturalised plants are rare in the county, but they are still firmly established. However, the tens rule predicts that only 1 per cent of the 'escaped' species should become pests, and, although whether a plant has pest status is a subjective judgement, perhaps the following 12 species can be regarded as significant pests, 1.8 per cent, which is a good fit to the rule. None are native British species, unless common cord-grass is so regarded (p. 217):

>water fern
>Sitka spruce
>Japanese knotweed
>rhododendron
>prickly heath
>shallon
>New Zealand pigmyweed
>pirri-pirri-bur
>sycamore
>Indian balsam
>giant hogweed
>common cord-grass

Some justification of the selection is necessary. Sitka spruce is on the list because it freely establishes from seed on all but the wettest of the mire nature reserves in Kielder Forest (Chapter 15), eventually, if not removed, destroying the interest of the habitat. As elsewhere in Britain there are worries about the spread into the wild of aquatic species introduced to garden ponds. New Zealand pigmyweed and water fern have both appeared in the last ten years or so as local pests in coalfield ponds. The knotweed, a nineteenth-century garden introduction, is a well-known, although localised, pest of gardens and waste ground. Pirri-pirri-bur is an invader of otherwise natural dune systems on Holy Island (Chapter 13, which see also for common cord-grass) and although it has spread inland has not there become a problem. Sycamore reduces the naturalness of woodlands which it too freely invades, but in other contexts is a welcome addition to the countryside. Indian balsam and giant hogweed, also nineteenth-century garden introductions, invade river banks and competitively exclude native species (Chapter 12). The spread of rhododendron into the wild is a rather localised problem in Northumberland, unlike the case in western Britain, invading woodland or moorland only around estate plantings. Large numbers of hybrids were bred and grafted onto *ponticum* stocks, and their neglect led to flowering and seeding of the stocks (Richards, in Swan, 1993). Shallon and prickly heath have similarly spread from estate plantings, particularly at Cragside where hundreds of hectares are co-dominated by the two species.

Possibly snowberry, planted for pheasant cover, could be considered a very local pest when it spreads by suckering into semi-natural habitats, and also beech – for reasons similar to sycamore. Taking all this into account, as Crawley (1997) has said, by world standards the problem plants of Britain are a pretty tame set.

Only two pteridophytes, out of 62 Northumberland taxa, were introduced – holly fern, a casual hortal and long extinct, and water fern – and all 47 *Carex* (sedge) taxa and all 32 orchid taxa, with the possible exception of creeping lady's-tresses, are native to the county. The pteridophytes and orchids are super-efficient dispersers, so that suitably adapted species would arrive here naturally, while sedges would be unlikely to be brought in as hortals.

Ballast plants
Many of the casual colonists were introduced as 'ballast plants' to the banks of the lower Tyne or of other coalfield ports. Ballast, in returning colliers and other vessels, usually consisted of sand and gravel, or chalk with flints. It contained the seeds of plants from the source areas of the ballast, many of which germinated on the ballast hills (dumps). Most failed to persist, but a few found our environment to their liking and became naturalised. Some were carried inland, perhaps when the ballast was recycled in laying rail beds, and others colonised adjacent ground. The ballast species originated both in southern England and further afield. Baker & Tate, in their 1868 *Flora*, listed 154 such species for Northumberland and Durham, and Winch had earlier listed ballast species in his 1831 *Flora*. Immigration ceased in the third quarter of the nineteenth century when wooden ships were replaced by iron ones, carrying water ballast, and most of the ballast hills themselves have long ago succumbed to development, although a few fragments of the habitat survive. Among the naturalised species are perennial wall-rocket and, probably, wild parsnip.

Non-vascular plants
(*Recent lichen information is from Janet Simkin.*)
Some of the more notable members of Northumberland's non-vascular flora (accepting lichens as honorary plants) are picked up in this section. Two extremely rare lichens are river jelly lichen (p. 195) and rock nail. The latter has three known, extant British localities, of which two are in Northumberland, both on the humid underside of slightly leaning, sandstone gravestones. Because leaning gravestones are regarded as a safety risk, the habitat is threatened. Petalwort, a liverwort, is also rare (p. 218), as is another liverwort *Lepidozia cupressina*, the only oceanic bryophyte more abundant in Northumberland than in Cumbria, occurring in shade on moorland sandstone outcrops. Northumberland is renowned for its *Sphagnum* mosses (*Sphagnum* species as well as the bog = *moss* habitat), and has several rarities. *Sphagnum balticum* was recently reconfirmed at Muckle Moss, where *S. majus*, *S. riparium* and *S. pulchrum* are also

found – Muckle Moss (pp.113–114) is a remarkable site in many ways. *Sphagnum riparium* is also in a marsh near Colt Crag Reservoir, and *S. pulchrum* on Boddle Moss and at Kielderhead. *S. imbricatum* occurs on *Sphagnum*-dominated bogs in west Northumberland, and fossil remains in the peat show that it was abundant until medieval times. Its demise, and replacement by *S. magellanicum*, represents a major and unexplained ecological change. *Sphagnum fuscum* is also on these bogs, as well as on some higher altitude blanket bogs, including on The Cheviot summit. Water rock-bristle is a minute, aquatic moss with a single locality in the county, on a moist, shaded rock face by an oligotrophic stream. It is not now known anywhere else in Britain.

There is prodigious growth of lichens on some upland sandstone crags, which, with their pure air and high humidity, are nationally important for their lichen floras (Gilbert, 1980). Important sites are Echo Crags in upper Redesdale, the Kielder Stone (Plate 6b), Muckle Samuel's Crag in the western part of Kielder Forest, the summit of Grey Nag (North Pennines) and Killhope Law, on the Durham border. Among rarer species are *Alectoria sarmentosa* and *Platismatia norvegica.*

Gilbert (1965, 1968) showed that the coalfield area of the lower Tyne valley and southeast Northumberland was then a bryophyte and lichen desert. Regarding bryophytes, the conspicuous moss *Grimmia pulvinata* is a sensitive indicator of air pollution (its presence denoting clean air), but various species disappeared in sequence with increasing pollution, the order of disappearance and distance in towards the urban area, however, varying with the substrate. For example, on the uniform habitat of asbestos roofs, only *Tortula muralis*, *Bryum capillare*, *B. argenteum* and *Ceratodon purpureus* survived in the inner suburbs and Newcastle city centre. Gilbert concluded that, for bryophytes, sulphur dioxide pollution was mainly culpable. The deeply incised Jesmond Dene, in the inner suburbs, retained a richer flora, apparently because shelter ameliorated the effects of pollution. Similarly for lichens, there was a drastic reduction in the number of species as SO_2 levels increased, and in central built-up areas only a few species survived, including *Candelariella aurella*, *Lecanora conizaeoides* (almost unknown before the onset of pollution) and *Lepraria incana*. With the decline in urban SO_2 levels since the late 1960s, however, there has been a dramatic recovery, with the number of lichen species increasing year by year. Noticeable now is the fruticose lichen *Usnea subfloridana*, common in parks near Newcastle city centre, while *Lecanora conizaeoides* is disappearing.

Birds

Northumberland has been very fortunate in the quality and number of its ornithologists, a tradition very much continued today. The main historical figures are described in Chapter 14, and annual reports of bird records are unbroken from 1933; they are now published by the Northumberland and Tyneside Bird Club. The county's east coastal position means that many vagrant species make landfall here, greatly exciting bird-watchers.

Breeding birds

There are 144 bird taxa regularly breeding in Northumberland, and 11 occasionally, 70 per cent of the 222 taxa featured in the British Isles breeding bird atlas (Gibbons *et al.*, 1993). Additionally, the dotterel breeds in the Cumbrian Pennines. Of the Northumberland breeders, five are introductions

to the British Isles: Canada goose, ruddy duck, red-legged partridge, pheasant
and little owl.

The birds that Northumberland lacks are predominantly those that have either
far northern/northwestern, western/southwestern, or far southern British Isles
breeding distributions. We therefore, not unexpectedly, have a 'middle British'
bird fauna. Missing species include 12 swans/geese/ducks, and ten waders.

Analysed by breeding habitats, and arbitrarily assigning a main habitat for
those taxa that are catholic in their preferences, the 144 regular breeders classify
as shown in Table 3.

Table 3 Northumberland breeding birds by habitat.

habitat	number of Northumberland taxa	per cent Northumberland taxa	per cent for all British Isles taxa
broadleaved/mixed woodland and scrub	37	25.7	22.5
conifer plantations	6	4.2	5.4
lowland farmland	25	17.4	14.4
moorland/crag	21	14.6	13.1
aquatic habitats/reedbed/other wetland	27	18.8	22.5
coast	21	14.6	13.5
lowland heath	–	–	1.8
montane habitats	–	–	0.9
other	7	4.9	5.9
	144	100.2	100.0

Northumberland, therefore, has much the same distribution of numbers of
breeding birds by habitat as has the British Isles as a whole, with the obvious
exceptions of lowland heath and high montane habitats, which the county lacks.

The 'abundance' maps in the British Isles atlas give an impression of the parts
of the country where each breeding species is particularly well represented
(allowing for different total bird populations). From these maps
Northumberland and, in some cases, adjacent counties, is the place to come for
nine taxa. However, for those indicated with an asterisk, Northumberland is
outstanding only within England. The birds, with their breeding habitat, are:

black-necked grebe	an estate lake
goosander	upland rivers
*black grouse	moorland (also Scotland)
golden plover	moorland
Sandwich tern	coastal (ca. one-quarter of British Isles population)
roseate tern	coastal (ca. one-third of British Isles population)
*siskin	conifer forest (also Scotland, Wales)
*common crossbill	conifer forest (also Scotland)

We should add the curlew, still plentiful in Northumberland, while declining
in many parts of Britain. It is characteristic of our lower moorlands and North
Pennine allotments, its song and call announcing the coming of spring to the
hills. Bolam (1912), has an anonymous writer describing curlew as 'plaintive
creatures who pity themselves on moorlands'. Indeed, the Northumberland

National Park has adopted the bird as its emblem. The puffin and eider duck are present in large numbers, and the goshawk and merlin are also good Northumberland species.

As regards breeding bird assemblages, the following habitats are the most notable:
upland woodland: redstart, wood warbler, pied flycatcher and many common woodland species;
conifer forests: goshawk, sparrowhawk, merlin (using old carrion crow nests), goldcrest, coal tit, siskin and crossbill (especially in Kielder Forest);
upland heather heath and blanket bog: merlin, golden plover, dunlin, red grouse;
marginal moorland: upland waders: lapwing, snipe, curlew, redshank; black grouse (the North Pennine moorlands, the Otterburn Training Area);
coastal islands: eider; colonial seabirds: fulmar, cormorant, shag, kittiwake, Sandwich, roseate, common and arctic terns, guillemot, razorbill, puffin (Farne Islands, Coquet Island).

We share a pair of golden eagles with a neighbouring area, and they breed successfully in some years.

Wintering birds

The tidal slakes between Holy Island and the mainland, and nearby Budle Bay, with vast flocks of wildfowl and waders, are the winter meccas for bird-watchers. Additionally, near-coastal ponds are habitat both for wintering wildfowl and passage waders. The whooper swan, for example, is normally present in numbers on several coalfield ponds, as well as at Lindisfarne, and small numbers of the Bewick's swan are regularly found in the same areas. The purple sandpiper is a notable wintering species of the rocky shores.

Butterflies

While the British Isles 'all-species richness' map in the breeding bird atlas shows a clear south to north decline in species richness, the map is based on 10x10 kilometre squares and is therefore unsuitable for comparing larger areas, for example, counties, which contain varied habitats. Consequently it is not clear that Northumberland is less species rich than a similar total area in the south. For butterflies, however, there can be no doubt. We are deprived. This is partly because of a lack of appropriate habitats (for example, chalk downland), but mainly because of our colder northern climate – and that despite several species having extended their ranges northwards in recent years owing to climatic warming. In the British Isles there are 59 species that are, or historically have been, resident (four are extinct in Britain), and another three (clouded yellow, red admiral, painted lady) are regular immigrants and reproduce in Britain. Asher *et al.*'s *Atlas* (2001), from which much of the following data is derived, gives 'records', and it is assumed that multiple records of non-migrant species for a locality imply breeding, i.e. residence. Butterflies are the best-known group of British invertebrates, and are the only invertebrate group considered in this chapter.

Of the 55 British Isles extant, resident species, only 11 are geographically widespread (all being present in Northumberland), the others therefore having range boundaries within the country. Northumberland has 23 currently resident species, plus the three regular migrants, which makes 45 per cent of the British Isles total. For three of our local resident species the range boundary, in each case the northern limit, is at present in Northumberland: small skipper, white-letter hairstreak and wall. Of the 32 resident species not found in

Northumberland, no less than 23 have northern limits that are to the south, or far to the south, of the county – hence our butterfly deprivation.

With regard to many of the 23, our inadequately warm and sunny climate is almost certainly our undoing – either through adverse effects of climate on some stage of the insect's life cycle or through climatic limitations on the food plants. Neither of the larval food plants of the brimstone, buckthorn and alder buckthorn, for example, occur this far north (the butterfly is, however, seen as a vagrant). For some other absent species, however, different missing habitat ingredients are probably the cause (although habitat and climate are much confounded). For example, several species formerly resident in Northumberland are now extinct here, and since climate has been generally warming in the past century, for most of these habitat loss, or fragmentation, are the likely proximal causes of local extinction. Bearing in mind the difficulty of establishing whether sparse early records indicate 'residence' or simply vagrants, it seems likely that extinct Northumberland species are:

        grizzled skipper
        small blue (extinct after 1945)
        holly blue (in recent years has appeared and disappeared)
        northern brown argus
        pearl-bordered fritillary (extinct after 1945)
        speckled wood
        gatekeeper

The northern brown argus has been considered to have two British races or subspecies, the mainly Scottish *Aricia artaxerxes artaxerxes* and the northern English *A.a. salmacis* – the locally famous Durham argus butterfly. The two races have been considered to overlap and hybridise on the Durham coast, with inland Durham colonies consisting entirely of the Durham argus, and it was this race which formerly inhabited outcrops of the Whin Sill in north Northumberland in association with the larval food plant, common rock-rose. However, the genetic relationships of the taxon require clarification. The butterfly's loss from the county is thought to have resulted from reduction and fragmentation of its semi-natural grassland habitat. It is likely that parallel causes, arising from agricultural intensification and changes in woodland management systems, are responsible for the loss of the other species from Northumberland.

Turning to extant species, the comma was not present at the time of Cook's local atlas in 1990, but was formerly present and has recently recolonised Northumberland (Ellis, 1999) and the Borders. It is possible that its spread has been assisted by widespread agricultural eutrophication, benefiting its main larval food plant, common nettle. However, in Northumberland, elm has so far been the main food plant, although the larva has been found on nettle (Ellis, 2001). Also absent in 1990, but now, as noted above, present at their northern limits are the small skipper and white-letter hairstreak. These, however, have advanced into brand new northern territory, presumably in response to climatic warming. The extent of northwards range shifts in Britain during the twentieth century of species not limited by specialised habitat requirements roughly coincides with the extent of northward shifts in summer isotherms as a result of global warming (Warren *et al.*, 2001), and, in any case, rapid changes in range are a feature of butterfly biogeography. The wall, also at its northern limit, was abundant until the 1860s, became extinct in the county, but has recolonised from the south, spreading into Northumberland in the 1970s.

Many of the 26 Northumberland butterfly species are localised within the county. The small skipper, dingy skipper and wall are exclusively or largely southeastern, with distributions similar to those of plants which are also confined to the warmest and driest part of Northumberland. The purple hairstreak and white-letter hairstreak reach only as far north as the main Tyne valley, and the large heath is concentrated on the western bogs. The ringlet has an interesting British and local distribution. Nationally it appears to be absent from the major industrial areas of the midlands and north, and in Northumberland it occurs mainly in the rural areas of the north and west, well away from the coalfield. Asher *et al.* (2001) suggest that it may be adversely affected by atmospheric pollution.

Mammals
Chillingham Park cattle
The cattle inhabit Chillingham Park, 134 hectares of open woodland and moorland, designed from the seventeenth century onwards as habitat for the cattle. The Park occupies a western slope of the Fell Sandstone cuesta. Of Britain's park cattle, only the Chillingham herd has been kept pure, and it shows no affinity with any other breed. It is a closed herd, highly inbred. Skeletally the animals resemble medieval British cattle They are white with partly red ears and are horned. Although the herd's origins are unknown, according to Yalden (1999) it is unlikely to be derived directly (as has been supposed) from native aurochsen; the animals are not particularly closer to their wild ancestor anatomically than are any other domestic cattle. More likely it is a feral domestic breed, medieval or earlier, descended from introduced, domesticated cattle from the Continent. Perhaps they were white mutants walled in as a curiosity, or for hunting. It is, nevertheless, one of the few herds of cattle in the world that is completely feral (although foddered in winter), with a natural sex ratio and age distribution. (They were, however, culled and males castrated in the nineteenth century.) Their normal social structure is with a king bull, whose dominance lasts for about three years. Like domestic cattle they have no fixed breeding season, but like wild cattle have high calf mortality, of around 50 per cent, in the first year. There are now on average 40–45 animals (with an even sex ratio), after the herd was reduced to 13 individuals in the very severe 1947 winter. The cattle are genetically very homogeneous, yet are clearly viable, and Hall & Hall (1988) and Visscher *et al.* (2001) have argued that rigorous natural selection, and inbreeding, have purged deleterious genes. The herd is managed by the Chillingham Wild Cattle Association and is backed up by a reserve herd in Scotland, established from the Chillingham herd (Fig. 58).

Feral goats
Another herd-dwelling mammal is the feral goat (goats were introduced to Britain in the Neolithic). There are now several populations in uplands along the Scottish Borders, which allows the billies to move between herds, maintaining gene flow. The nannies, however, are faithful to their home range. Four of the Borders populations are in moorland areas of Northumberland, at Kielderhead/Whitelee, Coquethead, and in two groups in the northern Cheviots, based respectively on Newton Tors and Yeavering Bell. Other herds have been extinguished at Christianbury Crag and elsewhere. There is no information as to when the goats became feral – probably incrementally over several centuries; there were herds of goats in Redesdale in the sixteenth century. They are now

Fig. 58 Thomas Bewick's *Chillingham bull.* Copy of a proof impression on vellum of the woodcut engraving made in 1789. Bewick considered it to be his masterpiece. The vellum impression is owned by the Natural History Society of Northumbria. (Natural History Society of Northumbria).

completely wild, although the populations are culled, or found new homes, at intervals in order to minimise browsing damage to plantations, and during the twentieth century they were at times a sporting quarry. Because they tend to graze the least productive moorland vegetation, they are now generally tolerated by hill farmers. They are regarded as of conservation importance in that Britain supports about half of the ancient feral caprines of Europe (Harris *et al.*, 1995), and the local goats, related to the Old English breed, are genetically distinct from continental populations (Fig. 59).

Their coat is long and thick, and of varied colour, often with a skewbald pattern. (They provided goatskin mats for hill farm bedrooms.) Kids are born in early spring, and most nannies (like hill sheep) first breed after two years, coming into season in autumn. The goats have a herd structure, with a dominant billy, and an old nanny with accumulated knowledge of the local environment who leads herd behaviour. They spend the greater part of the day feeding and ruminating, with a diet apparently similar to that of hill sheep and including heather, bilberry, hare's-tail cottongrass and deergrass, as well as finer grasses (McDougall, 1975). Like sheep they are hefted to their herd territory, and find ways to return if shifted for human convenience. McDougall observed that while hill sheep make and follow paths in single file (sheep tracks through long heather are a boon to walkers), the goats move on a broad front. The Kielderhead/Whitelee herd is now maintained at about 75 individuals by culling or relocation, but it is not known whether this constitutes a minimum viable population (conventionally taken to be 90 per cent survival probability after 100 years), given high mortality in hard winters and random variations in birth rate and survival levels. This herd was reduced to only nine animals after the exceptionally severe winter of 1962–3.

Fig. 59 Feral goats of the Yeavering herd. The dark animal is a dominant billy (John Steele).

Goats may seem unprepossessing, but to encounter one of the herds in wild moorland is an exciting experience. They are wary, with acute senses of sight, hearing and smell (and themselves smell strongly, especially the billies), and are difficult to approach closer than about 300 metres. They have become part of our wild fauna.

Other mammals (not discussed elsewhere in the book)
Many of Britain's 16 extant, resident bat species are at the northern edges of their European ranges, so it is not surprising that in Northumberland we have only half of that number as resident, breeding species: Natterer's, Daubenton's, whiskered, Brandt's, noctule, 45 kHz and 55 kHz pipistrelles, and brown long-eared bats. There has also been a single record of a Leisler's bat. It was noted in Chapter 5 that Brandt's and noctule bats are here probably near their northern limits in Britain. A very Northumbrian connection is summer roosts of Daubenton's bat in the roofs of bastle houses and castles, near to the rivers and burns over which they forage.

We have the harvest mouse, possibly introduced in prehistoric times (Yalden, 1999), but in what numbers it is impossible to say and there have been recent deliberate releases, obscuring the picture. The Normans are believed to have introduced the rabbit to Britain, partly to utilise poor land, and the early warrens were often installed on islands; Holy Island had a coneygarth by the early fourteenth century. Heslop Harrison (1931) noticed an association between rabbits and the small copper butterfly, in that sheep's sorrel, a main food plant of the butterfly, is a ruderal plant of disturbed soils and characteristic of rabbit colonies. Graham (1993) described solitary 'crag rabbits' living far out on the moors, untypically isolated from breeding populations. The brown hare was also probably introduced to Britain, perhaps in late prehistoric times, and like the rabbit has found agricultural landscapes to its liking; it is particularly associated in Northumberland with the upland allotments. There is no evidence of mountain hare currently in Northumberland; introductions have not persisted.

As regards predators, there are no modern polecat records from Northumberland, although they do occur not far over the Cumbrian boundary. There are, however, recent pine marten sightings (after its likely nineteenth-century extinction in the county), possibly of released animals, from widely scattered localities mainly in the vicinity of forest blocks, although not from the main part of Kielder Forest. The animal is, of course, an excellent climber, associated with both woodland and crags.

There is a herd of captive red deer in Hulne Park (in the nineteenth century; the park had albino red deer) and another on a holding in Kielder Forest west of Wark. Fallow deer are still to be found in Billsmoor, Hulne and Chillingham Parks, and there are escapees of both species.

Adder

The adder is extremely common in our moorland areas, both on heather heaths and in acidophilous grassland (for example in the Cheviots), and also in some upland woods, while being scarce in the lowlands. It seems to be less abundant in areas of blanket bog. Given the rarity of grass snakes (if they are still present), should you see a snake it is an adder, and therefore venomous. Often, however, it will be the sloughed skin that is encountered. Small mammals such as voles comprise much of its diet. Road casualties are common (Fig. 60).

Fig. 60 Adder, very common in the moorlands (Geoffrey Chaytor).

8

The Moorlands

Moorland occupies one-third of Northumberland, mainly in the western uplands. Here the cool, wet climate causes soils to be nutrient-deficient, acidic and often waterlogged, a combination which – together with the short growing season and difficult terrain – makes intensive farming uneconomic or physically impossible. Extensive grazing systems therefore prevail in the hills, with low inputs and low outputs, allowing the persistence of semi-natural and some near-natural ecosystems: the essence of the moorland environment.

Land use and zonation

Most of the moorland is sheep-grazed, mainly by Swaledale sheep, but in the Cheviots, with more fertile soils on the lower slopes, by the more demanding Cheviot sheep. Cattle also graze the lower, more productive moorlands. Much of the heather-dominated moorland is managed for red grouse, as well as being grazed by sheep, although sheep have been and are excluded from some grouse moors.

Moorlands above the natural tree line at 600–700 metres a.s.l. are montane (described in Chapter 11) and those below – most of Northumberland's moorland – submontane. The lower limit of the submontane zone is the moorland edge – the boundary against improved, enclosed farmland (Plate 6c). This, however, can be a somewhat elusive concept. The boundary is clear enough when a field mown for hay lies over the wall from open moorland supporting, say, heather, but less so where there is a gradual transition from improved fields through larger and larger allotments, with sequentially rougher and more acidophilous vegetation.

However it is defined, the altitude of the moorland edge varies considerably across Northumberland, being surprisingly high in the North Pennines. The high elevation of the valley floors there (in the upper dales they lie above the 300-metre contour) meant that enclosed farmland, if it was to exist at all, lay at relatively high altitudes. But, as explained in previous chapters, more important was the dual lead-mining and farming economy, encouraged by the mining concerns. Eventually, probably more miners had smallholdings than not, and as there was insufficient already improved land on the valley floors to meet demand, reclamation of adjacent open moorland or allotments, to make the small farms, pushed the moorland edge high up dale-sides to altitudes unmatched anywhere else in the British Isles. Exceptionally hay was mown even at 600 metres a.s.l., and the moorland edge was quite commonly above 500 metres a.s.l. Improvement was carried out by paring and burning the turf, culverting springs, installing stone drainage systems, and liberally applying lime and manure.

Although metal mining has ceased, this historic investment in land improvement has left a legacy of improved and semi-improved land to high altitudes in the North Pennines, both above and below the present moorland edge. This, despite now being at lower altitudes than formerly, is still commonly as high as 400 metres a.s.l. The highest farmhouses, however, have been abandoned and left derelict, their fields reverted to rough, acidophilous grassland, and most of the smallholdings are now parts of larger hill farms. North of the Tyne Corridor, in marked contrast, both topography and a different land-use history have not forced reclamation to such altitudes, and the moorland edge is characteristically much lower, at 200–250 metres a.s.l.

Some consequences, particularly for upland birds, of this distinctive land-use history in the lead-mining dales are discussed at the end of this chapter.

Some general characteristics of the moorlands

Within the submontane zone, the type of moorland vegetation present is determined partly by natural factors of climate, soil and slope, and partly by human factors such as grazing, burning and draining. As these management practices change, so does the moorland vegetation and its animal communities, often on quite a short timescale. Walls and fences frequently separate different vegetation types in response to differing grazing pressures across the boundaries – there may be more heather and/or bilberry on the one side than on the other (Fig. 61).

Fig. 61 The Scottish border line near Carter Bar, showing the effect of grazing on vegetation. There is a heather–hare's-tail cottongrass community on the left (Scottish) side of the fence, following the removal of sheep, and a cottongrass community on the still-grazed English side. (But which fence is the Border?)

The approximate areas covered by the main moorland vegetation types in Northumberland are given in Table 4. It can be seen that acidophilous grasslands account for 39 per cent of the moorland area, bracken communities 6 per cent, heathland (vegetation dominated by dwarf shrubs) 18.5 per cent, grass heaths (mixtures of heather and acidophilous grasses) 8.5 per cent and bogs (with a small amount of fen) 19 per cent. The remaining moorland consists of various transitions between the above types, and limited areas of gorse. Among the acidophilous grasslands, and accounting for 11 per cent of the moorland area, are the bent–fescue grasslands. They are the most productive type of moorland vegetation, providing the main forage for livestock. Only in winter, once they are grazed down, are sheep forced to turn to less palatable vegetation on the poorer soils. The bent–fescue grasslands occur on the lower moors, just above the moorland edge, and more widely on the fertile volcanic soils of the Cheviots. Here, their prevalence on valley floors and steep lower slopes (and to the summits of lower hills) can give a misleading impression of the extent of productive grassland on the lavas.

Table 4 Areas occupied by moorland vegetation types in Northumberland.

Type (on dominant species)	area (km²)		proportion of moorland area (%)	
acidophilous grassland				
bent–fescue	198		11	
Nardus	162		9	
Molinia	79		4	
Molinia–Nardus	41		2	
heath rush community	12		1	
other (mainly transitions				
between above types)	208		12	
		700		39
heathland and grass heaths				
heather	315		18	
heather–bilberry	7		0.5	
heather–*Nardus*	58		3	
heather–*Molinia*	52		3	
heather–heath rush	11		0.5	
other grass heath communities	32		2	
		475		27
peatland				
Sphagnum bog	20		1	
heather–cotton grass bog	233		13	
cotton grass bog	14		1	
other bog and fen	80		4	
		347		19
miscellaneous				
bracken communities	107		6	
heather–bracken	27		2	
gorse communities	23		1	
transitions from acidophilous				
grassland or heathland to bog	95		5	
		252		14
Totals (rounded)		1776		99

Notes

1. Source: Lunn (1976) *The vegetation of Northumberland: map at 1:200,000*. Areas measured by digitising map. The map is generalised so the areas are approximate.

2. The area of Northumberland is 5,227 square kilometres. The moorlands therefore occupy 34 per cent of the county, and the proportions of Northumberland as a whole occupied by the various communities are obtainable by dividing the right-hand column by 3.

3. The vegetation of Alston Moor (Cumbria) does not feature in these calculations.

4. Adding the estimated area of peatland under conifer plantations (say 100 square kilometres), and half of the area mapped as transitional between acidophilous grassland or heathland, and bog (47 square kilometres), the area of peatland is in the order of 494 square kilometres, 9–10 per cent of Northumberland.

This chapter describes the mainly acidophilous moorland types in Northumberland, and aspects of their faunas. Their floras are rather limited, owing to the stresses imposed by climate and soils. Some other moorland types, of much more restricted area, with neutral or basic soils and richer floras, are described in Chapter 11. Breeding birds not closely associated with any particular moorland vegetation type are considered later in this chapter.

Mires

Peat is formed where plant production exceeds its consumption and decomposition, leading to *in situ* accumulation of only partially decayed plant material. Oxygen deficiency owing to waterlogging, together with the durability of bog plant tissues, are normally the factors which inhibit decay. Mires are ecosystems developed on peat soils which still support vegetation that is normally peat forming. (Many former mire systems have been drained or otherwise modified and are no longer actively peat forming.) Mires, and peatlands generally, are either bogs or fens. Bogs are normally fed by atmospheric precipitation alone, in which case they are ombrogenous (or ombrotrophic), and are highly acidic and nutrient deficient. Fens are at least partly fed by ground or surface water (they are minerotrophic), and their soils vary from acidic to basic depending on local geology – they may be calcareous – and in nutrient status. The more acidic and nutrient-deficient fens are poor-fens. Fens are topogenous in sites where water stagnates or passes very gradually through topographic depressions, and soligenous in sites that are permanently irrigated by gravitational lateral seepage. Soligenous mires often take the form of linear soakways, extending down slope from springs; these – as well as more diffuse soligenous mires – are referred to as flushes (although many other flushes occur on mineral soils, not on peat). Fens colonised by shrubs or trees are known as carr. The vegetation of typical bogs and typical fens is very different, although there are transitions; fens have much richer floras than bogs. Bogs and poor-fens are oligotrophic, deficient in plant nutrients; other fens are mesotrophic or eutrophic, respectively moderately and very nutrient rich. These latter terms also apply to other habitats, such as lakes.

Peatland covers about 9–10 per cent of the area of Northumberland (Fig. 62), similar to the proportion for the British Isles as a whole, and although there is no information on the proportion that remains as mire (still with peat-forming vegetation), the plant communities recognised on my 1976 vegetation map indicate that it might be approximately one-third. The rest is either under conifer forest, or now carries a derived, drier type of semi-natural peatland vegetation or (a small part) has been improved as enclosed farmland. Most fens are fairly small in area, so most of the peatland depicted on Figure 62 is bog. Although most bog and some fen occur in the uplands, as part of moorland, some areas of both occur as isolated sites in the lowlands amidst improved farmland (Chapter 11). As noted in Chapter 1, our bogs are a special feature of Northumberland.

Ombrogenous bogs with us are mainly either blanket or raised bogs (also – if peat is still forming – referred to as blanket and raised mires). Blanket bogs originate primarily by paludification: the swamping of soils by heavy and persistent precipitation. This has occurred mainly on gentle slopes in the higher uplands, so that blanket bogs cover extensive and continuous tracts on plateaux and rounded hilltops from the North Pennines to the Cheviots (Plate 7a). The extent to which initial peat formation was triggered by human effects – especially forest clearance and resulting soil saturation owing to decreased transpiration

and decreased interception by the tree canopy and, perhaps, impermeable iron
pan formation during podzolisation – is unknown. Some blanket bog, apparently
as wild an environment as it is possible to find, may therefore, indirectly, be man-
made. Buried timber is frequently found under blanket peat, however, indicating
that natural swamping of woodland occurred (Fig. 63). Bolam (1916) observed
wasps using the sub-fossil wood for paper for their nests; keep something long
enough and it will turn out to be useful! Typically peat depth in blanket bogs
is up to 3 metres.

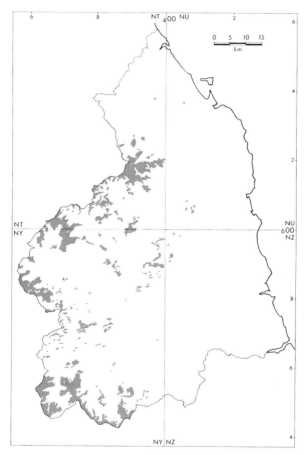

Fig. 62 Distribution of peatland in Northumberland. From Lunn (1976). The map shows all
larger peatlands, almost entirely bog, which were not wooded or afforested at the time of
survey. Rather extensive areas of former open bog had been drained and afforested in the
west of Northumberland in the twentieth century. A relatively small proportion of the
peatland shown on the map has later been afforested. The vegetation of large parts of the
peatland is *Calluna vulgaris–Eriophorum vaginatum* blanket bog, dominated by heather and
hare's-tail cottongrass, but there are also *Sphagnum* mires, especially in the area shown in
more detail on Figure 70. With permission of Department of Geography, University of
Newcastle upon Tyne.

Fig. 63 A 5-metre long oak trunk exposed from under blanket peat, Scaup Burn.
(V. Blankenburgs, with kind permission of Forest Enterprise and Northumberland Archives
Services: 2722-01-0485).

Raised bogs, in contrast, originate by terrestrialisation: the infilling of water
bodies, normally with topogenous (fen) peat, followed by bog peat accumulation
on the flat surface once this is raised above the influence of the ground water
table. Unlike the case with blanket bog, surface contours of raised bogs are
relatively independent of the mineral soil contours beneath the peat. Corings
through local raised bogs typically show that a shallow mere was infilled by peat
derived from reed-swamp vegetation (dominated by common reed). The reed-
swamp was subsequently colonised by carr (represented by brushwood peat),
which in turn was replaced by bog vegetation with dominant *Sphagnum* moss,
the remains of which built up the peat of the raised bog. *Sphagnum* species, owing
to their leaf structure of hollow, dead cells surrounded by live ones, can hold 20
times their own weight of water, which helps to perpetuate the high water tables
to which *Sphagnum* is adapted. Additionally, many *Sphagnum* species create high
acidity, to which they are tolerant and most other plants intolerant.

The natural replacement of one type of vegetation by another in this way –
from open water to reed-swamp to carr to bog – is known as succession.

Classic lowland raised bogs commonly assume the shape of a shallow dome
with a flat crown, and the much degraded lowland raised bog at Prestwick Carr
has this shape. The majority of Northumberland bogs that can be claimed as
raised bogs in terms of their origin by terrestrialisation (replacing former meres)
are, however, constrained between cuestas in the west of the county and are
therefore topographically lower than the adjacent ridges. Nonetheless, some
of these are shallowly domed (Fig. 64).

Fig. 64 A raised bog constrained between cuestas on the former Greenlee farm in west Northumberland. This bog, already with agricultural grips (drains), was later afforested.

Intermediate bogs are transitional between raised bogs and true blanket bogs. The example that has been particularly studied, Coom Rigg Moss, was shown by Chapman (1964*a*; 1964*b*) to have originated as several separate raised bog units by terrestrialisation. These later merged by paludification of the intervening mineral soils, so that the bog now consists of a single peat body about 1.5 kilometres in diameter. Even in the case of extensive higher-altitude blanket bogs, lenses of thicker peat, originating in basins by terrestrialisation, form part of the general peat blanket. Peat depth in raised and intermediate mires is up to 8 metres.

In a few cases, where bog vegetation is found on peat bodies occupying valleys along which there is some water flow or seepage, the ecosystem is known as valley bog (or mire). Normally there are indications in the vegetation of some slight mineral enrichment or of the presence of dissolved oxygen in the peat soil (the presence of various sedges, wavy hair-grass, tormentil, *Molinia*). However, much of the water input is from precipitation, and if bog species such as the acidophilous Sphagna, hare's-tail cottongrass, common cottongrass and cross-leaved heath remain dominant, the system is regarded as a bog. Muckle Moss and part of The Wou are thus valley bogs. Somewhat higher levels of mineral enrichment of mires in valleys and other depressions produce poor-fen vegetation. The soakway at the northern margin of Muckle Moss and the inflow and outflow ends of The Wou are poor-fens. Poor-fen indicators include marsh willowherb, bogbean, marsh cinquefoil, marsh violet, marsh arrowgrass, white sedge, common sedge and bottle sedge. The peat in such valley mires can be exceptionally deep, with ca. 13.5 metres recorded in the centre of Muckle Moss.

Despite the area, number and variety of Northumberland's mires, few are dangerous to walk over. Muckle Moss, however, is an exception. Towards the western end of this 2.5-kilometre long valley bog is a series of arcuate pools, concave to the east. Some of the pools are at least 7 metres deep, and some of these are thinly covered by rafts of *Sphagnum cuspidatum*. They are to be avoided. The mire surface slopes eastwards. Pearson (1960, 1979, pers. comm.), who investigated the structure of Muckle Moss, found that the part of the peat body east of the pools was floating. This part of the mire was therefore a *Schwingmoor* (the name describes the manner in which the mire surface sags under the weight of visitors). Pearson suggested that slow down-slope creep of the upper, western part of the peat body – rather like a valley glacier – generated fissuring as it impinged upon the Schwingmoor area; the pools occupy the deep fissures, and detached peat slices had clotted to become the floating raft. In support, two wire fences that cross Muckle Moss immediately to the east of the pools have been bowed several metres eastwards since their erection, and canes planted by Pearson had moved east-northeastwards – in one case by 3.59 metres in seven years.

Kielderhead Moors, Emblehope Moor and Whitelee Moor

An example of extensive blanket bog, large parts of which are now under conservation management so that grazing or burning no longer occur, is on the interfluve area between upper North Tynedale and upper Redesdale, and extending over the Border into Scotland. In fact, at Kielderhead there has been virtually no burning for half a century. Figure 69 shows the extent of peat in this area, virtually all of which is blanket bog. It covers both plateau surfaces and valley slopes with gradients of up to about 10 degrees from the horizontal, in an almost continuous tract of 6,000 hectares (Fig. 65). The gaps in the peat blanket represent steeper valley sides, or sandstone crags and knolls protruding through the peat.

The most widespread vegetation type in this huge area is *Calluna vulgaris–Eriophorum vaginatum* blanket mire, dominated by heather and hare's-tail cottongrass. A mossy understorey consists of species such as *Hypnum cupressiforme, Pleurozium schreberi* and *Plagiothecium undulatum*, while *Sphagnum* species are scattered: *S. capillifolium* forms large hummocks. Dwarf shrubs other than heather are crowberry, bilberry and cowberry. Cloudberry is frequent to very abundant. A different community occurs on flats and saddles, with higher water tables. Here crowberry, bilberry and cowberry are scarcer, even the heather is stressed and dwarfed, and deergrass and, at lower elevations, cross-leaved heath are abundant. *Sphagnum* species, especially *S. papillosum, S. magellanicum* and *S. subnitens*, have high cover. Overall, the appearance and composition of the blanket bog varies with altitude and slope, with corresponding dominance of any or a mixture of heather, hare's-tail cottongrass, common cottongrass (especially in level areas with high water table), deergrass and *Sphagnum*. The first two species dominate on steeper slopes with lower water tables.

Cloudberry is a special feature of the area. It flowers and fruits in abundance on the ungrazed blanket bogs, in contrast to poor flowering on sheep-grazed bogs. The white bramble-like flowers are produced in June and the orange fruits by mid-August. The plant is seldom found in Northumberland below about 500 metres a.s.l., and experiments by Grace & Marks (1978) showed that temperatures higher than those experienced at about this altitude depressed its growth (Fig. 66). Another notable plant is the less than glamorous orchid, lesser twayblade, the greenish flowers of which are found under leggy heather of both blanket bog and heather heath (Fig. 67).

Fig. 65 Kielderhead Moors. Blanket bog on the gentler slopes, upland heather heath on the steeper valley sides. The area is a National Nature Reserve.

Fig. 66 Cloudberry, abundant on blanket bogs above about 500 metres a.s.l.

Fig. 67 Lesser twayblade, found under heather in blanket bogs and heather heaths (Linda Reinecke).

Threading through the blanket bog are soakways with acidic, soligenous mire vegetation dominated by bottle sedge and *Sphagnum recurvum*. The soakways also contain bog-sedge, bog pondweed and bogbean (Fig. 68).

The only Northumberland locality for dwarf birch, a Boreo-arctic montane species, is amidst blanket bog on Emblehope Moor at about 420 metres a.s.l. There is a vigorous, and apparently spreading, patch some 30 metres in diameter, fringed by creeping willow. Another patch has recently been found on a bog in forestry plantations at Spadeadam, eastern Cumbria.

The west Northumberland/east Cumbrian bogs

Very different bogs occur in the zone of moderate elevation, at 200–300 metres a.s.l., adjacent to and north of Hadrian's Wall. The east Cumbrian bogs include Butterburn Flow and several on Spadeadam Waste. The pattern here, shown on Figure 70, is clearly different from that of the extensive blanket bogs just described. These bogs are islands in a sea of drier vegetation, rather than the reverse, and as explained earlier, consist partly of raised bogs replacing former meres, typically constrained between the cuestas, and partly – as the ground and rainfall rise northwards – of intermediate bogs. However, there is no hard and fast distinction between raised, intermediate and blanket mires – all are ombrogenous, and on low plateaux by the River Irthing level areas of bog appear simply to be blanket bog. There are scores of intercuesta bogs in Northumberland and ten or so large intermediate bogs – prior to afforestation there were many more.

Fig. 68 A soakway threading through the blanket bog at Purdom's Pike, above Kielder Forest, with acidic, soligenous mire vegetation (with permission of Forestry Commission).

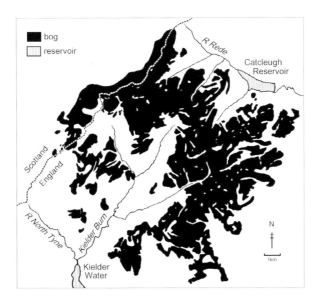

Fig. 69 Detailed distribution of bog in the area between the upper North Tyne and upper Rede. Virtually all is blanket bog. A substantial proportion of the bog is afforested. Based upon British Geological Survey one-inch drift maps, of various dates, by permission of British Geological Survey. IPR/45–25C British Geological Survey. Copyright NERC. All rights reserved.

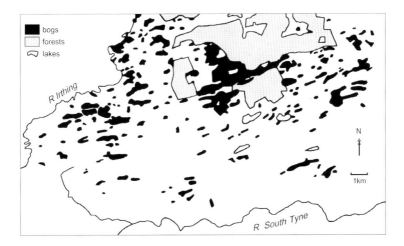

Fig. 70 Detailed distribution of bog in west Northumberland in and south of the Wark section of Kielder Forest and between the Rivers Irthing and South Tyne. Most is raised and intermediate bog. Source: author's manuscript field maps, dating from 1956–75. Some of the bogs have since been afforested, especially in the area between the large forest blocks. Because the data is based on vegetation mapping, afforested bog is not shown (unlike the case in Figure 69).

Until the arrival of the Forestry Commission in Northumberland in 1926, very many of the raised and intermediate bogs had survived as natural ecosystems, and this despite the general vulnerability of bogs to draining, burning, excessive trampling or grazing. Drainage, by digging or ploughing grips (open ditches) is particularly damaging, lowering the water table, with consequent loss of the *Sphagnum* carpet and its rapid replacement by dominant heather and hare's-tail cottongrass. Drained mires lose much of their botanical and other interest.

One reason why so many of these mires survived until the twentieth century was the inherent difficulty of draining sites, or of digging peat from them, in the absence of a pronounced downward marginal slope in the intercuesta depressions. Also, the high water tables reduced the impact of burning. Another reason probably lay in the troubled political history of this Border region, described in Chapter 2. It seems likely that types of moorland vegetation, including wet bogs, which further away from the Border were modified by hill farming activities, here remained in a more natural condition.

Yet a further reason is that much of the ground between the bogs carried *Molinia* grassland, together with a community transitional between *Molinia* grassland and bog which was co-dominated by *Molinia* and hare's-tail cottongrass (Plate 7b). As noted in Chapter 2, it was the practice, until the beginning of the seventeenth century, to summer cattle on these remote shieling grounds, making use of *Molinia*'s relatively high productivity and grazing value in that season, while leaving them ungrazed in winter. This was where 'round about in the wastes as they term them ... you may see, as it were, the ancient Nomads, a martial kind of men, who from the month of April, lie out scattering and summering (as they term it) with their cattle in little cottages here and there, which they call sheals or shealings' (Camden, 1610, but observed in 1599). (Summering sometimes had to be abandoned, however, for fear of raids.) Such transhumance was an effective method of cropping the *Molinia*, well adapted to moderate summer cattle-grazing, but unavailable in winter owing to the grass's deciduous habit. (It is less useful to sheep, owing to litter hampering the consumption of other grasses in winter and diluting fresh *Molinia* consumption in summer.)

This summer utilisation system would have obviated any need to drain the *Sphagnum* bogs in order to encourage heather and hare's-tail cottongrass, respectively for winter and early spring feed. Even when summering was superseded by year-round hill farming, the low winter carrying capacity of the *Molinia* grassland was reflected in the large size of the tenanted farms established after enclosure. Otterstone Lee, in North Tynedale, for example, covered 3,726 hectares and the farmhouse was 11 kilometres from the furthest boundary of the farm; West Kielder, also in North Tynedale, covered 3,240 hectares. Thus low grazing pressures were perpetuated and relict ecosystems survived – at least until afforestation in the twentieth century.

The undamaged inter-cuesta and intermediate bogs are *Sphagnum* bogs, with up to 100 per cent *Sphagnum* cover (Fig. 71). The main species are *Sphagnum magellanicum, S. papillosum, S. capillifolium, S. tenellum* and *S. cuspidatum*, the latter in hollows. The ground is spongy, and consists either of level *Sphagnum* lawns or complexes of low *Sphagnum* hummocks and hollows: the varied green, wine red and magenta hues of the Sphagna are quite delightful. In the moss carpet are rooted a number of dwarf shrubs, sedges and small herbs.

Fig. 71 Gowany Knowe Moss, a large *Sphagnum* bog in Kielder Forest, part of the Kielder Mires National Nature Reserve.

We have met some of these species already on the high blanket bogs: hare's-tail and common cottongrass, deergrass, cross-leaved heath and heather. Although heather is invariably present, it characteristically occurs in a depauperate form. More restricted to these *Sphagnum* bogs are round-leaved sundew, cranberry, bog asphodel and bog-rosemary (Plates 8a, b, c). The sundew is insectivorous, having yellow leaves with sticky red tentacles to which small insects adhere, and the plant supplements its nutrient budget on these infertile soils with nitrogen from this source. The closely related great sundew is, however, known from only three of the bogs. Cranberry's thread-like stems intertwine among the other plants, with conspicuous pink and white flowers. Bog asphodel, a small lily with a golden yellow flower, is *ossifragum* as a bone-breaker when eaten by sheep, but its reputation, according to Mabey (1996), is misdirected from the calcium-poor vegetation among which it grows.

Bog-rosemary was mentioned in Chapter 1 as one of the botanical specialities of the *Sphagnum* bogs and of Northumberland. Figure 72 shows its British Isles, Northumberland and Cumbrian distributions, and the plant's localisation in west Northumberland and east Cumbria is very clear.

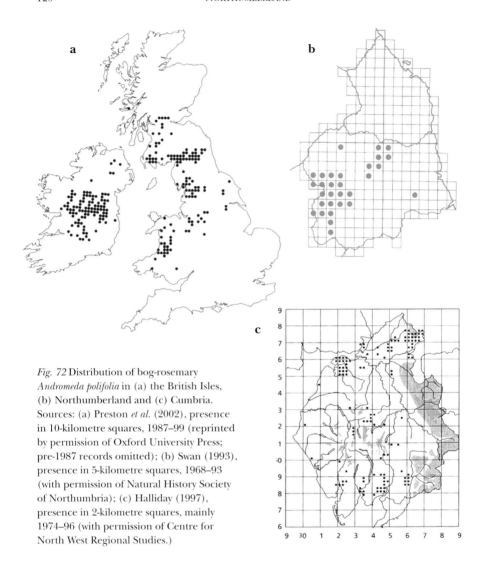

Fig. 72 Distribution of bog-rosemary *Andromeda polifolia* in (a) the British Isles, (b) Northumberland and (c) Cumbria. Sources: (a) Preston *et al.* (2002), presence in 10-kilometre squares, 1987–99 (reprinted by permission of Oxford University Press; pre-1987 records omitted); (b) Swan (1993), presence in 5-kilometre squares, 1968–93 (with permission of Natural History Society of Northumbria); (c) Halliday (1997), presence in 2-kilometre squares, mainly 1974–96 (with permission of Centre for North West Regional Studies.)

A number of rare or uncommon – and it has to be admitted not very conspicuous – sedges are also found on the *Sphagnum* bogs: bog-sedge, tall bog-sedge and few-flowered sedge. White beak-sedge is also present on a few bogs, and is rare in Northumberland. The bog-sedge occurs in soakways, sometimes with a depauperate form of common reed. The deergrass taxa of these bogs were described in the previous chapter. Intermixed with the Sphagna is the yellow-green moss *Aulacomnium palustre*.

These west Northumberland bogs are a main habitat of the large heath butterfly (Plate 8d), which otherwise in Britain is found principally in Scotland. Eales (1997) has found it on 145 sites in this area below about 400 metres a.s.l., and Dennis and he (1999) have suggested that its presence can be predicted on the basis of a few site attributes. The butterfly requires vigorous and contiguous hare's-tail cottongrass (as larval host plant) and cross-leaved heath (as nectar source for the adult), a water table at or near the ground surface, and cottongrass with a tussock habit (so that the overwintering larvae can avoid submergence). Its incidence also correlates positively with site area; presumably larger sites have larger populations, which are less extinction prone (the females being relatively immobile). Another, much less abundant, butterfly of the same part of the county is the small pearl-bordered fritillary, but associated rather with acidic flushes and marshes containing marsh violet, its food plant.

As noted in Chapter 1, many of the mires were drained and afforested by the Forestry Commission, or drained but not planted, or affected by forestry drains at their margins. Fortunately, many others remain intact, or nearly so.

The ground-water mound theory of bog hydrology (Ingram, 1982), which applies to thick lenses of peat, states that the hydrology of a bog system is based on a simple, single ground-water mass, the half-ellipse shape of which acts as a template for waterlogging, peat accumulation and the geometry of the bog surface. In a natural system the ground-water mound, owing to the low permeability of peat below a shallow depth, is more or less at the bog surface, at least in the central parts. Tapping the ground-water mound at any point, by digging drains or removing peat, will lower the water table throughout the bog, so damaging surface hydrology and altering the vegetation everywhere, and eventually lowering the peat surface through oxidation and shrinkage. The corollary is that blocking drains anywhere on the system, including at the margin, will have the opposite and whole-bog beneficial effect, and conservation programmes of drain-blocking based on this principle are described in Chapter 15. Monitoring shows that damming is indeed highly effective in raising water tables and restoring bog communities. However, there is still uncertainty as to whether the luxuriant growth of heather that characterises some bogs within Kielder Forest is caused by water table lowering owing to drains and afforestation at their margins, or is a consequence of removal of sheep-grazing. Probably both are implicated.

Bog pools

A feature of many bogs, including the high blanket bogs, is smaller or larger (up to tens of metres in diameter) pools in the peat. These are of both natural and artificial origin. The former include those impounded by slumped peat that has blocked gullies, while the latter are mainly those created for conservation purposes by damming agricultural or forestry grips, or natural erosion gullies, or by blasting. Other pools were dug on the edges of plantations as a source of water for quenching fires. Whatever the origin, their marginal vegetation consists rather uniformly of common cottongrass, bottle and common sedges (the latter as var. *strictiformis*, with long, narrow leaves) and *Sphagnum cuspidatum* and *S. recurvum*. Although the main objective of damming has been to restore high water tables, some pools have been created specifically to benefit breeding dunlin, and a general bonus has been to increase the numbers and expand the distribution of dragonflies and damselflies. Already using natural pools, these insects now breed in very large numbers in many of the artificial ones, for example in the numerous linear pools created by drain-blocking on Bellcrag Flow. At present we have no distribution maps for our local species.

Peat erosion

In some areas the blanket bog is gullied, either with sub-parallel systems down slopes (with gullies typically 30–40 metres apart), or dendritic systems, or gully networks on flats (for example, on Peel Fell). The gullies have typically cut right through the peat to the mineral substrate (Fig. 73). It is not known to what extent such gully systems follow disruption of the vegetation by sheep treading, or by draining and/or burning, and to what extent they are natural. Some gullies in all types of system are self-healing, and contain soligenous mire communities on newly forming peat. Some of the bright green *Sphagnum recurvum–Juncus effusus* (soft-rush) soligenous mires – which hill walkers learn to avoid – are in such healed gullies, which also contain cushions of the luxuriant, deep green moss *Polytrichum commune*. As well as the gullies (active only in wet weather) water flows in subterranean tunnels, at the interface between peat and mineral substrate. Tunnel roof sections collapse, and some of the deeper gullies may be unroofed tunnels.

Fig. 73 Erosion gully in blanket bog on The Cheviot.

While extensive tracts of blanket bog in the Kielderhead/Whitelee area have virtually no gullying, probably reflecting a long-sustained, relatively low human pressure on the ecosystem, gully systems are more extensive in the Cheviots and North Pennines. A survey by Wishart & Warburton (2001) found that gullies occupied 37 per cent of an area of blanket bog in the higher Cheviots, although there had been relatively little change in the gully systems during the last 100 years. Locally there is more extensive sheet erosion of blanket peat, where gullies have merged or, as in the case of the summit of The Cheviot, trampling by walkers has destroyed the vegetation cover. Here there are about 3 hectares of bare peat, another 15 hectares badly affected, and around the trig point 1.5 metres of peat (of the former 2-metre blanket) has been denuded since the column was constructed in the 1860s (J. Steele, pers. comm.). The National Park is addressing the problem by paving the footpath (here also the Pennine Way) and by revegetating with hare's-tail and common cottongrasses.

Flushes and fens

Throughout the moorlands, and in upland meadows and pastures, are larger or smaller soligenous mires or flushes. These are fed by springs varying chemically from highly calcareous, some producing tufa (calcium carbonate precipitated onto vegetation), to those only slightly less base-deficient and acidic than the surrounding soils. Springs emerge where, at outcrop, permeable limestones or sandstones overlie impermeable shales or mudstones, although the emergence of spring water is more complicated where drift overlies the solid rocks.

The flushes are either linear soakways, or more diffuse wet areas fed by a series of springs. Collectively they add enormously to the floristic diversity of the uplands, and additionally support a high diversity and biomass of invertebrates. These are a vital food for breeding waders and for red and black grouse, and, owing to the above-freezing temperatures at which ground water issues, remain available to insectivorous birds in hard winter weather.

The majority of flushes, even in the limestone areas, are acidic (the more calcareous flushes are described in Chapter 11) and are dominated by rushes – sharp-flowered rush, jointed rush or soft-rush. Frequently abundant are star sedge, common sedge, blinks, lesser spearwort, marsh violet and the mosses *Polytrichum commune*, *Sphagnum recurvum* and *S. palustre*. In a restricted area of upper Coquetdale they support a *Molinia*–bog myrtle community (Plate 9a), and bog myrtle also occurs on mires in the northeast of the county. There is a dense stand for example, with plants up to 2 metres high, at Kimmer Lough. The oddly disjunct local distribution of bog myrtle (Fig. 74) has not been satisfactorily explained. This aromatic shrub was the insect-repellent 'fleawood' of Northumbrian housewives. It contains a number of essential oils, a cocktail that helpfully paralyses the midge *Culicoides impunctatus* (Skene *et al.*, 2000).

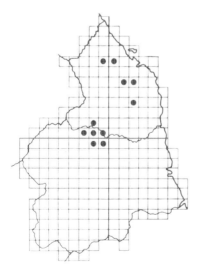

Fig. 74 Distribution of bog myrtle *Myrica gale* in Northumberland. After Swan (1993): presence in 5-kilometre squares, 1968–93. The plant is highly localised on acidic flushes and bogs in the northern part of the county. With permission of Natural History Society of Northumbria.

Two lowland fens are described in Chapter 11, but there are some fens set amidst moorland. They include Caw Lough (spring-fed; any lake was long ago infilled with peat) and the fens at Greenlee and Crag Loughs – all in west Northumberland. The Crag Lough fen consists of swamp, with much water horsetail and bottle sedge, and quaking mattresses of poor-fen vegetation, and contains a population of the very rare (in Northumberland) lesser tussock-sedge.

The mire ecosystems have been described at some length, being particularly characteristic of Northumberland. The other moorland vegetation types, while widespread in the county, are more typical of the British uplands generally.

Upland heather and bilberry heaths
Large tracts of moorland, and especially those seen from the road system, consist of upland heather heath (Plate 9b). Turner (1551) wrote: 'The hyest hethe that ever I saw groweth in northumberland which is so hyghe that a man may hyde himself in.' Eighteen per cent of the moorland is heather heath, another 11 per cent is drier, acidophilous vegetation with some heather admixture, and another 13 per cent is bog with co-dominant heather, so over 40 per cent of our moorland is heathery.

Much of the heather heath is managed in order to provide a surplus of red grouse for shooting, and the North Pennines has nationally important populations. The moors are crossed by lines of butts, variously constructed of timber, stone or peats – in the latter case heather, rooted in the turves, blends butt and moor. However, most grouse moors are also grazed by hill sheep, for which heather is an important food component in winter. In recent years large areas with patchy or unmanaged heather, especially in the Cheviots, have been purchased by landowners interested in shooting and are being intensively managed for heather and red grouse, reversing previous losses of the habitat.

A main management practice of gamekeepers is rotational burning of heather, and some heather heaths have probably been systematically burned for 200 years. Rossiter (1996) notes burning management of heather on the Hexham commons from at least the seventeenth century. Heather is burned to keep it physiologically young, and to prevent a degenerate canopy opening up, so allowing invasion by other plants. Burning is normally on a rotation of 10–15 years. Heather much older than this is less palatable, produces fewer flowers and seeds, has grown beyond the reach of grouse, is woody and burns with too hot a fire, and regenerates less well. Regeneration is both from the unburnt rootstock (unless fire heat is too great) and from seed. The pattern of burning is typically in narrow strips. This is because heather at different ages provides different resources for grouse: young, short heather, for example, is the most nutritious, while older, longer heather provides cover. Because pairs of grouse require this resource diversity within their individual breeding territories, burning narrow strips accommodates the diversity in smaller areas, promoting denser breeding populations.

Heather heaths managed in this way usually consist of virtually pure stands of heather (apart from mosses and liverworts), such that a range of former, more diverse heathland vegetation types, varying with soil and climate, have been impelled to converge on these heather monocultures. They are not, however, uninteresting. All moors contain larger or smaller patches of other vegetation, especially flushes, and heather itself supports a more diverse invertebrate fauna than most acidophilous grassland communities. For these reasons, and because of the cover that mature heather provides, the upland heaths are habitat for an important bird fauna, described later in this chapter.

Grouse shooting also takes place on the blanket bogs, where, as we have seen, heather is widely co-dominant with hare's-tail cottongrass or other bog species. Although burning is practised here too, this is damaging to the moss carpet, removes long heather as nesting habitat and may initiate gully erosion. It is probably unjustifiable even in grouse-management terms, since heather on blanket peat regenerates naturally by layering: prostrate stems readily develop adventitious roots in the damp peat substrate. The appearance of the blanket bog towards Cross Fell, when ascending by road to Hartside summit from Alston, has become an abomination of geometrical burnt patches in what was previously a wilderness landscape. It is also unlikely that draining of blanket bogs, too widely undertaken, does much to encourage heather growth except in the wettest bogs. Like burning, gripping is deleterious to the blanket bog ecosystem as a whole and destroys the flushes that are so vital for the chicks of breeding waders and red grouse.

Former heather heaths that have not been maintained for grouse shooting have been in decline for half a century or more. Areas that were heather dominated in the 1950s are now either mosaics of heath and acidophilous grassland, or have no heather at all, and moorland road verges have heather where there is grassland beyond the wall or fence. The losses have been severest on inherently more productive soils, where bent–fescue grassland replaced heather heath. The main immediate cause of heather decline has been heavy winter grazing, which favours grasses in competition with heather. Additionally, extensive tracts of heather heath have been afforested, particularly on the Fell Sandstone moorlands in the Rothbury area.

The distribution of heather heath is shown in Figure 75. There are four main areas: first the lower summits and gentler slopes in the Cheviot Hills, on both granitic and volcanic rocks; second the Fell Sandstone and other sandstone cuestas – especially on their long dip slopes; third the lower slopes of the tabular Fell Sandstone hills in upper North Tynedale and Redesdale (for example, of Carter Fell and Peel Fell); and fourth the lower, eastern plateaux of the North Pennines (in the Hexhamshire and East Allendale areas). All are areas of predominantly podzolic soils – sandy, freely draining, acidic and nutrient-deficient – to which heather is well adapted. Nutrient loss must have been exacerbated by frequent burning over the centuries.

At higher altitudes, above about 500 metres a.s.l., bilberry becomes increasingly abundant among the heather, as does crowberry, and more sparingly, cowberry. The increase with altitude of bilberry is partly a climatic effect. It is tolerant of, and protected against frost by, prolonged snow cover, and is also susceptible to drought, benefiting from the higher humidity at higher altitudes. In addition, the ground becomes rockier above the limit of glacial drift, and bilberry, better than heather, thrives on these ranker soils. It is locally dominant, as 'Vaccinium edge', on sandstone cuesta scarps. A habitat where the heaths must be in a near-natural condition is the tops of huge sandstone blocks, tumbled from crags or (like the Kielder Stone) shifted by the ice sheet, and which are inaccessible to grazing mammals. Here humic ranker soils support heather, bilberry, crowberry and cowberry. Very rare with us, however, is bearberry, occurring only near to Blanchland and by the Darden Burn, also on ranker soils. The broken, rocky ground of bilberry heath is wheatear habitat, and their purple droppings decorate boulders in the berry season.

More basic soils under heather support a more floristically diverse vegetation with, for example, sneezewort, bugle, wood anemone, harebell and common dog-violet.

Among the more conspicuous insects of the heather moorlands are emperor, northern eggar and fox moths (Fig. 76). The caterpillars of the emperor moth are at first blackish, cryptic against heather stems, but when larger are bright green with light dots, now cryptic on heather foliage. Ford (1955) noted that people suffering from red-green colour blindness perversely see the caterpillar as conspicuous. The hairy caterpillars of the northern eggar and fox moths,

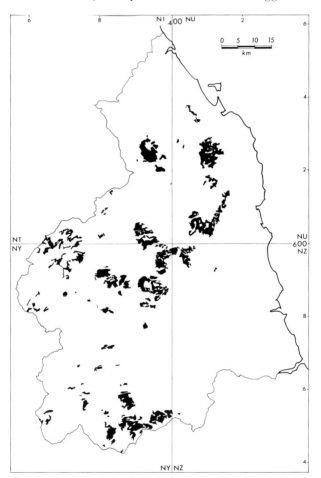

Fig. 75 Distribution of heather heath in Northumberland. After Lunn (1976). The eastern tendency within Northumberland is a consequence of the wetter, western uplands carrying extensive blanket bog rather than the podzolic soils and gleys with which upland heaths are associated. In the west, heather occurs instead as an important component mainly of *Calluna vulgaris–Eriophorum vaginatum* blanket bog. With permission of Department of Geography, University of Newcastle upon Tyne.

on the other hand, can afford to be conspicuous, because their defensive hairs are irritating to predators. Cuckoos, however, especially an upland fringe bird in Northumberland, cope with hairy caterpillars by having a specially adapted gizzard, regurgitating the hairs as pellets. (The normal cuckoo foster parent on the moors is the ubiquitous meadow pipit.) Population explosions of the heather beetle, whose larvae feed on the leaves and bark of heather, can temporarily devastate stands, normally on wetter heaths or on bogs, where *Sphagnum* is favoured for egg-laying.

Fig. 76 Emperor moth, characteristic of the heather moorlands (Geoffrey Chaytor).

Molinia grassland

A century ago, the moors west of North Tynedale, and stretching away to Spadeadam Waste in Cumbria, consisted of the raised and intermediate bogs described above and otherwise mainly of enormous tracts of a prairie-like grassland dominated by purple moor-grass *Molinia caerulea*. Purpleness came from both the grass inflorescence and from the tips of older leaves. Locally *Molinia* is 'flying bent' on account of its deciduous habit and the propensity for dead leaves to blow in the wind and collect in drifts in winter. The *Molinia* grassland occupied the dip slopes of the cuestas north of Hadrian's Wall and the lower slopes of the rounded hills further north, where it merged upwards into blanket bog through a transitional zone characterised by the *Molinia*–hare's-tail cottongrass community. The grassland occurred on stagnohumic gley soils, which are particularly widespread on the heavy tills in this part of west Northumberland, and was climatically restricted to moorland lying below about 400 metres a.s.l.

Molinia sprouts in late spring from food reserves stored in the roots and a swollen stem base. It then grows rapidly, so that by August it forms a knee-deep greenish-purple sward – sometimes tussocky and very difficult to walk through. In winter *Molinia* grassland appeared as a cream-coloured, straw-like litter. Normally also present in the grassland were sweet vernal-grass, wavy hair-grass, heath bedstraw, and tormentil. Mosses included *Dicranum scoparium* and *Rhytidiadelphus squarrosus*. Heath spotted-orchid was common.

The preceding paragraphs have been couched in the past tense because much of the *Molinia* prairie has gone. It was at the heart of the vast territory acquired in the mid-twentieth century by the Forestry Commission, which soon learned that these comparatively low-altitude stagnohumic gleys suited Norway spruce rather well. Much of the lower part of Kielder Forest was planted on *Molinia* ground. Outside of the forest, however, there are still a few hill farms with extensive *Molinia* grassland, and until well into the twentieth century the grass was cut for hay and stacked on the moor. The late-medieval/early modern stacksteads identified by archaeologists in this area would be partly for *Molinia* hay. *Molinia* is tolerant of fire, and the litter was commonly burnt in spring, in the expectation that its removal, and the release of nutrients in ash, would increase both availability and palatability.

Further eastwards in Northumberland, where annual rainfall is less than about 1,000 millimetres and gley soils are less peaty, the community is more restricted, being replaced either by a *Molinia*–heather community or *Nardus* grassland.

The agriculturalist Sir George Stapledon, writing in 1935, claimed that these west Northumberland *Molinia* grasslands represented the biggest example of agricultural waste in Britain, citing unconsumed biomass and also their low altitude and easy improvability. It was to be forestry, however, not farming, which effected the transformation. I estimate that, prior to afforestation, the combined area of *Molinia* grassland and the *Molinia–Eriophorum vaginatum* community in Northumberland was about 300 square kilometres, mainly between the North Tyne and Cumbrian border. Of this only about 80 square kilometres survive, comprising 6 per cent of the county's moorland area, as a relict of a former landscape and land use.

Nardus grassland

Large areas in the Northumberland uplands, in common with much of upland Britain, carry an acidophilous grassland dominated by mat-grass, *Nardus stricta*. It occupies about 9 per cent of the moorlands, and is particularly widespread in the Cheviot Hills (Fig. 77) and in West Allendale. *Nardus* grassland is characteristic of both podzolic soils and stagnogleys, to the highest altitudes. The grassland varies in composition from a virtually pure sward of *Nardus* to various admixtures with other acidophilous grasses and sedges and a limited range of acidophilous herbs; the mixed communities occupy about another 9 per cent of the moorlands. The grass is tussocky, wiry and unpalatable, and is ignored by sheep for much of the year. Its wide distribution is accounted for partly by overgrazing of bent–fescue grassland, which it invades and gradually replaces through selective grazing of the more palatable grasses, and partly by loss of heather heath (whether by overgrazing or inappropriate burning), which it also often replaces. Both in the Cheviots and on the Fell Sandstone cuesta dip slopes there are sharp contrasts between black land, carrying heather, and white land, with *Nardus* – the latter has a bleached appearance for much of the year. In the North Pennines, reverted fields and allotments have also become invaded by *Nardus* and other acidophilous grasses and sedges.

A variant of *Nardus* grassland is co-dominated by heath rush, which, having a high light requirement, is favoured by heavy grazing pressure. Heath rush itself is little affected by grazing (being unpalatable), burning or treading. Parts of the heavily grazed West Allendale commons have this type of vegetation. Heath rush becomes dominant on slightly wetter substrates.

Fig. 77 Nardus grassland on the Scottish Border line, north of The Schil (Cheviot volcanics), in winter. There is shallow blanket bog in the saddle in the foreground.

There is a clear geographical zonation in the North Pennines, from mainly blanket bog in the west (on the slopes above South Tynedale), to mainly *Nardus* and related acidophilous grasslands (in West Allendale where the moors are managed for sheep), to mainly heather heath (in East Allendale and Hexhamshire where they are managed for red grouse). This sequence reflects both decreasing altitude and precipitation towards the east, and different land management practices.

Bracken

Bracken is one of the few British ferns able to thrive in the open at low altitudes. Originally a species of open woodland, after forest clearance it expanded onto suitable soils below its general upper altitudinal limit in northern England of about 450 metres a.s.l. (locally to 100 metres or so higher), wherever agricultural management was less intensive. It now occupies about 6 per cent of Northumberland's moorlands. Bracken is poisonous and carcinogenic, and is not normally grazed. It usually occupies ground that would otherwise carry bent–fescue grassland and, where it is dominant, significantly reduces forage. Colonies expand via an aggressive rhizome system. Rapid spread during the twentieth century was partly due to fewer cattle being grazed in the uplands, since their trampling and bruising checks bracken. The plant will grow on most acidic, freely draining soils, including brown soils, brown rankers and podzols, provided that soil depth exceeds about 20 centimetres. Burning has also favoured its spread, because the deep rhizomes are unharmed by most fires, including those that kill the root systems of heather. In recent decades, however, the area of bracken has been reduced by herbicide spraying, including from the air.

The altitudinal constraint means that bracken communities are not extensive in the North Pennines, owing to the high altitude of the moorland edge there. Nor are bracken communities at all extensive in west Northumberland, owing

to the prevailing gley soils with impeded drainage, although there is dense
bracken on the lower slopes of some unforested North Tyne and Rede tributary
valleys. At the Battle of Otterburn (1388), in Redesdale:

'This deed was done at Otterbourne,
About the breaking of the day;
Earl Douglas was buried at the braken bush,
And the Percy led captive away.'

The parts of Northumberland where bracken is extensive are the Cheviots,
and the Fell Sandstone cuestas. In the Cheviots it is found on steep to moderate
slopes on both andesite lavas and granite, on brown podzolic soils and brown
rankers. It is, however, much more extensive in the north and east of the
igneous massif (Fig. 78) than in the south. On the Fell Sandstone, bracken is
characteristic of the scarp slopes and of the sides of valleys incised into the dip
slopes. The soils on these steeper slopes have resisted extreme podzolisation and
are typically brown podzolic soils, in contrast to the fully developed podzols of
the gentler dip slopes carrying heather heath. However, here and there, even
on the dip slopes, are patches of bracken amidst the heather. The soils under
these may also have undergone less podzolisation, in this case owing to late
patchy survival of woodland fragments. Although the trees have gone, the better
soils that they maintained are now picked out by bracken (Payton, 1987).

Few other plants are found under dense bracken, partly owing to allelopathic
compounds released by the plant (substances injurious to competing vegetation),
but where it is sparser, and light penetrates, patches of bent–fescue grassland

Fig. 78 Extensive bracken in the Breamish valley, Cheviots. The view is northwestwards from
Brough Law towards Cunyan Crags. Note the extensive scree developed on the volcanic slopes.
There has been some bracken cutting.

occur. If grazing is light the grassland contains herbs such as bluebell, wood sorrel, climbing corydalis and common dog-violet – there are some extensive and colourful drifts of bluebell amidst patchy bracken in the Cheviots and on some Fell Sandstone slopes. Chickweed wintergreen, with a strikingly attractive white flower, is also locally found among bracken, as well as in some acidophilous grasslands and woodlands. It occurs mainly in the northeast of the county, especially in moorland on the Fell Sandstone cuestas, and is rather uncommon in west Northumberland, although found growing through brash after Kielder forest fellings. Its British distribution is centred on the Scottish Highlands, and northeast Northumberland and the North York Moors are its only English strongholds. Experiments by Matthews (1942) suggested that low winter temperatures increase the germination percentage of chickweed wintergreen's seeds, which may explain this geographical distribution (Fig. 79).

Fig. 79 Chickweed wintergreen, not uncommon on the more easterly moorlands of the county (Geoffrey Chaytor).

Walkers often pick up common sheep ticks (or ticks pick up walkers) from bracken. The tick has three consecutive hosts with intervening free-living stages. The final host is a larger mammal such as deer, sheep, hares, dogs and humans, or red grouse. The adult female gorges on her host's blood, which she then converts into egg production. Ticks acquire hosts by climbing up the stems of bracken and other plants to await passing animals (questing behaviour). Ninety per cent of their life cycle, however, is spent away from their hosts, when they require a humid microclimate that they find under long heather or in *Molinia* and – especially – bracken communities. Farmers associate long heather as well as bracken with tick infestation, and, unsurprisingly, are not keen on conservation management that increases tick microhabitat. Ticks not only cause distress to sheep but transmit various diseases, particularly the viral disease louping ill, among sheep and red grouse populations. More seriously for humans is the transmission by ticks of Lyme disease, which can have serious permanent effects if untreated.

Moorland birds

The blanket bogs and heather heaths of the North Pennines are nationally important for their upland breeding birds. There are in the order of 450 pairs of golden plover breeding or probably breeding in the county, and, following afforestation of its former moorland habitats west of the North Tyne, by far the main concentration is in the North Pennines. Its piping call is evocative of the bogs and heaths. On the latter it breeds especially in recently burnt heather – where a bonus is likely to be the control by gamekeepers of carrion crows. During the incubation period, it forages in inby fields, preferring fields with an abundance of earthworms, as indicated by mole hill density (Whittingham *et al.*, 2000) (Fig. 80). The dunlin, too, breeds mainly in the North Pennines, on blanket bogs, and altogether there are about 75 to 90 pairs in the county. It nests near to pools and flushes that supply invertebrates (especially craneflies and other Diptera) for adult and chick feeding. Another bird that, in Northumberland, is associated with blanket bog is the twite. This finch bred widely in the county in the nineteenth century, but declined and ceased to be a regular breeder by the late 1950s. It has recovered somewhat, with about ten pairs, almost entirely in the North Pennines, where nest sites are in the banks of peat gullies with overhanging heather or crowberry. Day *et al.* (1995) suggest that the bird has in general been adversely affected by agricultural intensification involving the loss of rough fields adjoining the moor, as a source of grass and herb seeds. In the North Pennines, however, the trend, as we shall see, has rather been in the opposite direction, with the highest improved fields reverting to rough grassland.

Fig. 80 Golden plover breeds on the blanket bogs and upland heather heaths (Geoffrey Chaytor).

North of the Tyne Corridor, the great black-backed gull, a rare and irregular breeder on the coast, bred successfully on blanket bog on Carter Fell in 1923, but a nest was destroyed the following year by a gamekeeper (Bolam, 1932). The lesser black-backed gull nested colonially (with a few pairs of herring gull) on the large intermediate bog near Hindleysteel early in the twentieth century (Bolam, 1912), but the colony was already declining owing to game preservation (the gulls took grouse eggs) and has long since disappeared. There had also been scattered colonies and pairs on other bogs in the area, including Butterburn Flow.

Fig. 81 Female merlin with meadow pipit prey (copyright Allan Potts).

Northumberland's upland heaths are also nationally important for the merlin. Most of the county's 35–40 breeding merlin pairs are distributed between the moorlands of upper North Tynedale and Redesdale, and of the North Pennines (Fig. 81). The merlin is Britain's smallest raptor, feeding mainly on meadow pipits, skylarks and other open-country bird species, which are taken on the wing. It prefers to nest in long heather, which is scarce on intensively managed grouse moors, so that the merlin is associated with more casually managed heather moorland, often in steep-sided, headwater valleys amidst blanket bog. Merlins have been monitored in and around Kielder Forest since 1961, and studied more intensively in Northumberland than anywhere else in Britain, with Brian Little the central figure. Up to 1979, in his main study area, the birds nested at traditional sites on the ground amongst heather or on small crags, and where projecting rocks provided plucking stations. They also used old carrion crow nests – in isolated broadleaf trees or in coniferous shelter belts, secure from mammalian predators. Merlins then began to nest in disused crow nests in trees at the edges of the young forest plantations, with higher breeding success (Newton *et al.*, 1978), and numbers so nesting have continued to increase.

Nesting is now up to 2.5 kilometres into the forest. A result of this availability of secure forest edge nesting sites has been to allow merlins to forage successfully over adjacent acidophilous grasslands – previously neglected, and commonly at lower altitudes than the heather-dominated moorlands. The traditional heather nesting and foraging areas, however, continue to be used, so that the overall breeding population has increased (Little *et al.*, 1995), although not necessarily to beyond pre-afforestation levels. There are indications that crows and their disused nests are becoming less numerous, at least at higher altitudes, perhaps owing to predation by goshawks (Chapter 10) and to control measures.

The raven is almost always associated with hill sheep farming, with sheep and lamb carrion being its staple diet (Ratcliffe, 1962). And, just as lambing in the hills is timed by farmers to coincide with the first flush of spring grass, raven breeding is timed so that the young birds can exploit placentas and the ewe and lamb carrion inevitably arising during lambing in the hills. At least in this respect regulations requiring the removal of dead farm stock are unfortunate, and improved sheep husbandry has also reduced food supplies. Marquiss *et al.* (1978) showed that the twentieth-century decline of the raven throughout the Scottish Borders and Northumberland was related to the loss of sheepwalk, and hence carrion, owing to large-scale afforestation. Galloway & Meek (1983) said that at least 11 pairs may have bred in 1967, but there was a rapid decline in the early 1970s, and numbers remained low up to the mid-1990s, with from 1–3 pairs, since when there has been a slow recovery supported by birds from the southern Scottish population. Ravens have additionally suffered from severe gamekeeper persecution on North Pennine grouse moors. They have in fact declined almost continuously from the eighteenth century, first from the lowlands (a pair nested in the spire of St Nicholas Cathedral in Newcastle in the late eighteenth century) and then in the hills. Brian Harle, in 1983, compiled an unpublished list of 41 locations where ravens had nested in Northumberland at some time, nearly all in the Cheviots, Simonside area and the Wanneys. Abel Chapman (1924) noted how they alternated eyries from one year to the next. The Northumberland ravens mainly nest on crags.

Also a crag nester, the peregrine falcon is likely to be seen soaring in the higher hill areas. As Galloway indicates (in Day *et al.*, 1995), the bird has been subjected to a multitude of threats: persecution by gamekeepers and shepherds, egg collectors, falconers (taking young from the nest), rock climbers, photographers and organochlorine insecticides. Numbers were not known to exceed five to six pairs in the years up to 1960, after which the pesticidal effects of the early 1960s caused its decline to extinction in Northumberland by 1970. Recovery had begun by 1981, with four pairs, reaching eight by 1984. In 1991 no fewer than 13 pairs attempted to breed, including in areas (South Tynedale and Allendale) where there was virtually no historic evidence of nesting. The recovery has continued, with over 20 pairs breeding recently, and is despite ongoing illegal nest robbing of eggs and young, pointing to greater forbearance by keepers. The peregrine specialises on birds as prey, capturing them in the air in spectacular fashion, taking what is most readily available. This, unfortunately for grouse-moor owners, includes red grouse and, unfortunately for racing pigeons, domestic pigeons (during the Second World War protection status was locally removed from peregrines to protect carrier pigeons). The prey available in greatest numbers in the hills, however, is the meadow pipit.

The buzzard remains very much a western species in southern Britain, but regular breeding recommenced in Northumberland in 1988, probably owing to reduced persecution, and there are now 90 or so breeding pairs in the county, nesting in trees. This is part of the general expansion of the buzzard into eastern Britain during recent years. The bird takes rabbits and a variety of other prey (Fig. 82).

Fig. 82 Buzzard with chicks (copyright Allan Potts).

The heather heaths can potentially support hen harriers, but, as is well understood, larger raptors have been illegally persecuted by grouse moor managers. Hen harriers were supposed to reduce grouse populations available for shooting, a claim supported by a study of Langholm Moor in Dumfriesshire, and other moors (Redpath & Thirgood, 1999), at least for the mix of habitats found there. Because of persecution, the hen harrier as a breeding species is extremely rare in Northumberland, even though this was the first English county to be recolonised from Scotland in recent decades. Henry, in Day *et al.* (1995), suggests that the reason why the birds do not nest in the grassy sheepwalk areas along Hadrian's Wall and in upper Coquetdale, where they would be unmolested, is precisely because of the absence of the vital ingredient of rank heather for nesting, although they do nest in dense rush beds.

The short-eared owl is thinly distributed over the heather moors, but tends to be more constant in numbers there than on sheepwalk grassland where its population, depending on a very variable vole food supply, fluctuates more widely. It is most abundant in the North Pennines. The kestrel is common throughout the county, nesting in a variety of sites, but in the moorlands its population too fluctuates with vole numbers.

On *Molinia* grassland, and other grass moorlands with tall enough vegetation to provide cover, meadow pipit and skylark are abundant, the former being by far the commonest moorland bird with an estimated 15,000–30,000 pairs in the county, and densities locally of more than 70 pairs per square kilometre. The bird particularly associated with bracken, especially in sheltered valleys of the lower moorlands, is the whinchat (although it also nests in other, mainly upland, habitats, especially in patches of soft-rush and in low scrub). This insectivorous summer visitor has its densest Northumberland breeding concentrations among the bracken of the Cheviots, and its numbers are much lower in the North Pennine dales, where bracken is of restricted distribution. There are an estimated 1,000 to 1,500 pairs in Northumberland, out of a national 14,000 to 28,000 pairs. Another Cheviot breeding species, but in this case shared with the North Pennines, is the ring ouzel. It is associated with diverse, valley-bottom habitats, mainly above 300 metres a.s.l., and the county holds perhaps 130 to 180 pairs.

Birds of the North Pennine moorland fringe

Internationally important populations of breeding waders – curlew, redshank, snipe and lapwing – are associated with the various grassland communities occurring just above and below the present moorland edge in the North Pennines. Their flights, songs and calls (and snipe drumming) are amongst the most evocative and joyful sights and sounds of spring, and population densities of all species combined are up to 140 pairs per square kilometre.

Part of the explanation for the wader densities is a land-use history driven by the former lead-mining industry.

Firstly, the historic investment in land improvement on the smallholdings and semi-improved allotments raised the overall productivity of the grassland ecosystems, leaving residual fertility even after the demise of mining, when fields reverted and allotments were neglected (Fig. 83). This is reflected in the invertebrate biomass available to the waders.

Secondly, the remarkably high former moorland edge meant that, almost uniquely in central and southern Britain, the general trend in the North Pennine dales in the second half of the twentieth century was a lowering of the upper limit of improved meadows and pastures. Wader habitat has not only survived, but has expanded, as formerly improved land has become less intensively managed.

Thirdly, a mosaic of neutral and acidophilous grasslands, marshes, flushes and rills is now found in remaining traditionally managed fields, reverted fields, neglected allotments and adjacent unimproved moorland. This habitat diversity meets the requirements both of individual species and of the bird community as a whole. The soils of the moorland fringe are typically stagnogleys, developed on clayey parent materials. Because of their impeded drainage, especially following neglect of drains and culverts, they are exceptionally prone to invasion by soft-rush – as trampling of the wet soils by stock presses seeds into the soil. Other stands of rushes – sharp-flowered rush, jointed rush and soft-rush – occur in acidic flushes. The rushes are important as cover, and, with other wetland habitats, provide energy-rich invertebrate food.

Fourthly, the still high moorland edge has prevented large-scale afforestation and consequent wader habitat loss.

[Agricultural intensification has, however, occurred on the better land nearest to the valley floors. Many fields below the present moorland edge have been radically improved by the installation of more efficient drains, the application

Fig. 83 Allotments in the valley of the Thinhope Burn, North Pennines. They are the large, semi-improved, rectilinear enclosures, normally resulting from Parliamentary enclosure awards. Allotments commonly lie between smaller, irregularly shaped, intensively managed fields below and unimproved moorland above. Often, as here, they contain extensive stands of rushes.

of artificial fertilisers and herbicides, and (often) reseeding. Such improvement leads to significant decreases in the breeding densities of most wader species, compared to traditionally managed fields. In particular there are losses of stands of rushes, and of wet patches (as a source of invertebrates), and the creation of a more uniform vegetation composition and structure (Baines, 1988).]

Hence the present breeding wader populations. The curlew is Britain's largest wader (Fig. 84). Altogether in Northumberland there are in the order of 3,000 breeding pairs, a significant proportion of the UK population of 33,000 to 38,000 pairs, and it is in the North Pennines that most birds occur. For example, 12.6 pairs per square kilometre have been recorded in the South Tynedale/West Allendale area. Redshank is even more concentrated in the North Pennines, breeding near to flushes and small pools, and there are somewhere between 500 and 1,000 breeding pairs in the county. Snipe, however, is more evenly distributed across Northumberland's uplands. Like the redshank it nests near to pools and flushes and is particularly associated with stands of rushes. It was formerly widespread in the lowlands, but agricultural drainage has restricted its habitat there. Its county population is about 1,300 pairs (Fig. 85). Lapwing (Plate 10a) is more widely distributed than the previous three species, remaining abundant in the lowlands, but the North Pennines has the densest breeding population. It feeds on earthworms from the more fertile grasslands, and needs moist areas as a source of insects for the chicks. According to Bolam (1912) 'peeseweep land' is characterised by blue 'peeseweep grasses': field wood-rush and common sedge. These are plants of the short, acidophilous grasslands, favoured by breeding lapwing. The total Northumberland population is perhaps 4,000 pairs, but with indications of recent decline.

Fig. 84 Northumberland has in the order of 10 per cent of the UK's breeding curlew population; they are concentrated in the North Pennines (Geoffrey Chaytor).

Fig. 85 Snipe, particularly associated with stands of rushes (copyright Allan Potts).

Not all the rushy, moorland fringe grassland in the North Pennines, supporting breeding waders, lies in the former lead-mining area. Outside of the orefield the floors of the dales are still at a high altitude, reflected in a relatively high moorland edge (although not nearly as high as in the mining areas), and these areas have experienced parallel land-use trends to the former mining areas. An additional general factor favouring large wader numbers throughout the North Pennines is the presence of numerous base-rich flushes and marshes – owing to the influence of the local limestones – providing a high biomass of invertebrate food.

The mosaic of habitats at the moorland fringe also meets the requirements of black grouse, with three-quarters of the current English population being found in the North Pennines (although Speyside remains the British stronghold). There are about 800 North Pennine cocks, with Alston Moor having a particular concentration. The bird, a generalist herbivore (but its chicks requiring invertebrate larvae), depends upon access to all the components of its varied diet within reasonable radius from the lek, or mating arena. It needs stands of rushes for cover and seeds, good quality herb-rich grassland, diverse moorland including flushes and rills, and patches of broadleaved woodland or scrub, or of conifers (Fig. 86).

Fig. 86 Blackcocks at the lek (Geoffrey Chaytor).

In much of Britain, afforestation, together with culling in the interwar period to protect new forestry, and upland farming intensification, have been adverse to the species. It is noteworthy that the only other part of Northumberland where black grouse survive in significant numbers is the Ministry of Defence's Otterburn Training Area, with its traditional hill farming practices. Even in the North Pennines, however, there has been a drastic decline in black grouse numbers in recent decades. This is probably due to overgrazing, which removes or reduces key food plants, and reduces vegetation height and therefore cover and invertebrate biomass. Reseeding of herb-rich meadows and pastures is also adverse. Reduced control of foxes, stoats and carrion crows – predators of eggs and chicks – may also be a factor in black grouse decline. The more easterly Pennine dales contain too much heather heath for the necessary habitat diversity, and black grouse are scarce there. A North Pennines Black Grouse Recovery Programme is encouraging appropriate land management and there are indications of recent increases in the population.

Abel Chapman (1907) particularly associated black grouse with a different part of Northumberland, west of the North Tyne. Here, amidst the *Molinia* prairie, were 'tortuous cleughs or glens, shaggy with lichen-clad alder and saugh' [willow], together with birch, hazel and hawthorn. The ground-water gley soils on the alluvial flats beside the burns carried stands of rushes, there were patches of heather and bracken on the steep cleugh sides, and numerous acidic flushes amidst the *Molinia*. Chapman recorded 39 birds being shot at Chirdonhead in one day of 1901. He regarded the black grouse as 'a rigid Conservative ... He abominates improvements, and anything in the form of reclamation is anathema to him ... a three-inch pipe is his notice to quit ... [Better that] improved breeds of mutton in the future be brought from the Antipodes, or the Cape, or from British East Africa ... and leave the blackcock in unmolested enjoyment of these primeval moorlands – swampy, rush-clad, and ill-drained ...' Since Chapman's time, large-scale afforestation rather than agricultural improvement has largely destroyed the black grouse habitat here.

9

Woodland

Northumberland has a high proportion of tree-covered ground. Woods more than 0.1 hectares in area cover 16 per cent of the administrative county (Forestry Commission, 2002) and, in England, only counties in the south of England which include the Weald and New Forest have a higher proportion. (Overall, England has 8.4 per cent woodland cover and Britain 11.8 per cent.) However, two-thirds of Northumberland's woodland consists of large twentieth-century conifer plantations, and a substantial part of the rest is either smaller conifer plantations or coniferised older woodland. The area of ancient, semi-natural woodland (woods of over 2 hectares: Cooke, 1987; Carter, 1988) is only about 0.5 per cent of the county, distributed in 409 individual woods very few of which exceed 10 hectares in size. The equivalent figure for Britain is 2 per cent. None of our woodlands are totally natural, but semi-natural woods are those where native trees have arisen spontaneously by natural regeneration. They are said to be ancient if they have had a continuous tree cover since AD 1600, and many of these are likely to be directly descended from the wildwood; they are primary.

Some ancient woods, however, have arisen from secondary natural regeneration on once cleared sites. Horsley Wood, for example, was more extensive in the thirteenth and seventeenth centuries than it had been in Romano-British times (Tolan-Smith, 1997*a*).

Ancient, semi-natural woods with varied habitats and composition, and rich field layers, include those in the Derwent Gorge, at Whitfield, along the lower Allen, in Hareshaw and Whittle Denes, at Howford (the confluence of the North and South Tynes), Plessey Wood on the River Blyth, those along the Wansbeck above and below Morpeth, and the woods in the Holystone Burn valley. In the north are Roddam Dean and the woods in the College valley. The steep-sided, lowland denes are typically wooded, and even on Tyneside retain some semi-natural woodland. Best known is Jesmond Dene, gifted to the City of Newcastle by Sir W.G. Armstrong in 1883, but also cut into the Coal Measures of the northern flank of the Tyne valley, upriver from Newcastle, are Denton Dene, Throckley Dene and How Dene. The sides of denes provide an intimate variety of habitat: sandstone crags, rock benches, landslips, flushes and rills.

Apart from the ancient, semi-natural woods, many other woods are now conifer or broadleaf plantations on ancient woodland sites. Where such planted woods are of native species, they commonly retain relict woodland ground floras, although the dense shade of beech, non-native in northern England, is an adverse factor. In Northumberland there has been a 44 per cent loss of ancient, semi-natural woodland since the mid-1930s, mainly by replanting with alien species.

It is to be expected that, as elsewhere in Britain, much woodland was in medieval times managed as coppice or coppice-with-standards. The same would be true in later centuries, given the huge demand for small wood from the coal and lead mines, but there is rather little local information on the practice. Bailey

& Culley (1805) refer to the early felling of trees, after 25–30 years, for small wood, and to the cutting of hazel every three or four years for corf rods (corves were the baskets used for carrying coal out of the mines). Rossiter (1999) suggests that there was a dearth of mature woods with decaying trees in Northumberland in the eighteenth and nineteenth century owing to this demand, with consequential adverse effects on the birds of older woodlands: green and great-spotted woodpeckers, wryneck, nuthatch and redstart. Today some ancient, semi-natural woodlands show every sign of former coppice management, in multi-stemmed or irregularly butted growth form.

We can speculate on why Northumberland has a low proportion of ancient, semi-natural woodland compared with most other English counties. Reasons might include the wholesale redesign of the landscape in the eighteenth and early nineteenth centuries, noted in Chapter 2, which rationalised land use in relocating woodland to the poorest soils, and the continued dominance of lowland Northumberland by large estates, which until recent years have continued to replant former native woodlands. Be that as it may, the ancient, semi-natural woodlands that survive are all the more important to us, both because of the large number of species they support, common and rare, and as a direct link to the original wildwood.

Today only 13.3 per cent of Northumberland's woodland cover (of over 0.1 hectare) is broadleaved, and 3.7 per cent mixed, with 71.7 per cent coniferous, the remainder being recently felled, windblown or open space within woods. However, changing national woodland policies have promoted broadleaf planting, and between 1980 and 1999 the relative proportion of broadleaves to conifers in Northumberland increased from 11.4 per cent to 17.4 per cent.

We noted in Chapter 7 that 16 per cent of Northumberland's vascular plants are primarily woodland species, but because woodlands often contain other habitats – for example, glades, flushes, streams – they may contain twice as many species again. About one-quarter of the county's regular breeding birds are primarily broadleaved woodland species, and many others are associated with woods, so that all told perhaps half of all the county's higher plants, and perhaps one-third of its birds, can be encountered in less than 3 per cent of the area (non-coniferous woodland).

Distribution

Bailey & Culley observed that woods growing in a natural state (our ancient, semi-natural woods) are mostly on the banks of rivers, and, if we include the narrow valleys of burns and the denes, this is still the case. They tend to occupy steep valley-side slopes, where they have survived either by deliberate choice (restricting woodland to sites incapable of agricultural use or of low grazing potential) or by benign, casual neglect. That said, there are fewer woods on steep valley-sides in the uplands, because such sites are subsumed in the general moorland and are accessible to sheep.

Ancient woodland indicators

In the absence of documentary evidence, there is interest in trying to deduce which woodlands are genuinely ancient and semi-natural on the basis of shape, species composition and structure. Woodlands with irregular shapes are strong candidates (most of the woods in denes and along rivers are necessarily irregular). A varied canopy composition according to soil, and a diverse age structure, are also supportive, and the presence of a wood bank (an earth bank that would have been topped by a fence or hedge) is thought to indicate a medieval wood, barred against livestock. Horsley and Slaley Woods each have one. The presence of assemblages of rare lichens on tree bark is considered to indicate ecological continuity, and Gilbert (1980) has recorded 11 woodlands with a concentration of 'old forest indicator' lichens, mainly in the uplands and with a concentration in the North Pennines. Best known of the lichens is tree lungwort, which, however, is declining. Also, the death of old ashes, the most favourable habitat with the least acidified bark, is adversely affecting the lichen communities.

More accessible to most naturalists are vascular plants, and again there have been attempts to construct lists of ancient woodland indicators, mainly based on Peterken's (1974) and Peterken & Game's (1984) methodology for Lincolnshire woods. The idea is that certain of the species requiring woodland shade, or being in some other way limited to woodlands, are also very poor dispersers and colonisers, and are unlikely to be present, at least as assemblages of species, in secondary woods (ones planted on bare ground in the last century or so). The presence of such assemblages therefore indicates long ecological continuity as woodland. Peterken distinguished ancient from secondary woods using documentary evidence and was therefore able to list species confined to the former. It was realised, however, that indicator species would differ in different parts of the country. An interesting exercise for North East England's woods was carried out by Durkin (1997). His procedure was as follows:

1. The total native flora of Northumberland and Durham was listed.

2. Species occurring in 2x2 kilometre squares (Durham) and 5x5 kilometre squares (Northumberland) devoid of woodland were removed.

3. Rarities whose habitat was known not to be woodland, or which were known to occur in non-woodland habitats, were removed.

4. Species occurring frequently in surveyed, known secondary woodland were removed – these included generalists and casual arrivals from other habitats.

5. Species not recorded in a representative sample of surveyed, known ancient, semi-natural woodlands in the region were removed. (Some of these species, however, were woodland rarities not encountered in the survey.)

This filtering process produced a suite of 54 probable indicator species. I have modified Durkin's list as follows:

1. Species not uncommon in Durham woods but extremely rare in Northumberland woods were removed.

2. Species considered, in Northumberland, to be too catholic in their habitat requirements to serve as indicators were removed.

3. Other extreme woodland rarities were removed.

4. Two species previously filtered out, herb-Paris and bluebell, were reinstated as reasonably characteristic of likely ancient woodland, at least in lowland Northumberland.

Fig. 87 Toothwort, regarded as an ancient woodland indicator (John Reinecke).

The result is a list of 43 species that are suggested as collective indicators of ancient semi-natural woodland in lowland Northumberland. The 11 species that are probably the best indicators are marked with an asterisk:

wood horsetail
beech fern
oak fern
hard shield-fern*
juniper
wood anemone
goldilocks buttercup*
wood stitchwort
downy currant
alternate-leaved golden-saxifrage*
wood vetch
spindle
dog's mercury
wood sorrel
sanicle
wood forget-me-not
wood speedwell
common cow-wheat
toothwort* (Fig. 87)
giant bellflower*
woodruff*
guelder rose
moschatel*
lords and ladies

hairy wood-rush
greater tussock-sedge
remote sedge
wood-sedge
smooth-stalked sedge
wood millet
wood fescue*
giant fescue
wood meadow-grass
mountain melick*
wood melick
hairy brome
bearded couch
false brome
herb Paris*
bluebell
ramsons
broad-leaved helleborine
bird's-nest orchid*

The list does not include Northumberland rarities, even though they may be good ancient woodland indicators, since they are unlikely to be encountered during survey. These are:

soft shield-fern
small-leaved lime
upland enchanter's-nightshade
field maple
wood barley
yellow star-of-Bethlehem
creeping lady's-tresses

Clearly not all even of the first list of plants will occur in all ancient, semi-natural woods, although some of the larger ones, with the most diverse habitats, have remarkably many of them. Perhaps a total score of 16 or so species from the two lists might be indicative of ancient, semi-natural woods in lowland Northumberland. It is certainly the *sum* of species that is more important than the *particular* species present, since the whole concept is concerned with statistical probability (Rose, 1999), and as the number of plants from the above lists in a site increases, so does the probability of the wood being ancient. It is all somewhat rough and ready, since the presence or absence of particular species depends on topography, soils, the size of the wood and past management – past or present grazing by sheep or cattle will reduce the score. Moreover, many of the species listed also occur to some degree outside of ancient woodlands.

The list is inappropriate for the uplands for two reasons. First, a number of the species listed are quite widespread in the uplands, and at times locally dominant, away from any sort of woodland. Presumably the upland climate compensates for absence of the woodland canopy either in suppressing competitors or releasing the plants from physiological stresses incurred in the open at lower altitudes. As we saw in the previous chapter, there are carpets of bluebells in some moorland areas on better soils, and some Pennine meadows are dotted with wood anemone in spring. Clearly, since these and other plants occur in the open they could equally well occur in secondary woods planted on their sites. Nor, since they have long survived in the open in the hills, can they be taken as indicators of the recent presence of woodland on the sites where they occur, although this may sometimes be the case. Second, some of the lowland indicator species are simply absent from the uplands, presumably limited by some aspect of temperature. These include spindle, lords and ladies (absent from South Tynedale woods above the Cumbrian boundary), wood stitchwort and wood speedwell.

Bluebell is curiously absent from a number of woods for no apparent ecological reason. Perhaps it is just chance – perhaps the plant was patchy in its distribution in the wildwood and today's relict woodlands simply sample both its former presence and its former absence (Plate 10b).

Composition
The natural vegetation of Northumberland was discussed in Chapter 6, and the fragments of ancient semi-natural woodland that survive – often on atypical sites, which is why the woodland persists – cannot represent the full range of types that was formerly present. In the uplands, in particular, the steep slopes carrying woodland are unrepresentative of the generality of former woodland on the prevailing acidic and poorly drained soils below the blanket bog. Additionally, the composition of most surviving woodlands has been altered by management.

Oak woods
Most semi-natural woods in both the lowlands and uplands are either oak dominated or have a substantial oak component (Figs 88 & 89). Wych elm was also normally present but has been much affected by elm disease, although elm re-sprouts from the base and grows until the stems are stout enough to be reinfected. Some woods are still partly elm dominated through re-sprouting, for example parts of Horsley Wood, and elsewhere there are undiseased trees. In many woods there is a sequence of dominance from wet, valley-floor woodland with much alder, to oak and birch on drier upper slopes.

The existence of oak and other woodlands in the Holystone Burn valley, together with juniper scrub, *Molinia*–bog myrtle flushes (Chapter 8) and the valley-side common reed community (Chapter 12), all relict communities, indicate a history of low intensity land use in this area. Is it possible to relate this to the easy accessibility of upper Coquetdale to raiding parties from over the Border and from adjacent Redesdale – just a few centuries ago?

The upland oak woods on acidic, freely draining soils have a ground vegetation of bracken, heather and bilberry, together with great wood-rush, hairy wood-rush and common cow-wheat. This is the vegetation that, after woodland clearance, gave rise to bracken communities and upland heather heaths. A feature of some of these woods is hemispherical cushions of the pale green moss *Leucobryum glaucum*.

Many upland woods, in particular, are grazed, and consequently with a floristically impoverished, grassy floor. The National Park has concluded numerous agreements with woodland owners and managers to exclude livestock in future. Ungrazed, hitherto mainly lowland woods, have more bramble and ivy.

Fig. 88 Yardhope Oaks, Holystone Burn valley, upper Coquetdale – probable ancient, semi-natural woodland.

Fig. 89 Mixed ancient, semi-natural woodland in Hareshaw Dene, with a field layer of ramsons (copyright Allan Potts).

Alder woods
There are alder woods in the Cheviots (Plate 11a; Fig. 90) – in the Harthope
valley, on Yeavering Bell and elsewhere – and in Redesdale and the valley of
the Grasslees Burn. In the North Pennines they occur on surprisingly steep
slopes. Their ground vegetation may contain greater tussock-sedge and lesser
pond-sedge, together with a variety of common plants of marshy ground
including marsh valerian, marsh hawk's-beard, meadowsweet and water mint.
Woods of this type occur on the heavy, coalfield clays, sometimes with peaty soils.

Fig. 90 Woodland of alder and birch along the Dunmoor Burn, Cheviots (John Steele).

Ash woods
Although there are strips of ash on more basic soils in many woods, ash woods
are a feature of the North Pennine dales (Plate 4a). In upper South Tynedale,
where they occur on steep banks along the main river and burns, they begin
to have a boreal aspect. The trees are late to leaf in spring and the woods have
lost field-layer plants of lower altitudes such as brambles (which are largely absent
above Alston), and have gained its congener, stone bramble, together with other
characteristic upland species such as beech fern and oak fern. The field-layer
flora of these woods, with wood horsetail, wood crane's-bill, melancholy thistle,
globeflower and marsh hawk's-beard, gave rise to that of the Pennine hay
meadows, described in Chapter 11. The ash woods contain much bird cherry
(Figs 91 & 92).
    The floors of the ash-dominated Pennine gills, sheltered by both topography
and tree canopy, have a permanently humid, cool, sheltered microclimate, and
boulders, rock surfaces and fallen trees are luxuriantly covered by bryophytes.
Particularly abundant is the moss *Thuidium tamariscinum*, and perhaps indicative
of continuity of woodland cover is another moss *Hookeria lucens*, its large
translucent leaves resembling those of a leafy liverwort. These sheltered gill
woods are also fern rich, with male-fern, broad buckler-fern, lady-fern, hard fern
and hard shield-fern. The dead fronds provide camouflage for nesting or resting

woodcock. In the lead-mining area mine entrances are frequently encountered in the gill and river-bank woods, often with a curtain of hard shield-fern or hart's-tongue hanging from the stonework (Fig. 93). Rock gorges below waterfalls support a vegetation as near to natural as it is possible to find in our woodlands.

There are also ash wood fragments on andesite lavas in the Cheviots, by burns and on rock faces, with a ground flora similar to that of the North Pennines.

Fig. 91 Young ash wood, naturally regenerated on an ancient woodland site after felling, Nattrass Gill, Alston Moor.

Fig. 92 Beech fern, not uncommon in upland woods (Linda Reinecke).

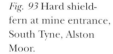

Fig. 93 Hard shield-fern at mine entrance, South Tyne, Alston Moor.

Birch woods
Most woodlands high in upland valleys are birch woods (Plate 11b). Some are probably the last relics of more mixed native woodlands, more valuable trees having long ago been felled. Birch is a short-lived tree, and has probably survived by abundant regeneration from seed in periods of reduced grazing pressure, or through protection of seedlings from sheep among long heather or boulders. The woodlands in cleughs have probably also been protected from moorland fires. It is impossible however, in most cases, to distinguish between such woodlands as relics, and as secondary woods on formerly bare moorland. Because most of the woods are open to sheep-grazing, and birch does not cast heavy shade, their ground vegetation is similar to that of the surrounding moorland – often grassy and mossy, and with hummocks of *Sphagnum palustre*.

Pine woods
In 1961 Herbert Edlin, an officer of the Forestry Commission, published an article *The wild pines of Kielder Forest – are they truly native?* He was referring to a small group of Scots pines – fewer than a dozen trees – in William's Cleugh (Fig. 94). There was another by the nearby Scaup Burn. Edlin was considering the possibility that the pines were relict from native pine woods, rather than being derived more recently from seed blown in from plantations. In favour of native status was their morphology (akin to that of native pines) and the remoteness of the site, but Edlin reached no firm conclusion. Subsequent pollen analyses of nearby peat, and chemical assays of needles, have been similarly inconclusive. That the pines may indeed be native is, however, supported by:

1. Pollen diagrams, and dated stumps preserved in peat, demonstrating the late survival of pine woods elsewhere in Northumberland.

2. The discovery of other local populations of pines in apparently natural contexts – at Leehouse Rigg (Ottercops area) and by the Lilswood Burn (Hexhamshire).

3. Possible 'pine' place names dating from post-Roman times in Northumberland (p. 85).

4. The occurrence of a limited pine wood flora associated with the Williams Cleugh pines – chickweed wintergreen and Issler's clubmoss, the latter otherwise known only from native pine woods in Scotland.

5. The occurrence of the lichen *Alectoria sarmentosa* at the nearby Kielder Stone, otherwise – apart from two other Northumberland sites – restricted to the Scottish Highlands, and perhaps a relict from former pine woodland (Gilbert, 1980).

None of the arguments are conclusive, but the Williams Cleugh pines are being used as a seed source both to bolster that population and for new woodland planting.

Scrub
Northumberland lacks large areas of scrub, owing to the scarcity of unmanaged lowland sites (such as lowland heath) and to the near-ubiquity of sheep-grazing

Fig. 94 Scots pines at William's Cleugh, a possible native population.

in the non-forested uplands. However, there are patches of scrub in the southeastern coalfield area, occupying disused industrial or commercial sites, or parcels of farmland isolated by roads, railways, etc. Many disused railways (throughout the county) and colliery waggonways have been colonised by scrub, although with the passage of time the scrub has often become woodland, particularly of ash. The esker in the Bradford kame complex, a surrogate railway embankment, is locally flanked with scrub. Scrub is variously dominated by hazel, birches, willows, bird cherry, hawthorn, blackthorn or gorse, with much bramble, raspberry and rose. Disused quarries also contain scrub. Steep scarps of outcrops of the Whin Sill in the northeast of the county are commonly gorse-covered.

Willow
In less intensively managed moorland areas, notably in upper North Tynedale and upper Redesdale, are numerous patches of willow scrub – additional to fringes of various willow species along rivers and burns (p. 198). Some patches have been browsed down almost to ground level, but others contain bushes a few metres high. Eared willow is the most frequently encountered species on wetter soils, while creeping willow is more characteristic of drier moors on the Fell Sandstone outcrop of central Northumberland.

Juniper
Juniper was much more abundant than now in the nineteenth century, but declined in the twentieth, partly because of shading under conifer planting (Clifton *et al.*, 1995, 1997). It occurs in woodlands, and on moorland, in the Pennines and the Fell Sandstone area. At many sites the bushes are old or moribund, and the population is not regenerating. In moorland areas this is due to sheep-grazing pressure, as may also be the case with roe deer in woodlands.

Eales (2001 *a*, *b*) has surveyed the insects associated with juniper, noting the limited number of species known to use the plant as a food source. He found the juniper shield bug, which feeds on ripe berries, on female bushes at almost all the sites examined, thus extending its British range northwards. It was, however, absent from the Holystone Burn woods, probably owing to the depredations of the wood ant, which has numerous large nests throughout the woodlands and forages high into shrubs and trees (Fig. 95).

Fig. 95 Juniper scrub among birch, Holystone Burn valley, upper Coquetdale.

Overview

An overview of the composition of Northumberland's woodland is given in the Forestry Commission's *National Inventory* (2002), based on sampling. It shows that Sitka spruce is by far the commonest tree today, accounting for 68 per cent of the conifer area and 56 per cent of all woodland, and that birch is the main broadleaved woodland component, slightly ahead of oak. This is presumably accounted for in part by birch's ready invasion of felled and subsequently unmanaged woodland, and its regeneration on neglected sites. The third most abundant broadleaved component in the county is sycamore. As regards trees outside of woods, of which there are about a quarter of a million in the county, boundary trees consist mainly of ash and oak (60 per cent between them), but taking all trees outside woods (of at least 0.1 hectare in area) into account, willow species are the second most numerous, after ash, mainly in small groups. This is probably accounted for by clumps on poorly drained land in a variety of land-use contexts. The *Inventory* also provides information on the main species planted in the county by period (judged by extant woods). Prior to 1861 beech was the predominant species, from then until 1920 it was oak, in the 1920s it was sycamore, and thereafter, up to the present, Sitka spruce. The changing pattern reflected perceived market demand.

Woodland vertebrates

Most woodland vertebrates are found in plantations of native trees, as well as in ancient, semi-natural woodlands, but ancient woods are more likely to have a favourable diversity of niches for our native woodland fauna. This diversity includes holes in trees, standing and fallen dead and rotting wood and a varied shrub layer.

None of our amphibians or reptiles are particularly associated with woodland, although slow-worms occur in woods as well as in open country.

We have the normal community of broadleaved, deciduous woodland birds, but particularly characteristic of the valley woods of the upland margins are the pied flycatcher, redstart and wood warbler. A lack of old trees with holes was clearly limiting the pied flycatcher, because about half of the over 300 pairs in Northumberland use nest boxes; the bird was rare until the end of the nineteenth century. The redstart, another hole nester, has also been assisted by nest box schemes; it has a somewhat wider distribution into lowland woods, and its feeding and courtship behaviours make it more characteristic of open woods and edges. Both the pied flycatcher and redstart make use of the numerous holes in old alders. The wood warbler, sparse in lowland woods, occurs mainly in upland valley woods in the southwest of the county. It requires tall trees as song posts, but unlike the other two species, nests on the woodland floor. All three species are insectivores and summer migrants. In an upland wood there is a sharp contrast between the noise and activity in the canopy in early summer and the quietness of winter – apart from parties of tits foraging for dormant insects.

The nuthatch is a relatively recent arrival in Northumberland woodland, spreading northwards mainly within the last 100 years, but with its main expansion in the last few decades. It is still mainly in the southern half of the county, especially in the valleys of the Tyne and its tributaries. The nuthatch is a resident and, as its name implies, a tree fruit and seed eater. The green woodpecker, associated particularly with valley woodlands on the upland margins, is attracted to some oak woods by the abundant populations of wood ants, whose nests it raids. The smallest patch of birch at the head of a moorland cleugh will support the willow warbler.

Many woodland birds are edge species, breeding and finding cover in the wood while feeding on the ground or in the air outside the wood. They are thus favoured by the long, narrow shape of many of Northumberland's riverside, dene and cleugh woods. In this group are two more insectivorous summer migrants, the tree pipit and spotted flycatcher; the pipit also thrives at the margins of conifer plantations.

The roe deer is now ubiquitous in all but the smallest woodlands, having spread from the Forestry Commission's great plantations (Chapter 10). It has become a significant ecological factor, browsing and fraying seedlings and saplings, and altering the composition and structure of the ground vegetation. Broadleaved woods that have compartments with dense young conifers where the roe can lie up are particularly favoured (or disfavoured, owing to damage).

The red squirrel is still abundant in the larger woods, as well as in conifer plantations, but is threatened by the advancing greys (Chapter 10). The dormouse is now known only from one woodland area in the Allen valley, with the most northerly populations in Britain, well isolated from its nearest validated neighbours in southern Cumbria. Many woods contain badger setts, but this is a very common animal, and setts occur widely in other habitats, including moorland, particularly there among dense bracken.

Estate woodlands

As noted in Chapter 2, Northumberland has long been a county of large, landed estates, and it has a strong forestry tradition. The Royal Forestry Society was formed at Hexham in 1882, as the English Arboricultural Society. From the late seventeenth to the mid-nineteenth centuries there was much estate woodland planting, and the lowlands are now well provided with both broadleaved deciduous, and coniferous, plantations. Most have been managed for timber production, and lack the structural and species diversity of ancient semi-natural woodland. They nonetheless provide habitats for the more freely dispersing woodland flora and for many woodland birds.

Much planting was for effect. Lancelot 'Capability' Brown (1715/1716–83) was a Northumbrian, and the elements of his carefully informal, structurally varied, estate landscapes, in his naturalistic 'English' landscape style, included clumps of trees, encircling belts of woodland, larger woods in valleys, grazed grassland and water features. Although he learned his trade in the county, working at Kirkharle, it is not clear how extensive was his direct involvement in reshaping the local countryside, although his indirect influence, through his reputation and family and friendship ties, is undoubted. There seems to be no doubt, however, that he advised the Duke on the design of the parkland around Alnwick, worked at Wallington, and directed the design of Rothley Lake and woodland.

In the uplands, most estate woodlands were shelter plantations, normally of Norway spruce, Scots pine or sycamore. Sycamore is wind-firm, does well on low-nutrient sites and was extensively used to shelter hill steadings. A local tradition in the uplands was a plantation design in the shape of a squashed four-pronged star, providing stock shelter whatever the direction of the wind. In the North Pennines it was the lead-mining companies that were largely responsible for establishing upland plantations, mainly of Norway spruce for mine timber.

In specimen plantings around the houses, and in some cases in timber-producing woodlands, estate owners fashionably and competitively experimented with newly introduced species, many from the cool temperate regions of North America. The long summer daylight hours of northern England, equable climate, and moist soils (owing to cool summers and, in coastal areas, the haar) promoted rapid growth of many of these species and there are fine individual trees in Northumberland, some of exceptional height in sheltered sites. Mitchell (1996) described many of them, referring to Northumberland as an outpost for conifers of the far north and west of Britain, where many conifers do exceptionally well. He mentions individual trees at Cragside, Howick, Kyloe, Beaufront Castle, Minsteracres, Wallington, Alnwick and Etal (Fig. 96). W.G. Armstrong planted seven million trees and shrubs at Cragside, including a still-famous rhododendron collection; the latter has thrived on the acidic soils of the Fell Sandstones.

Northumberland played a role in the development of Leyland cypress as a nursery taxon. The tree is a hybrid of Nootka cypress and Monterey cypress, respectively from the northwest and southwest of North America. The hybridisation events occurred in 1888 and 1911, in the grounds of a home near Welshpool, in Montgomeryshire, of the tree collector Christopher J. Leyland (1849–1926). Some young trees were taken in 1892 to Haggerston Castle, his other, Northumberland, home. The first cuttings from the Haggerston trees were planted in Leyland's nearby Kyloe Wood in 1892, from where further cuttings were distributed. The hybrid was later named after Leyland, who after a naval career, became a North Eastern businessman. 'Leylandii' of course, is a useful tree in the right place.

Fig. 96 Giant sequoia, Kyloe Wood. They were planted in 1902 by Christopher Leyland.

10

Kielder Forest

Hugh Dalton, Chancellor of the Exchequer after the Second World War, claimed (perhaps ironically) Kielder Forest as a Black Forest in the making. It is a twentieth-century, mainly coniferous, plantation complex created by the Forestry Commission (FC) on former moorland and occupies 62,000 hectares, 42,500 hectares of which are planted (Fig. 97). It is the largest planted forest in northern Europe, and the largest continuous area of upland forest in the UK by a considerable amount. The only other concentrated landscape change in twentieth-century Britain matching it in scale was the interwar expansion of suburban London into the Home Counties. Kielder Forest stretches from upper Redesdale across upper North Tynedale, almost to Hadrian's Wall, and westwards into Cumbrian Spadeadam Waste and Kershope (the Cumbrian section accounts for about 22 per cent of the total area). There is also contiguous forest in Scotland. Other FC forests in Northumberland are at Kidland, Harbottle, Harwood, Thrunton and Slaley. Altogether the Forestry Commission manages, either as forest or as open land, 12 per cent of the county of Northumberland, and 60 per cent of woodland of more than 2 hectares is owned or leased by FC.

The establishment of Kielder, and the other twentieth-century upland FC and private forests, largely accounts for the increase in forest and woodland cover in Northumberland from less than 4 per cent in 1895 to 16 per cent today. Most upland private afforestation has been in the Cheviot Hills.

The Kielder landscape prior to afforestation was the vast *Molinia* prairie of Chapter 8, interspersed with largely undamaged *Sphagnum* bogs, rising to upland blanket bog on the higher hills. Eastwards towards North Tynedale and Redesdale, with lower rainfall, was heather heath. Along the burns was a scatter of native woodland. This was the wild moorland, England's empty quarter, divided into huge sheep farms, described in the books of the local naturalist Abel Chapman.

The forest
Kielder is largely a coniferous forest, the species used being able to produce marketable timber quickly on the prevailing poor soils. The main species planted have been Norway spruce (12 per cent of the initial planting) and Sitka spruce (72 per cent), with smaller proportions of Scots (2 per cent) and lodgepole (9 per cent) pines, together with larches (2 per cent) and other conifers, including Douglas fir. Norway spruce was planted on the stagnogleys of the lower slopes, below about 275 metres a.s.l. (it is also relatively frost hardy, and therefore suited to valleys into which cold air drains), and Sitka higher up on the stagnohumic gleys and blanket bogs. Scots pine was planted (often in mixture with Sitka) on podzols, usually carrying heather heath, and lodgepole pine on the high blanket bogs, also usually in mixture with Sitka. Along the burnsides, on the better soils and frequently in bracken, European larch was originally used, but

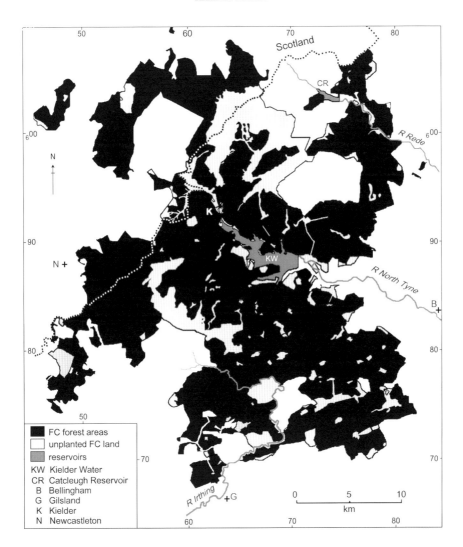

Fig. 97 Kielder Forest. With permission of Forestry Commission. Reproduced from Ordnance Survey based mapping on behalf of The Controller of Her Majesty's Stationery Office © Crown Copyright 2004 100042457.

it gave way to Japanese larch, and later to hybrid larch – a hybrid of the two with superior growth to both of its parents on most soils. The belts of larch along the burns functioned as firebreaks, being less flammable than the spruces and pines and, owing to fast early growth, rapidly suppressing ground vegetation. Douglas fir was planted on a small scale on the best available soils, including by restocking old plantations acquired with the rest of the land. Hardwoods were planted for amenity from the beginning, along public roads: birch, rowan, horse chestnut, ash, wild cherry, together with ornamental conifers. Such planting is conspicuous along the A68 through Redesdale.

Nowhere else in the world, at the time, had large-scale reafforestation of land that had been bare for centuries been attempted – nor on such poor land. The earliest planting was therefore experimental, trying various species, varieties and techniques of establishing nursery-grown transplants. It was an unpleasant surprise, for example, that heather proved to be antagonistic to spruces, probably owing to a heather mycorrhiza suppressing a spruce mycorrhiza involved in nitrogen uptake from the soil. In the early days every operation was manual, including cutting the drains and planting in turfs.

The earliest planting in Northumberland was in 1926, near Falstone. After major land acquisitions in 1932–3, planting proceeded on a larger scale, mainly on the lower, more accessible ground, on *Molinia* grassland and heather heath. Further major land acquisitions, at depressed prices, followed between 1937 and 1942, particularly in the southern area west of Wark. During the war, planting continued on a reduced scale, but it was then, with acute labour shortages, that mechanisation began – especially the use of tractor-drawn ploughs capable of cutting drains and turning over continuous strips of turf. Young trees were planted on the upturned turfs, and the resulting furrows assisted drainage. The way was thus prepared for a rapid expansion of planting onto the more difficult stagnohumic gleys and high blanket bogs after the war. A 1943 report by the Forestry Commissioners on *Post-war forestry policy* had advocated a much expanded afforestation programme, accepted by Government, and this combination of policy, mechanisation and the reservoir of land previously acquired led to a huge increase in the annual rate of planting between 1945 and 1960, when about half of the forest was planted – making full use of Sitka spruce (Figs 98 & 99).

Fig. 98 First-rotation forest, Kielder Burn.

Fig. 99 Ploughing rough ground, Akenshaw Burn, 1955. (V. Blankenburgs, with kind permission of Forest Enterprise and Northumberland Archives Services: 2722-01-0303).

Planting was in dense, even-aged blocks, to be harvested by clear-felling. Access was by a network of metalled roads, and by usually straight rides (containing relicts of the moorland vegetation).

Most planting at Kielder was completed by 1980. There was little more land available to acquire (the Duke of Northumberland having retained Emblehope, on the North Tyne/Rede interfluve, as a grouse moor and hill farm), Government policy changed to favour private afforestation and then – partly in the light of public concerns about loss of valued moorland landscapes – changed again in 1988 to embargo further large-scale, upland planting in England. This was also the death knell for private tax-avoidance forestry here. Some of the lower-altitude forest land in North Tynedale was lost to Kielder Water reservoir, and a few peripheral plantations were sold to private forestry interests.

Conservation issues

The establishment of the first-rotation forest followed a single-objective, production-forestry strategy, involving the loss of some ancient woodland, and of vast areas of open moorland, with bogs and bird populations that would now be regarded as of international importance (Fig. 100). Birds suffered not only through loss of their habitats to forestry, but because of the inhibiting effect on breeding waders of nearby plantation edges. Golden plover, curlew, dunlin, red grouse, wheatear, raven and ring ouzel all declined considerably. The then numerous black grouse, which severely damaged the early Scots pine plantings, were shot as pests. (Now, in Harwood Forest, on the Simonside dip slope, Scots and lodgepole pines are being managed as continuous-cover, open, mature forest, at a timber production loss, to benefit black grouse and red squirrels (Fig. 101).) Landscape considerations were ignored, and there was much regret at the loss of the wilderness qualities of these remote moorlands.

Fig. 100 The environment that was lost: Hope House farm, upper Chirdon Burn, 1952, soon to be afforested. (V. Blankenburgs, with kind permission of Forest Enterprise and Northumberland Archives Services: 2722-01-0202).

Fig. 101 Lodgepole pine managed as continuous-cover, open forest for black grouse and red squirrels, Simonside.

PLATE 1

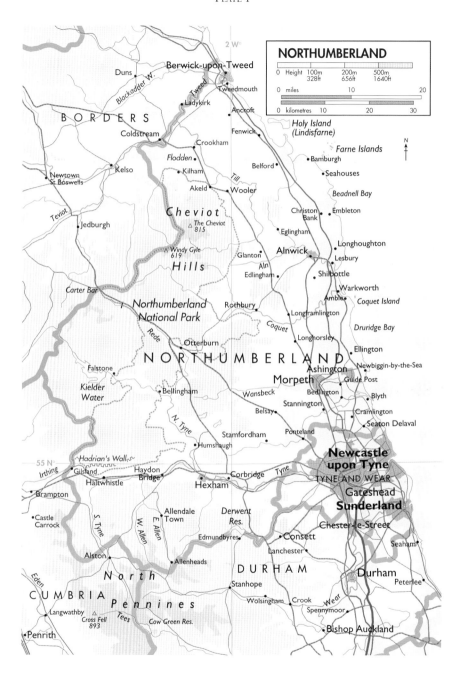

Roads, towns and selected villages in Northumberland.

PLATE 2

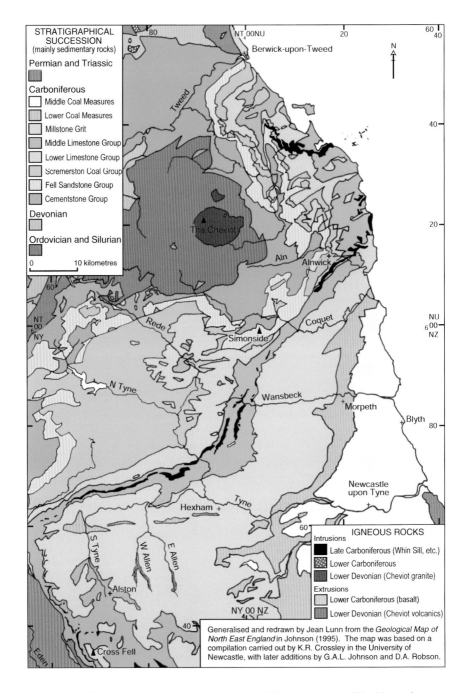

Geology of Northumberland: solid geology. *With permission of the Natural History Society of Northumbria.*

PLATE 3

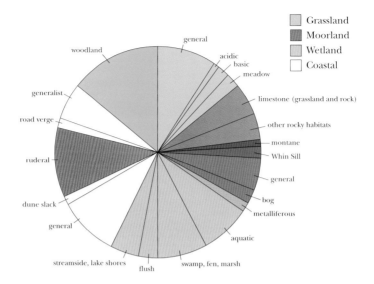

(a) Northumberland's vascular plants classified by the habitat in which they most commonly occur.

(b) The granite hills of The Cheviot (left) and Hedgehope, from the southeast, looking over Thrunton Forest (David Noble-Rollin).

PLATE 4

(a) Ashwood and Ashgill Force, Ashgill, upper South Tynedale.

(b) Hadrian's Wall at Houseteads Crags, looking eastward. The Wall here follows the crest of the Whin Sill cuesta.

PLATE 5

(a) The Cheviot, and College valley, view southwards. Higher ground underlain by granite, lower hills by Cheviot volcanics. The Bizzle (corrie) is mid-background, and a tor – Braydon Crag – is on the skyline.

(b) Cheviot volcanic country, Rowhope, upper Coquetdale (copyright Allan Potts).

PLATE 6

(a) Crag Lough, below the Whin Sill scarp, is in a basin eroded by ice sheets. Open fen, carr and a raised bog indicate that a once larger lake has been reduced in area by peat accumulation.

(b) *Usnea* and other lichen species on the Kielder Stone – sandstone with pure air and high humidity (Janet Simkin).

(c) The moorland edge near Garrigill.

PLATE 7

(a) Blanket bog on the Cumbrian boundary above Kielder Forest. The edge of the peat blanket is clearly visible above the headstream valley.

(b) Spadeadam Waste, representative of landscape of west Northumberland/ northeast Cumbria prior to afforestation. *Sphagnum* bog, *Molinia* grassland and (foreground) *Molinia*–hare's-tail cottongrass community.

PLATE 8

(a) Round-leaved sundew (about 3-times life-size), an insectivorous plant of the *Sphagnum* bogs.

(b) Cranberry, abundant on many of the *Sphagnum* bogs (Geoffrey Chaytor).

(c) Bog-rosemary, a *Sphagnum* bog species and one of our botanical specialities (Linda Reinecke).

(d) Large heath butterfly, abundant on the west Northumberland bogs (John Steele).

PLATE 9

(a) Bog myrtle growing in an acidic flush, amidst upland heather heath, in the valley of the Holystone Burn, upper Coquetdale.

(b) Upland heather heath, Tosson, upper Coquetdale (copyright Allan Potts).

PLATE 10

(a) Lapwings have their densest Northumberland breeding populations in the North Pennines (Geoffrey Chaytor).

(b) Bluebells at Harbottle, upper Coquetdale (copyright Allan Potts).

PLATE 11

(a) Alderwood, Langlee, Harthope valley, Cheviots (John Steele).

(b) Birches, Barrow Burn, Alwinton (John Steele).

PLATE 12

(a) A metallophyte, alpine pennycress (Linda Reinecke).

(b) Another metallophyte, mountain pansy – characteristic purple form.

(c) Unimproved, upland hay meadow, Alston Moor in June. Pignut and meadow buttercup are prominent.

PLATE 13

(a) Wood crane's-bill, characteristic of unimproved upland meadows (Geoffrey Chaytor).

(b) Globeflower, another upland meadow plant (Geoffrey Chaytor).

(c) Dark-bordered beauty moth, a rare species occurring at Newham Fen (Nick Cook).

PLATE 14

(a) Gorse on the floor of the College valley in the Cheviots. In the background are the Collingwood Oaks on The Bell, planted by Admiral Collingwood early in the nineteenth century (John Steele).

(b) Early marsh orchid, a plant of calcareous flushes (Linda Reinecke).

(c) Coppery monkeyflower, upper South Tyne shingle.

PLATE 15

(a) Kielder Water (copyright Allan Potts).

(b) Bloody crane's-bill, a characteristic Northumberland dune plant (Geoffrey Chaytor).

(c) Six-spot burnet moth on viper's-bugloss (Geoffrey Chaytor).

PLATE 16

(a) Puffins (Ian Armstrong).

(b) The author, almost half a century ago, on Grain Heads Moss, not then (as it is now) a gap in Kielder Forest. Now one of the bogs comprising the Kielder Mires National Nature Reserve.

In 1974, Government policy and Forestry Commission objectives were recast to include *inter alia* conservation and recreation. Because significant harvesting was about to begin at Kielder (about a quarter of the forest is now into its second rotation), there was opportunity to restructure the forest according to these multipurpose objectives. As a result the mid-twenty-first century forest will be very different from the bleak, spruce monoculture blankets inherited from the twentieth century. Redesign plans take into account natural landscape features for boundaries, widening the range of tree species, mixing compartment ages, matching the scale of the planting units to that of the landscape, eliminating rectilinear rides, leaving some trees until biological maturity, creating glades for roe grazing (and to facilitate culling), developing parkland transitions to moorland above the forest, and above all pulling back the forest from the burns. The result of this last policy will be to create a pattern of wide riparian corridors through the forest, some planted with native broadleaves, some regenerating broadleaves naturally, others remaining open. It will also improve the stream habitat by reducing shading (which cools the water), increasing useful organic input to the streams, diversifying the bank-side vegetation and stabilising the banks – dense conifer shade, by killing ground vegetation, causes bank erosion. Conifers are being cleared back a variable distance averaging about 30 metres from the burns, and about 600 kilometres of waterway will benefit.

Overall, about 15 per cent of economically plantable land will be open space integral to the plantations (for example, rides, riparian corridors) and a further 7 per cent will be broadleaved planting. About 30 per cent of the forest estate as a whole, including non-plantable and agricultural land, will not be under plantations – much will be managed, or, as the case may be, not managed, for wildlife.

Tribute should be paid to a succession of enlightened foresters, at Kielder and, when it was separately administered, Rothbury, who have enthusiastically embraced, and in some cases pre-empted, the new objectives, particularly with regard to nature conservation. Overall, the replacement of moorland by forest has perhaps increased upland Northumberland's biodiversity – but only because large moorland areas still remain, as well as the vast forest. (Conservationists of 30 years ago would be flabbergasted by this statement, and there is still regret at the loss of that great western wilderness.)

Other potential environmental impacts of the forest were soil and stream-water acidification owing to the capture of airborne pollutants by conifer needles, and increased sediment input into watercourses during preparation for afforestation and harvesting. The new riparian corridors, as buffer strips, should help in these respects (Newson, 1992).

Forest management
Despite the welcome new approach, there is no getting away from the fact that Kielder Forest is primarily a Sitka spruce forest (Fig. 102), and Sitka is by far the main crop, owing both to its high growth rates and market demand. Although in the early period of establishment there was a policy of matching species to sites (Fig. 103), Sitka is so much the most productive crop that it came to be planted on virtually all sites – in future, however, constrained by the other forestry objectives. Sitka spruce is a temperate rainforest species from the coastal seaboard and islands of British Columbia and Alaska, with a climate not dissimilar to Kielder's.

Fig. 102 Young Sitka spruce, Wark section of forest, planted in *Molinia* grassland.

Fig. 103 Norway spruce at about 30 years, Ridge End Burn area. (V. Blankenburgs, with kind permission of Forest Enterprise and Northumberland Archives Services: 2722-01-0496).

For the first rotation, phosphorus and potassium were commonly applied, when planting or by helicopter spraying of older trees. The main risks in any forest are fire, disease and insect damage, and although the fire risk is less than when grazing was first removed from the *Molinia* prairie, it remains a hazard, particularly in dry weather in spring. Disease clearly threatens any monoculture, but has not as yet proved a major problem. The main insect pest is a pine weevil, which damages the bark of young trees.

It was originally intended to manage the forest by thinning, taking out a crop of poles and giving more space to the trees that were left. On the gley soils, however, with their high water table – despite the furrows and drains – root penetration was shallow, and thinning on these high, exposed slopes increased susceptibility to windthrow; a familiar sight in the forest came to be a chaos of tangled trunks and branches (Fig. 104). From the 1960s, therefore, and because of a reduced market for poles, thinning and brashing were abandoned in much of the forest (on ground over approximately 250 metres a.s.l.), and most of the plantations are now clear-felled before maximum yield is achieved to pre-empt windthrow – normally when the crop is 20 metres or so high, at 40 to 50 years. A consequence of the shortened rotation is that individual trees are correspondingly smaller, so that a high proportion of output (45 per cent) goes for paper, particle board, etc. Larger sawlogs go for general constructional timber, pallets and packaging. The forest is now in full sustainable production – about 1,000 hectares are felled and restocked annually, and it is expected that the sustainable harvest will be about 400,000 cubic metres per year. At present Kielder accounts for about 5 per cent of British timber production.

Fig. 104 Wind damage, Wark section of forest. (V. Blankenburgs, with kind permission of Forest Enterprise and Northumberland Archives Services: 2722-02-0104).

It was mentioned that Kielder Forest was a giant experiment, and experimentation continues: on the provenance of species (a preferred high-yielding strain of Sitka spruce is from the Queen Charlotte Islands in British Columbia), on selection and breeding of preferred genotypes, on vegetative cloning, on techniques of restocking by planting on machine-formed mounds with spruce rooted in plugs, and on continuous-cover forestry with the reintroduction of thinning on more windfirm sites.

The forest landscape
Figure 97 shows that the forest is broken up by numerous strips and fragments of unplanted land (as well as by some non-FC land). There are also the rides, and, in future, there will be the riparian corridors. Unplanted areas are:

1. Bogs with very high water table, which were difficult to drain and were temporarily spared. They were later to be drained by more advanced machinery, but fortunately by then their nature conservation value was recognised by FC, and 58 of them are now managed as nature reserves (the Border Mires; Chapter 15). A number of them suffered, however, from the effects of forest drains at their margins (see Chapter 8 on the ground-water mound) – Coom Rigg Moss National Nature Reserve is an example.
2. Land above the commercial planting limit at about 520 metres a.s.l., mainly blanket bog. The main areas are the Kielder Western Moors (west of the North Tyne, on the Cumbrian boundary) and the Kielderhead Moors (against the Scottish border). These areas are also now in nature conservation management.
3. Land, mainly along the floors and lower slopes of the tributary valleys, which was of better quality and was allocated for forest workers' smallholdings (based on the former hill-farm steadings). Such holdings normally included both inbye fields and rough grazing, and also provided firebreaks through the forest. (There are now no such holdings; some of this land was planted up, and some survives as rough grazing.) Its vegetation is varied acidophilous grassland, upland heath and bracken.
4. Unplanted firebreak strips through the forest, mainly orientated north–south, and also normally grazed. The orientation related to dry easterly winds in spring, when the dead *Molinia* foliage presents the main fire hazard (the same winds that bring haar to our coastal regions).
5. Areas of better land, left or reassembled as full-time farms under tenancy from FC.

Within the forest itself are relics of the former landscape: walls, boundary stones, sheep stells, bridges, the railbed of the old North Tyne railway and its splendid viaduct at Kielder, ruined dwellings (although many survive, some as holiday homes – others were demolished to reduce supposed fire hazards from campers), even old shelter plantations of Scots pine, Norway spruce or sycamore. The overall pattern of the forest during the first rotation – the boundaries between crops of different ages and the location of the fire breaks – also reflected the previous pattern of land ownership, and the order in which FC acquired the various holdings. Moorland was normally afforested down to the boundary with inbye land, thereby fossilising the former moorland edge as the lower forest edge. The amenity woodland of Norway spruce and Scots pine, planted by successive Dukes of Northumberland around their eighteenth-century shooting box, Kielder Castle, survives (Fig. 105).

Fig. 105 Forest landscape with Kielder Castle and village. (V. Blankenburgs, with kind permission of Forest Enterprise and Northumberland Archives Services: 2722-01-0394).

Why Kielder?

Before describing the habitats and wildlife of the forest, it is worth asking why Kielder Forest was established here, in the Borders, in the first place. Following First World War timber shortages, the 1919 Forestry Act set up the Forestry Commission, with a remit to establish a strategic reserve of standing timber. This included new planting by FC. In 1943, as noted, the target was expanded. Factors favouring Kielder as a forest region were:

1. Government policy, particularly after the Second World War, was that the least agriculturally productive moorland was to be acquired for planting, and the moorland that was to be the core of Kielder Forest fitted perfectly; we saw in Chapter 8 how the landscape inherited from the period of Border warfare and raiding consisted of vast areas of *Molinia* grassland and blanket and raised bog, with a very low stock-carrying capacity.
2. Nonetheless, much of the area was below the ca. 520 metres upper climatic limit. Indeed, much of the forest is on land between 200 and 300 metres a.s.l. Precipitation was adequate for temperate rainforest species such as Sitka spruce, and slopes were comparatively gentle, facilitating mechanisation.
3. Although the land was currently unproductive, the widespread gley soils, after the water table was lowered by dense networks of open drains and furrows, were well suited to spruces.
4. Land values were low in the 1930s, owing to agricultural depression, and much of Northumberland was and is owned as large estates, making large acquisitions possible. No less than 24,000 hectares were acquired, almost entirely in 1932 and 1933, from only two estates: those of the Duke of Northumberland and of the Ecclesiastical Commissioners (owners of the former Swinburne estate). Large acquisitions also provided economies of scale in forest management.

5. Local markets for the timber were available, particularly as pit props for the still flourishing coal mines of the Northumberland and Durham coalfield.
6. Critically, all these advantages were apparent to Roy L. Robinson (1883–1952), the Chairman of the Forestry Commission for the entire period from 1932 to 1952. An Australian, he was a passionate and stubborn advocate of forestry. Already in a report to the Board of Agriculture of 1910 he had focused on Kielder, and he was later to make the forest happen. On being ennobled in 1946, he took as his title *Baron Robinson of Kielder Forest in the County of Northumberland and Adelaide in the Commonwealth of Australia.* He felled the first tree to be harvested in the forest, in 1948, and there is a monument to him at the head of the Little Whickhope Burn, in the midst of the forest in which his ashes were spread. A large chunk of Northumberland habitat has a Robinson stamp upon it (Fig. 106).

Fig. 106 Lord Robinson (Chairman of the Forestry Commission), Kielder village, 1952.
(V. Blankenburgs, with kind permission of Forest Enterprise and Northumberland Archives Services: 2722-01-0187).

Other upland areas in northern England do not have FC forests on anything like the same scale. The North Pennines, with their high moorland edge, have relatively small areas of moorland below the altitudinal planting limit, and much of this is common land, virtually precluding acquisition for forestry. The central Lake District, after a vitriolic 1930s conservation battle between FC (and Robinson) and amenity organisations, became a no-go area for forestry. Hence Kielder.

Wildlife in the forest

Habitat and species in the unplanted areas are largely as for the general moorland and are not further dealt with in this chapter. The plantation areas themselves can conveniently be subdivided into (a) planted, fenced areas before canopy closure; (b) closed plantation; (c) replanted fellings, before canopy closure; (d) rides; (e) roads; (f) stream sides. The short rotation of the spruce crop, of course, means that there is constant change in the forest landscape and distribution of habitats.

(a) **Planted, fenced areas before canopy closure.** In the now rank vegetation, released from grazing pressure, populations of rodents, especially short-tailed field vole, build up, attracting their predators: short-eared owl, kestrel, stoat, weasel and fox. On heather ground before the first rotation, with both abundant prey and leggy heather for cover, hen harriers arrived. A peak of about eight breeding pairs was reached in the mid-1960s following the time of maximum afforestation, and even one or two pairs of the extremely rare (for Northumberland) Montagu's harrier bred. The latter has not bred in the county since 1992, and the extensive new forest was probably a one-off opportunity for the species. As the young trees become taller, birds associated with scrub take up temporary residence: willow warbler, whinchat, stonechat, grasshopper warbler, reed bunting and redpoll. From about 15 years after planting the canopy begins to close, and the scrub species – as well as the vole predators – are replaced by woodland birds.

(b) **Closed plantation.** Once the densely planted trees close canopy, so little light reaches the forest floor that no vascular plants can survive and even shade-tolerant mosses are patchy: *Plagiothecium undulatum, Rhytidiadelphus squarrosus, Eurynchium praelongum*. There is very little food for small mammals, and it is the roe deer that is particularly associated with this habitat, where it lies up. Roe graze and browse in adjacent unplanted areas, road verges and well onto moorland.

In England, roe, as a native mammal, had become virtually or entirely extinct by the end of the eighteenth century, although it may just have survived in woodlands in the English Border counties (Cowen *et al.*, 1965). There are no records of deliberate introductions to Northumberland, and if roe had become locally extinct, it must have spread in the nineteenth century from Scottish and/or Cumbrian populations because it was present, though comparatively rare, in Northumberland early in the twentieth century. Subsequently, the reduction in the number of keepers (who controlled roe), and in the influence of the hunts (hounds are distracted by roe), during and after the First World War, the widespread birch scrub that developed on plantations felled during that war, and then the establishment of Kielder Forest allowed its population to explode, and roe is now an extremely common animal both in the forest and elsewhere. It has spread to all Northumberland woodlands large enough to accommodate it. It is rare, in the forest, not to see one, even during daytime, although roe feeds mainly at dawn and dusk, and the Kielder population is estimated to be about 6,000. In order to minimise damage to young trees by browsing and fraying, roe numbers are controlled by the forest rangers and through commercial stalking, with about 1,200 individuals officially culled per year, bucks and does in equal numbers. Roe no longer has any natural predators in Britain, although foxes may take calves (Fig. 107).

Analysis of roe droppings in Kielder (de Jong *et al.*, 1995) indicates that the main food plants are heather, bilberry, rosebay willowherb and other herbaceous species, and broad buckler-fern – all characteristic species of recently felled areas. The deer are highly selective in their diet, tending to avoid grasses, which they

Fig. 107 Roebuck in the forest. (V. Blankenburgs, with kind permission of Forest Enterprise and Northumberland Archives Services: 2722-01-0486).

cannot readily digest, apart from Yorkshire fog. Although terpenes in the spruces, and prickliness in Sitka, limit browsing, and Sitka is avoided altogether except in spring, browsing has caused considerable damage to young trees. Norway spruce saplings, in particular, become topiarised. The deer are most abundant in the younger parts of the forest, where there is more ground vegetation for food.

The other plantation mammal is the native red squirrel, whose main food is tree seeds. As noted in Chapter 9, it is threatened by the advancing grey squirrel, introduced into Britain from North America in the 1870s, but it is hoped that the major conifer forest blocks, if appropriately structured, may be a permanent refuge for viable populations. Red squirrel is still present throughout the county and Alston Moor, in most types of woodland. The grey advance is both from the south (County Durham is largely lost to it and it has crossed the Tyne) and the north (it has crossed the Tweed), so that the county has two interface zones. There has been much local research on red squirrel ecology and behaviour, notably by Drs Peter Garson and Peter Lurz of the University of Newcastle, from whose publications much of the following information is derived. Distribution data came from survey work since 1991, with public involvement, under the banner of *Red Alert North East*. Within England, Northumberland and northern Cumbria are the last extensive strongholds of the animal (Fig. 108).

Fig. 108 Red squirrel (copyright Allan Potts).

The main cause of replacement of the red by the grey appears to be competitive exclusion through food competition, partly through the grey being an acorn specialist and able to cope with their tannins, while the red cannot. Additionally the grey is bigger, eats more, probably pilfers the red's winter caches (Wauters *et al.*, 2002), converts food into energy more efficiently, and has higher breeding success and juvenile recruitment. Because it lays down more body fat it has higher winter survival and can sustain greater population densities than the red squirrel in broadleaved and mixed woodlands. It is also likely that the red succumbs to the probably flea-borne parapox virus carried by the grey, and to which the latter is immune (Rushton *et al.*, 2000).

In coniferous forests, however, the grey is at a dietary disadvantage to the red, which should therefore maintain its populations in the larger forestry blocks – a case of alien trees saving a native mammal. The current conservation strategy is to use Kielder (especially Spadeadam Forest in east Cumbria), Kidland and Slaley Forests as red squirrel refuges, and the forest design plans take red squirrel needs into account. A diversity of conifer species and ages (staggering mast years), increased areas of long-term retention for the seed crop, introduction of more early seeding species such as lodgepole pine, and a high proportion of large-seeded conifers (Norway spruce, and Scots or lodgepole pine) are the prescriptions, providing a food resource throughout the year. Sitka spruce has smaller, less palatable seeds and is less favourable, so that forest management to benefit the red squirrel involves some sacrifice of the highest yielding conifer. Mixtures of conifers, with nurses for Sitka spruce, are becoming favoured for sylvicultural reasons, and these will also benefit red squirrels. Predictive computer models have been developed to assist the Forestry Commission in squirrel-friendly forest design. Regrettably from other points of view, large-seeded broadleaved trees (oak, hazel, beech, sycamore) favour the grey, so that conservation planting of these species in significant quantity is to be avoided in the red squirrel refuge areas. Small-seeded broadleaves such as birch and alder, however, are not important grey food sources.

To ensure red survival, control of greys will also remain necessary in a buffer zone, which foresters are normally happy to do anyway owing to grey damage to trees; unfortunately reds strip Scots pine bark near the top for sugar, causing forking and broken tops – they used to be trapped as a pest by FC. Clearly, with regard to the potential (although not the certainty) to maintain a red squirrel population, Northumberland is favoured in having a large area of conifer forest in a part of Britain where the species is still prevalent – between 6,500 and 10,000 red squirrels are estimated to live in the forest. The survival of the species in Northumberland outside of large forest refuges is most doubtful, and Kielder Forest probably already holds the most important English population.

As to forest birds, they divide into those using the trees for cover and nesting while feeding both inside and outside of the forest, and those that breed in the forest and feed in the tree canopy. Among the former are the raptors and owls: merlin and buzzard (Chapter 8), sparrowhawk, goshawk, and tawny and long-eared owls. The sparrowhawk, which hunts small and medium-sized birds during the day, has now recovered from the population crash of the 1950s caused by organochlorine poisoning (the result of the birds eating prey that had consumed dressed cereal seeds). In the early 1960s very few, if any, pairs bred in Northumberland. Now, unlike prior to the population crash, there is a very strong preference for breeding in conifers, so that a high proportion of the Northumberland sparrowhawk breeding sites is now in Kielder Forest. The tawny owl is a nocturnal hunter at the edge of forest blocks, taking small mammals and small birds. In Kielder, owing to the scarcity of veteran trees equipped with holes, it nested on the ground – frequently in the root-buttresses of spruces, or on crags. Predation by foxes, however, led to the erection of numerous owl nest boxes in the forest, which are well used. Long-eared owls nest in old carrion crow nests and in red squirrel dreys. Goshawks had become extinct in Britain by the end of the nineteenth century, mainly owing to gamekeeping in the interests of pheasants. In the mid-twentieth century there were escapes and deliberate releases by falconers of imported Finnish birds, and successful breeding in Northumberland began in 1977, mainly in the forest area where they nest high in the trees. There are normally about 10–20 successful broods per year in the county. Goshawk prey is mainly pigeons and corvids, but they also take game birds including red grouse, and are one of the birds that is illegally killed (although not in the forest). There has been concern that goshawks prey on red squirrels and could therefore depress squirrel numbers, but Petty *et al.* (2003) have shown that too few are taken to have any likely significant effect. Other species making use of the trees for nesting include many of the common woodland edge birds, including song thrush. Its anvils are often found on the edges of forest roads, where calcareous road metal locally favours snails. Carrion crows nest relatively securely in the forest, allowing them to prey on nests on adjacent moorland.

A bird whose home is entirely in the plantation compartments is the crossbill, a specialist on conifer – especially Norway spruce – seeds. The crossbill was rare in Northumberland in the nineteenth century, but visiting and breeding numbers have grown as the forest matured. It periodically irrupts from the Continent, and some birds remain to breed during the winter, with the number of breeding pairs in the county varying from over 10,000 pairs in good cone years to as few as 100 in poor years. Enormous numbers were recorded in the forest after an irruption from northern Europe in 1990–91, with one estimate of more than 13 birds per hectare. It nests high in the trees. The other bird to have taken particular advantage of conifer seed crops is the siskin. It was not certainly known to breed in Northumberland in the early twentieth century, whereas it is now not only a winter visitor but an extremely common breeding species. As with the crossbill, breeding numbers and success appear to depend on food availability, which includes alder seeds from the gallery woodlands along the burns, as well as conifer cones. Estimates are of at least 10,000 breeding pairs of siskin in Northumberland, mainly in Kielder Forest. It also nests high in conifers. Other birds characteristic of conifer woodland, which have taken advantage of the forest, include the goldcrest and coal tit. In winter most of the non-migrating forest birds move down into the valleys or further afield.

The most spectacular insect of the forest is the truly magnificent, black and yellow wood wasp or horntail, whose female (about 4 centimetres long) has a long ovipositor that bores into wood and deposits the eggs; the larvae tunnel in the wood, usually of unhealthy trees. The insect is probably not native, but introduced with timber.

(c) **Replanted felled areas, before canopy closure.** The forest is harvested by clear-cutting, with cuts between 5 and 100 hectares in area. Replanting follows immediately, although some natural regeneration of Sitka spruce occurs and is in principle welcomed, although higher yielding varieties are preferred. Just as was the case after planting of the first rotation crop, rank ground vegetation develops in full daylight conditions. Whereas before the first rotation this consisted of ungrazed, former moorland vegetation, it now consists of a mixture of acidophilous plants that survived in rides and gaps in the forest, and new species seeded in (Wallace & Good, 1995). Among the former, *Molinia* is abundant at middle altitudes, tufted hair-grass at lower levels (its inflorescences making a silver carpet), and heather and wavy hair-grass on drier sites. Among the latter are foxglove, rosebay willowherb, soft-rush and broad buckler-fern, all taking advantage of the disturbed soil after felling. On mineral soils Yorkshire fog is abundant. Field vole populations build up to peaks of 150 to more than 350 per hectare (Petty *et al.*, 2000) and persist for about 12 years until renewed canopy closure. Tawny owl is now the most abundant bird of prey. The scrub bird species return in sequence, and a scarce, but fairly regular, winter visitor from the Continent is the great grey shrike, also preying on voles.

(d) **Rides.** Anyone who has walked along forest rides will know what hard going it can be, typically through tall, tussocky *Molinia* and bushy heather and bilberry. Often the heather has appeared only after fencing of the forest against sheep, though whether from stunted plants or from the seed bank is not known. The damp, sheltered conditions favour the biting midge, the animal most characteristic of the forest and most feared by every resident of and visitor to Kielder. Midge larvae are found in any tiny patch of moisture, and the biting females can drive the unprotected human to shelter faster than any tiger. Other pests of the rides and gaps in the forest are horseflies and their relatives, where again it is the female that bites. These include the absolutely silent-on-approach, dull grey cleg.

(e) **Roads.** The 640-kilometre network of unsurfaced, metalled road adds ecological diversity, particularly in providing disturbed habitats for ruderal plants, and the many small quarries in sandstone outcrops within the forest, source of the road material, provide similar habitats. Some of the sandstones are calcareous. Characteristic of the road edges are annuals and short-lived, widely dispersing perennials, such as thyme-leaved sandwort, common whitlowgrass, wall whitlowgrass, greater plantain, weld, sticky groundsel, sand spurrey, wall speedwell and thyme-leaved speedwell. Plants of neutral or calcareous soils are fairy flax, yellow-rattle, autumn gentian, common twayblade and quaking grass. Both stag's-horn clubmoss and fir clubmoss grow on sandstone material on forest roadsides and in the quarries. Sitka spruce seedlings locally form swards on road verges and in the centre of the track, as well as in recently felled plantations.

Where the road has been made through more base-rich soil, the removal of grazing pressure has allowed the survival on undisturbed banks of tall-herb communities with meadow species: melancholy thistle, globeflower, wood crane's-bill, great burnet and wild angelica.

A feature of turning areas and lay-bys appears to be the nuptial flight of ants. One August day of walking in the forest brought midges and flying ants, and, on the open moor, pestering swarms of sheep headfly, causing my much-travelled daughter to remark that only in Alice Springs in Australia had she been so bothered by insects.

(f) **Stream sides.** It is along the burn-sides that the more natural pre-forest vegetation survives. Willows are abundant, mainly rusty willow, eared willow and goat willow. Rowan, downy birch, bird cherry and hawthorn occur in inaccessible niches away from (former) sheep and (now) roe browsing. A bankside fringe of alder is commoner on the lower reaches of the tributary burns and along the main rivers. The late Mr V. Blankenburgs, one of a number of Second World War refugees from Latvia who found work with the Forestry Commission at Kielder, in his case as an engineer, mapped the woodland and trees along the burns prior to afforestation. He found strings of individuals, and groups of trees, penetrating far up the burns into the heart of the blanket bog, and it would be interesting to record what has survived the intervening half-century.

A wide variety of marsh and damp grassland plants occurs near the burns. Cuckooflower is a food plant of the ubiquitous green-veined white butterfly. In late summer there are the white flowers of sneezewort. Birds of the forest burns include mallard and grey wagtail. Feeding on alder and birch seeds is the redpoll, whose breeding distribution in Northumberland during the twentieth century switched from the east, with habitat loss on agricultural intensification, to the forest area of the west. In some years bird cherry, here as elsewhere, becomes enveloped in a dense web of white silk threads, protecting the caterpillars of a small ermine moth.

The creation of riparian corridors through the forest will hugely expand these habitats, and the valley floors are also the main locations for the numerous ponds that have been dug in order to add habitat diversity in the forest.

11

Other Inland Terrestrial Habitats

Montane habitats

As noted in Chapter 5, only a very small part of the county of Northumberland is above the temperature- and wind-determined natural tree line at 600–700 metres a.s.l., and even when Cross Fell and adjacent summits in the Cumbrian Pennines are added the area is still not large. The climate at these elevations imposes severe limitations on both plant and animal life.

Vegetation and flora
Much of the montane zone supports acidophilous plant communities, not conspicuously different from those at lower altitudes. However, a component of acidophilous grassland or bare peat on most high summits in the North Pennines and Cheviots is stiff sedge, an Arctic-montane plant. The Cross Fell summit bent–fescue grassland also contains viviparous sheep's fescue, and The Cheviot, on sites below the summit with long-lying snow-beds, supports luxuriant bilberry communities, protected by the snow against frost. Also on The Cheviot, the local rarity dwarf cornel (Fig. 109) grows among the bilberry, and common under bilberry in the Cheviots is an attractive, small, pale yellow form of common cow-wheat. On sandstone block scree, which is well developed on the north face of Cross Fell, fir clubmoss roots between the boulders (Fig. 110), and parsley fern also occurs on screes, although in nothing like the profusion in which it is found in the Lake District. Woolly hair-moss (*Racomitrium lanuginosum*) partly clothes the block scree, and locally, on the Cross Fell range, forms summit heath.

Fig. 109 Dwarf cornel, rare on The Cheviot and on Fell Sandstone moorland, usually under bilberry on north-facing slopes (Linda Reinecke).

Fig. 110 Fir clubmoss, sandstone block scree.

Botanists tend to concentrate on more basiphilous montane habitats, which are famously species-rich, but Northumberland, even including Cross Fell, comes nowhere near emulating either upper Teesdale, the Lake District or the calcareous parts of the Scottish Highlands for mountain plants. We have only a depauperate version of their flora.

Table 5 is a complete list of Arctic-montane vascular plant species (Chapter 7) found in Northumberland and upper South Tynedale/the Cross Fell range, indicating the montane area(s) in which they occur.

Table 5 Arctic-montane vascular plants (* occurs only in Cumbria; ** a coastal species).

species	Cheviots	other hills north of Tyne Corridor	Cross Fell range/Alston Moor
alpine clubmoss	✓	✓	✓
alpine meadow-rue*			✓
dwarf willow		✓	
Pyrenean scurvy-grass	✓		✓
roseroot	✓		✓
starry saxifrage	✓		✓
yellow saxifrage		✓	✓
alpine willowherb	✓		✓
chickweed willowherb	✓		✓
spring gentian*			✓
alpine saw-wort	✓		
three-flowered rush*			✓
(curved sedge**)			
stiff sedge	✓	✓	✓
alpine meadow-grass*			✓
alpine foxtail	✓		✓

Alpine clubmoss, chickweed willowherb and starry saxifrage have other Northumberland North Pennine localities. Pyrenean scurvygrass, as *Cochlearia pyrenaica* subsp. *alpina*, is in the Cheviots and on the coast. As subsp. *pyrenaica*, a metallophyte, the plant is widespread along Pennine rivers. There is an old record by George Bolam – Chapter 14 – of spring gentian on the Northumberland side of Gilderdale, but both Professor Swan and I have searched for it in vain.

Not all these plants are basiphilous, but the majority are. They occur, together with other mainly montane species, on crags and in flushes, rills and grassland. In the Cheviots, such montane habitats are largely confined to The Bizzle and Hen Hole. In Chapter 3, it was explained that in the metamorphic aureole surrounding the Cheviot granite the andesite lavas are competent enough to support crags. Here, on ledges and in crevices, some of the basiphilous mountain plants escape both sheep-grazing and, owing to thin soils or adverse climate, competitors. Crag species are roseroot, mossy saxifrage, starry saxifrage, chickweed willowherb, alpine willowherb and cat's-ear, together with numerous herbs also found at lower altitudes: wild angelica, marsh hawk's-beard, wood crane's-bill, goldenrod, dog's mercury and limestone bedstraw. Shrubs include burnet rose and stone bramble, and in other habitats are flea, star, common yellow-, stiff and smooth-stalked sedges. On blanket bog on the Cheviot is bog bilberry, which also occurs at lower levels, near to Gilsland.

Also, on these damp, shaded crags and rocky slopes in the Cheviots, is a variety of ferns, not all confined to basic soils: green spleenwort, brittle bladder-fern, mountain male-fern, oak fern, beech fern, lemon-scented fern, parsley fern and northern buckler-fern. The profusion of ferns also reflects the ability of many of them to deter sheep from eating them, owing to their batteries of biochemical defences. Two rare montane mosses, both in The Bizzle, are *Tetralophozia setiformis* – at its only locality south of the Highlands – and *Splachnum vasculosum*; the latter grows on dung in flushes.

Birds and beetles
The special bird of the high North Pennine fells is the dotterel, a plover that
winters in North Africa and breeds mainly in the arctic tundras. It clearly regards
our high moorlands as near enough to that, and they are its southern breeding
limit in Britain. The dotterel nests on flat stony tops in dry, short vegetation,
often *Racomitrium* heath, relying on camouflage for protection (Fig. 111). There
are also early twentieth-century records of it nesting in the Cheviots. Additionally,
all of golden plover, dunlin, meadow pipit, skylark and wheatear are at home in
the montane zone, as well as on lower-altitude moorlands.

Fig. 111 Dotterel in breeding habitat (Geoffrey Chaytor).

Living in woolly hair-moss and scree on Cross Fell summit is the snowfield
ground beetle, which preys on cold-numbed insects at the edges of snow patches,
and a rove beetle *Olophrum assimile* is known in Britain only from the Dun Fells
and a single Scottish site (Key, 1996).

Metalliferous habitats
The habitats contaminated by heavy metals were introduced in Chapter 3 (the
common presence of zinc has led to the use of the adjective 'calaminarian' for
the metalliferous habitats, although lead ore dominated production). They
are both the mines themselves, mainly spoil dumps, and river alluvium (Fig. 112).
While it may seem unlikely that such polluted habitats are of natural history
interest, they have developed a specialised flora consisting of species able to
tolerate moderate concentrations of normally toxic metals in the soil. A number
of the plants are very attractive, and this, their rarity, and their association with
a vanished mining industry that caused their existence, makes their habitats
rather special places.

Historic sources of mineral waste to the river systems were described in Chapter
6. Today the main source of new deposits of metalliferous fine-grained sediment

Fig. 112 Partly bare, metalliferous alluvium, Low Nest, South Tyne. (The Scots pine has naturally regenerated).

is the reworking by streams of contaminated alluvium. According to Macklin (1992), 18 square kilometres of Tyne system alluvium contains lead, zinc or cadmium above agriculturally acceptable levels. The dominant mode of heavy metal transport and deposition is as suspended fine particles of the ore minerals, although there is also transport in solution, particularly of zinc. Zinc production was concentrated in the Nent valley, so that zinc in South Tyne alluvium occurs in high concentrations mainly below the Nent confluence at Alston, although there are also toxic levels higher up the South Tyne, and in the Allen system.

The mechanisms of heavy metal tolerance vary according to the plant species, but include harmless sequestration in certain tissues (as, for example, with alpine penny-cress), and barriers to uptake by the root system. In some species the tolerance appears to evolve rapidly in populations exposed to the toxic stress, so that appropriate genes were already present.

Many of the metallophytes are poor competitors, being small and slow-growing herbs. This accounts for their scarcity in other habitats, including non-contaminated river alluvium that, owing to the vagaries of river deposition, often occurs adjacent to contaminated sites. On the polluted alluvium, however, they escape competition and thrive, their normal competitors being unable to cope with the heavy metals. It is this very distinctive flora that is more abundant in the North Pennines than anywhere else in Britain. Some of its members, however, also occur in other local habitats, presumably as normal varieties.

The metallophytes include:
  spring sandwort (Fig. 113)
  bladder campion
  thrift
  mountain pansy (Plate 12b)
  Pyrenean scurvygrass
  alpine penny-cress (Plate 12a)
  kidney vetch
  common restharrow
  sheep's-fescue
  meadow oat-grass
  common bent
  narrow-lipped helleborine (lately considered to be dune helleborine)
  There are probably other species, strains of which have some degree of
tolerance, including *Mimulus* taxa. Spring sandwort and alpine penny-cress are
the most characteristic of the species, and, unlike the other metallophytes, alpine
penny-cress is almost confined to heavy metal-contaminated sites in Britain.
Thrift is, of course, common on the seashore, but the metallophyte is a different
ecotype (genetic variant). The mountain pansy has a variety of striking colour
forms, but the populations on contaminated sites are often purple. The orchid,
narrow-lipped helleborine, has only in recent years been identified on alluvium,
where it typically occurs under birch. Janet Simkin has studied the lichens of the
alluvium, and has found that the bare stones and intervening fines can support
up to 25 species per square metre, some of which are heavy metal tolerant.

Fig. 113 A metallophyte, spring sandwort.

The river alluvium has much larger populations of the metallophytes than the
mine dumps, although some of the latter support spring sandwort and alpine
penny-cress in enormous profusion (in some cases there are girdles of one or
the other on the margin of otherwise bare, toxic spoil). This may be because the
alluvium is a more benign habitat in other respects, with higher nutrient levels,
higher pH (which reduces toxicity) and higher soil moisture, as well as being

less extremely toxic. Some of the river shingle complexes, which include non-polluted areas, are extraordinarily floristically rich. They support not only the metallophytes but an array of casuals from a variety of habitats, including adjacent meadows, and, in the case of the South Tyne, montane species whose propagules have been washed down from the Cross Fell area. The metallic influence extends well down the rivers, far beyond the Orefield itself, and even to the main Tyne below Hexham as far as the tidal reaches of the river. Some of the best sites are Garrigill, Low Nest, Williamston, Lambley and Beltingham (all South Tyne), below Nenthead (Nent), Ninebanks (West Allen), and Close House (on the main Tyne). The metallophytes are typically found on the low terraces (described in Chapter 6), up to a few metres above the river, and seldom or never currently flooded. One of the best mines is Whitesike, near Garrigill.

Perhaps surprisingly, these metalliferous habitats are subject to various threats. River Authorities, oblivious to costs and benefits, straightened and canalised rivers at considerable cost to protect farmland of mediocre quality, destroying some terraces as well as the river beds. Upland farmers have turned increasing numbers of cattle onto the terraces, the dung complexing and locking up the heavy metals and so converting the soils into more normal and productive ones. And, forgivably, the extensive mine dumps in the village of Nenthead have been deeply covered with soil to reduce the health hazard of toxic dust. More widely, birch or gorse colonise the alluvium, apparently tolerant of the heavy metals, and their leaf fall ameliorates the surface soil, allowing a more normal ground vegetation to develop. Sheep and or rabbit grazing, however, arrests this succession, beneficially for the metallophytes.

As to the origin of the metallophyte flora, either the plants have evolved tolerance since intensive mining began in the seventeenth century, or there were already adapted varieties clinging to the limited exposures of ore-bearing veins at outcrop on river and stream banks. Early botanical records indicate that the specialised flora on the low terraces dates only from the nineteenth century (Swan, 1993), but on the mine dumps, some of which are much older, evolution can be allowed more time to do its work.

The Whin Sill

This highly distinctive geological formation was described in Chapter 3. Its outcrops occur from high in the North Pennines to sea level. The rock is a quartz-dolerite, weathering into base-rich, although relatively nutrient-poor, soils. It is, however, extremely tough – hence the vertical crags it supports – so that soils are thin and drought-prone. The combination of base richness, modest nutrient stress and relatively severe physical stress leads to a distinctive vegetation and flora, including a number of both national and Northumberland rarities. At the coast there are additional maritime influences: possibly some alleviation of moisture stress, owing to the moderating effect of the sea and the haar on summer heat. The higher Pennine outcrops are less interesting botanically, probably because of the cooler, wetter climate and more leached soils.

Where the whin forms cuestas, two main habitats are present. On the gentler dip slopes there is a short, grazed turf, interspersed with bare patches and rock slabs (these often remaining damp long after rain, owing to seepage over the impermeable rock), while on the scarp slopes crags overlook block scree. However, some ledges on the scarp slope, whin dykes on Holy Island, and various quarry habitats have a vegetation and flora similar to that of the dip slope (Fig. 114).

Fig. 114 Open grassland on the Whin Sill dip slope, Craster.

On crag ledges and on block scree the main plants – not particularly confined to the whin – are ferns and their allies, benefiting from the humid shelter and freedom from stock trampling afforded. They include fir clubmoss, parsley fern, mountain male-fern, lemon-scented fern, oak fern and beech fern.

By contrast, the dip slopes are characterised by annuals and drought-tolerant perennials. Most of the former complete their life cycles in spring or early summer, so avoiding mid-summer drought stress. They include slender parsley-piert, little mouse-ear, long-stalked crane's-bill, blinks (*Montia fontana* subsp. *minor*), rue-leaved saxifrage, annual knawel and lesser chickweed. Common whitlowgrass grows in white-flowered profusion on otherwise bare slabs after a damp spring. The annuals also include several members of the pea family, Fabaceae (Leguminosae): slender trefoil, rough clover and knotted clover, presumably because of their ability to gain nitrogen via bacteria in their root nodules – nitrogen is in short supply in the thin, droughty soils.

Among perennials, members of the onion genus *Allium* are well represented, including chives. Although this grows on the whin dip slope (on slabs, wet in winter) adjacent to Hadrian's Wall it was not, as local legend has it, introduced as a culinary herb by the Romans, but is native. The chives, however, seldom flower, perhaps owing to grazing and/or drought on the thin soils (Fig. 115). Also on the whin are wild onion and field garlic. The reason for the association of whin and onions is not obvious, except that these alliums all require well-drained soils (nor will woodland ramsons tolerate waterlogging). The whin is notably richer in iron, magnesium and calcium than other local igneous rocks but poorer in potassium and phosphorus. Does the distinctive onion biochemistry require such a combination? Presumably the occurrence of the calcicole common rock-rose on the whin, as well as on limestone and on Cheviot andesites, is due to the calcium content of the rock. The same may be true of dropwort and hairy stonecrop.

Fig. 115 Chives on the Whin Sill, Walltown (Geoffrey Chaytor).

The following species are found in Northumberland only on the Whin Sill: upright chickweed, heath pearlwort, spring cinquefoil, rough clover, spignel, the hawkweeds *Hieracium dicella*, *H. schmidtii* and *H. subplanifolium*, spring squill, chives and angular Solomon's-seal. Additionally, two subspecies are confined to the whin here: *Festuca rubra* subsp. *juncea* (a red fescue) and *Bromus hordeaceus* subsp. *ferronii* (a soft-brome), both on coastal outcrops. Spring squill is almost entirely coastal in Britain, and then mainly on the west coast, but in early summer produces blue carpets in whin turf near the coast at Dunstanburgh, Craster, Cullernose Point and Hips Heugh. Spignel, a white-flowered umbellifer, grows in profusion at a single locality, a low whin hillock, Houky Hill, at Thockrington.

Each of its fruits, leaves and roots have powerful smells and the plant was used as a culinary herb and stimulant; according to Halliday (1997) the roots of this 'Westmorland herb' (it is abundant in part of the old Westmorland) were sold in London as an aphrodisiac. Could the Whin Sill chemistry be performing its magic here too? The local name for the plant was *howka* or *hook-a*, so which came first, the plant name or that of its hillock? Wallis (1769) claimed the plant was much dug up – locally 'howked' – for the root, hence the name of plant and hill. However, Thockrington is named for Old Englishman Thocker, 'the unsteady one'. Was this nickname from his spignel-abuse, with houka and howky simply formations of Thocker (Fig. 116)?

Fig. 116 Spignel. In Northumberland it occurs only on the Whin Sill, at Houky Hill, Thockrington.

All this amounts to a distinguished flora, with several nationally rare or scarce species as well as local rarities. It is also distinctive to Northumberland, in that the Whin Sill is a formation confined to North East England and its outcrops in Durham and eastern Cumbria are in different, upland environments. Some southern Scottish igneous outcrops, however, have similar soils without quite the same diverse flora. Although extensive areas of the Whin Sill dip slope support acidophilous vegetation, and even heather heath, chemical analyses indicate general homogeneity across the outcrop, and it seems more likely that thin covers of till explain the soil differences.

Most of the characteristic whin plants are unlikely to have survived under a woodland canopy, lending support to the idea that, on the thin soils and bare slabs of the dip slope surfaces, there would have been glades in the natural woodland. However, thick gorse, blackthorn or hawthorn scrub occurs in patches on the whin surface, both at the coast and inland.

Threats to the habitat include cessation of grazing (leading to scrub invasion), very heavy grazing, and use for foddering cattle and application of fertiliser (both favouring more competitive herbaceous vegetation). These various adverse factors have caused loss of the distinctive plants on many outcrops, and, together with quarrying and golf course management, have greatly fragmented and reduced the area of the habitat in the last half-century.

Upland hay meadows

The only old, lowland hay meadow surviving in Northumberland that I am aware of is one deliberately maintained at the University of Newcastle's Cockle Park farm, others having been altered out of recognition by changes in farming practices. There are, however, a few score of traditional upland meadows surviving in the county. These are famously rich floristically, and also support a rich invertebrate fauna. They have developed through traditional hay-making practices in an upland climate of high rainfall, low temperatures and short growing season, and in these respects and in their flora somewhat resemble meadows in the Alps and Scandinavia. They are found principally in the Cheviot valleys, North Tynedale, Redesdale and the North Pennine dales, and there is one superb meadow, Gowk Bank, on the Cumbrian bank of the River Irthing. Meadows are grazed before and after being shut up for hay, and include the main lambing fields. My family owns some fields on Alston Moor, but because they are too banky and stony to be mown by modern machinery (they were formerly cut by more robust horse-drawn mowers and by scythe), we simulate traditional management as best we can by light cattle-grazing beginning in early June and excluding cattle from one field until August.

Of all our Northumberland habitats, old meadows, along with bluebell woods and coastal dunes, are the most colourful. For meadows, the seasonal floral succession, in approximate order, is lesser celandine, wood anemone, daisy, primrose, marsh marigold, pignut, meadow buttercup, germander speedwell, wood crane's-bill, cat's-ear. Yellow and white is later mixed with blue and purple. The number of species of flowering plant in a square metre may be 30 or more, and in a field up to 120 (Plate 12c).

The reasons for this richness (i.e. what allows so much coexistence) is much discussed and still incompletely understood, and knowing some of the answers is important in managing and restoring meadows. Part of the story is the suppression of dominance (Grime, 1979). Dominant plants are those which, through growth rate, stature, root competition or in other ways simply crowd out other species. They are said to be competitors. But, in order to dominate, they require good growing conditions – adequate nutrients, light, moisture and so on, and also an absence of physical disturbance, by cutting, grazing or natural soil disturbance. Denied these optimum conditions they cannot flourish, and are replaced by other species that can tolerate stress (factors restricting photosynthesis: such as nutrient deficiency, water shortage), disturbance (destruction of plant biomass), or some modest combination of the two. Such plants are respectively stress-tolerators and ruderals. Stress-tolerators typically have slow growth rates, but often have physical or biochemical defences against herbivores. Ruderals have short life cycles (they are often annuals) with abundant seed production – we know many of them as garden or agricultural weeds. Grime hypothesised that moderate levels of stress and/or disturbance should allow coexistence of plants with all three strategies, as well as those with intermediate strategies, producing maximum species-richness. Conversely, the absence of stress and disturbance would benefit competitors, able to establish dominance and exclude other species, and extreme stress or disturbance would sharply limit the number of species able to survive.

Grime's ideas work rather well for these old, unimproved hay meadows. There is moderate stress because soils are only moderately fertile (through applications of farmyard manure and lime – but not of artificial fertiliser), and because of the cool, upland climate and short growing season. The vegetation is also moderately disturbed, by mowing, grazing and cattle trampling opening up niches for seedling regeneration. In contrast, improvement of these meadows by fertiliser application, drainage, etc., removes stress (although not disturbance), shifting the balance in favour of more competitive species. These establish dominance, altering a species-rich herbage to a species-poor one, often dominated by perennial rye-grass. This has happened to the majority of our upland meadows. (Ploughing and re-seeding have the same outcome.) It is also thought that artificial fertiliser knocks out some of the mycorrhizal fungi that assist the meadow species to obtain nutrients.

Additionally, there is often considerable habitat variety within a field, adding to the possibilities of floristic variety: steep banks, small valleys, flushes, rills, springs, marshes, shelter from an adjoining wood or plantation, and varying soil texture and chemistry.

Turning to composition, characteristic herbs are a lady's-mantle (*Alchemilla glabra*), frog orchid, marsh hawk's-beard, wood horsetail (Fig. 117), wood crane's-bill, fragrant orchid, yellow-rattle, great burnet, common valerian and globeflower (Plates 13a, b). A rarity is small-white orchid, and now uncommon in meadows, though common enough in semi-natural woodland and by river banks, is melancholy thistle, with its huge, bright purple heads. Yellow-rattle is a hemi-parasite, partially dependent on grasses. It weakens them by parasitising their roots, further reducing competition.

Research by Smith *et al.* (1996*a*, 1996*b*) has shown just how critical timing of hay making is to meadow composition. The more competitive grasses are late seeders, so too late a cut (September) is not desirable. The (blue-flowered) meadow crane's-bill also ripens seed only late in the year and is not therefore a normal component (although it was abundant in lowland meadows, where it ripened earlier); instead we have the (purple-flowered) wood crane's-bill, which is so characteristic that the European Union's *Habitats Directive* (1992) lists as one of the habitats it is important to conserve 'Mountain hay meadows (British types with *Geranium sylvaticum*)'. Leaving mowing until late summer – the norm before mechanisation – allows most of the plants to flower and ripen seed, which is important because soil seed bank longevity is low for most meadow species.

Clearly agricultural improvement impoverishes meadow floras, but so does the abandonment of grass conservation with year-round grazing – the fate of many meadows over recent decades. With the widespread loss of traditionally managed meadows, their flora has survived in the often wide road verges (resulting from enclosure awards requiring wide corridors for moving stock), particularly in the North Pennines. Once-a-year verge mowing by Highway Authorities simulates to some extent meadow management, and the verges are now a main habitat for *Alchemilla glabra*, melancholy thistle, northern hawk's-beard, wood crane's-bill, common bistort and great burnet.

The nearest approach to the traditional meadow vegetation outside of the

Fig. 117 An upland meadow species: wood horsetail, with its fossil Carboniferous-age relative, *Stigmaria*. Acton Burn (Geoffrey Chaytor).

remaining old meadows, however, is in various river- and burn-side habitats, ungrazed or only casually grazed. The flowery banks of North Pennine burns are delectable in summer, especially when hawthorn is in blossom, and the footpath from Ashgill via Garrigill to Alston is particularly rewarding. However, in most parts of the uplands, including the Cheviots, there are tall-herb community fragments alongside the burns, where they are fenced off from stock or difficult to access.

As to birds, the characteristic bird of the meadows was the corncrake, now lost as a breeding species owing to earlier cutting for hay or silage, and to mechanisation destroying chicks. It bred sporadically at least until the 1950s, may have bred since and still calls in some years.

Another bird associated with damper upland meadows has been the yellow wagtail, but recent confirmed breeding records are rather sparse in the North Pennine dales, part of a general decline of the species in Britain. In many North Pennine meadows the most conspicuous bird is actually the pheasant, which manages to raise a brood during the hay-growing season and hangs around for the rest of the year causing palpitations when exploding before the feet of walkers.

An insect that takes the eye is the black, day-flying, chimney sweeper moth, whose caterpillar feeds on the flowers of pignut.

Lowland mires
In Chapter 8 we looked at the extensive mires in the uplands. There are also lowland mires, once much more numerous and extensive than now, and notable in the contrast they provide with the intensively farmed landscapes in which they

are set. Three well-known examples – Prestwick Carr, Newham Fen and Ford Moss – will illustrate something of their range of variation. Another site contains Holburn Moss and Lake; the moss is a lowland raised bog in the northeast of the county and is noted as a winter roost for huge flocks of pink-footed and greylag geese. The origin of the lake is uncertain, but late medieval Lindisfarne Priory had peat-digging rights there. Only Kemping Moss, another raised bog in the northeast of the county, is now commercially worked for peat, although another site in the same area has planning consent. A fen and swamp at Healey are also worthy of note.

Prestwick Carr
Prestwick Carr, formerly Mersfen Moor, lies inside the Newcastle City boundary in open country, adjacent to Newcastle Airport. Being so close to the city it was a mecca for nineteenth-century naturalists, who regretted its drainage and substantial loss as a semi-natural habitat complex. It had been a mosaic of meres, swamp, fen, carr and raised bog, the meres varying considerably in extent depending on seasonal weather and the state of connections to the River Pont for which it served, and still serves, as a flood reception area. The site occupies a broad basin, excavated by ice sheets, in Coal Measure shales, and the peatland systems extend to some 300 hectares. Borings through up to 5 metres of peat have revealed layers of sand and gravel, representing flood events during fen peat accumulation, and a 2-metre thick sheet of lake marl, indicating the presence of a once substantial lake.

Prestwick Carr remained more or less wild until the nineteenth century (although a new cut to the Pont had been excavated in the eighteenth century), with some peat working and cattle-grazing, but was substantially drained (the meres extinguished), enclosed, and ownership partitioned, between 1853 and 1860 (Harbottle, 1995). It is now a flat area of pasture and meadow (and formerly some arable), geometrically divided by hedges, fences, lanes and drains. Much of the pasture, however, remains ill-drained, and in wet winters part of the Carr still floods. Drains are deteriorating and part of the area is affected by coal-mining subsidence. A Scots pine plantation, now with much birch regeneration and bracken, was established on the raised bog, which nonetheless survives as a recognisable bog ecosystem (with heather, hare's-tail and common cottongrasses and cross-leaved heath) where the planting failed and despite open drains. Altogether the reclamation of Prestwick Carr has been an agricultural failure and a biodiversity disaster. There is hope, however, that part of the site can be rehydrated by slowing water runoff (part is now in the ownership of Newcastle City Council and managed as a nature reserve, although still being grazed). Reflooding to form a new mere is, however, unlikely owing to the perceived danger to aircraft of bird strike.

The pre-drainage flora and fauna was impressive. The meres contained pike, perch, roach and eels – the latter were sold in Newcastle. Bittern, teal, pintail, shoveler, hen harrier, water rail, spotted crake, corncrake, redshank, dunlin and ruff all bred. In winter the wetlands were used by large numbers of other ducks, geese, and whooper and Bewick's swans. Most famous, however, was the wood sandpiper, the Carr claiming the first and, until 1959 when it bred in northern Scotland, the only definite breeding record for this wader for the British Isles. In 1853 John Hancock (1874; see Chapter 14) took its nest and eggs, as well as an adult male, for his collection. Victorian naturalists did that sort of thing, and in any case the habitat was soon to be lost. The very wood sandpiper, stuffed by Hancock, is on display in the Hancock Museum bird gallery in Newcastle, and the nest is in the collections.

An expedition of the Tyneside Naturalists' Field Club in 1850, before drainage, recorded *inter alia* fine-leaved water dropwort, lesser water-plantain, greater bladderwort, intermediate bladderwort and pillwort. These are all lost to the Carr and either extremely rare in Northumberland now, or, in the case of intermediate bladderwort and pillwort, extinct in the county. Bog-rosemary grew on the raised bog, and amazingly it is still there, despite drainage and planting.

Today Prestwick Carr still contains some fen-type vegetation, with stands of meadowsweet, yellow iris, soft-rush – a general impression of the Carr is of a vast rushy grassland – and reed canary-grass. The drains are particularly interesting, supporting a number of locally rare or uncommon aquatic and semi-aquatic plants, including tubular water dropwort and slender tufted-sedge. A carr wood contains willows, birch and alder. Breeding birds include woodcock, snipe, curlew, sedge warbler and reed bunting. Winter sees teal, wigeon, pochard and whooper swan. Brown hare is present, and otter hunts along the drains – all within 10 kilometres of central Newcastle.

Newham Fen

Newham Fen, also known as Embleton's Bog, a National Nature Reserve, is on the northern coastal plain 6 kilometres southwest of Seahouses. It is underlain by Middle Limestone Group strata, and sits in a basin, probably a dead-ice hollow, which formerly contained a shallow mere. The esker that forms part of the Bradford kame complex bounds the site to the east, and the East Coast Mainline railway to the west. The mire, part-reclaimed and much less extensive than formerly (bittern and marsh harrier bred here), is seepage-fed by calcareous water and is eutrophic. It consists of a central open fen, surrounded by carr of birch and willow, including dark-leaved willow and bay willow. The carr was advancing onto the open fen to the detriment of habitat diversity, but clearance and recent high water tables have solved that problem while leading to extensive dominance by common reed. This in turn is being controlled by mowing and removal of the litter. The fen vegetation includes the following Northumberland rarities: lesser tussock-sedge, slender sedge, coralroot, narrow-leaved marsh orchid, marsh helleborine, lesser butterfly-orchid, round-leaved wintergreen and black bog-rush. Stonewort (*Chara*) species occur in pools. The fen contains no fewer than 16 species of *Carex*, and calcicolous mosses such as *Tomentypnum nitens*.

Newham Fen is one of only five known British localities for the dark-bordered beauty moth, deserving of mention if only for its fine appearance: its food plants are willow and birch (Plate 13c).

Ford Moss

Ford Moss, in northeast Northumberland, is a nature reserve of Northumberland Wildlife Trust and is a lowland raised bog occupying an ice-scoured depression in Scremerston Coal Group strata. Adjacent to the bog is the former village of Fordmoss Colliery, abandoned in about 1914: coal seams were worked under the moss (Fig. 118).

The raised bog peat overgrew a mere and fen, and the peat is now at least 12 metres deep in the centre of the moss (Parkinson, 1978). Long-continued drainage attempts have lowered the water table over much of the site, leading

Fig. 118 Ford Moss. Note the drains, and birch and pine encroachment.

to downy birch and Scots pine encroachment from the slopes south of the moss; some of the pines at the margin are substantial trees, with more recent colonisation towards the centre of the moss. The site is no longer grazed or burned, although it is still occasionally shot over, and the water table is being restored by damming the drains and ditches.

Despite the lowered water table, parts of the mire surface remained wet, with *Sphagnum* lawns supporting cranberry and round-leaved sundew, although the prevailing vegetation is dominated by heather and hare's-tail cottongrass. Some of the wetter areas are in circular depressions, which may be the result of pitfalls. Ford Moss is one of the northeast Northumberland group of localities for bog myrtle, whose disjunct Northumberland distribution was described on page 123.

Limestone habitats
Although the county is widely underlain by Carboniferous strata, which include limestones, apart from the Great Limestone the beds are thin, and they are largely covered by glacial drift or, in the higher uplands, peat. Consequently we have no extensive limestone habitats. The strips of limestone grassland on limestone cuestas (north of the Tyne) and dale-side benches (in the North Pennines), on rendzinas and calcareous brown earths, contain a characteristic suite of calcicoles: the lady's-mantle *Alchemilla filicaulis*, quaking grass, limestone bedstraw, common rock-rose, fairy flax, hoary plantain and salad burnet. Wild thyme, though not a calcicole, is always present and scented underfoot. The fern, moonwort (Fig. 119), is found in turf on limestone at higher altitudes, where lesser clubmoss is also frequent.

Fig. 119 Moonwort, a fern of upland limestone grassland.

On limestone crags and old quarry faces, free from grazing, an attractive plant is small scabious, and at higher altitudes in the North Pennines are maidenhair spleenwort, green spleenwort, wall-rue and brittle bladder-fern. These ferns (apart from green spleenwort) are also common in the terraced walls of dales gardens, and on mortared walls of ruined buildings associated with lead mining (Fig. 120).

Fig. 120 Brittle bladder-fern, on limestone crags and old quarry faces.

Calcareous flushes

Moorland flushes were introduced in Chapter 8, but the calcareous ones left until this chapter. North of the Tyne Corridor they are a feature of the Ottercops area, of part of the Otterburn Training Area and of the upland fringe southeast of Simonside (Fig. 121). In the North Pennines they occur locally on dale-sides below limestone scarps. They form species-rich islands amidst species-poor acidophilous moorland, although the combination of species depends on just how base-rich the flushes are. They are sedge- rather than rush-dominated. The more neutral flushes contain dioecious sedge, tawny sedge, carnation sedge, flea sedge and common yellow-sedge. They are also likely to contain marsh willowherb, marsh lousewort, common butterwort, lesser clubmoss, devil's-bit scabious, marsh arrowgrass and marsh valerian. Characteristic mosses are *Ctenidium molluscum*, *Palustriella commutata*, *Cratoneuron filicinum* and *Campylium stellatum*, giving a golden hue to the vegetation, and the flushes are often edged by basiphilous sphagna: *Sphagnum contortum*, *S. warnstorfii*, *S. teres* and *S. subsecundum* (sens. str.).

Fig. 121 Thistly Holes, a calcareous flush amidst birch wood in the MoD's Otterburn Training Area.

In addition to many of the species just mentioned, the most calcareous of the flushes support greater tussock-sedge, long-stalked yellow-sedge, few-flowered spike-rush, broad-leaved cottongrass, grass-of-Parnassus, and orchids such as fragrant orchid, common twayblade and early marsh orchid (Plate 14b). Very locally in upper South Tynedale (in Cumbria) bird's-eye primrose makes a glorious pink show in diffuse flushes on bank-sides, as does hairy stonecrop; the latter also occurs in flushes in the Cheviots. A number of the calcareous flushes contain deposits of tufa.

The Spetchells
This name has, through usage, been transferred from the rough grassland and scrub of the low river terrace on the south side of the Tyne at Low Prudhoe to the 1-kilometre long ridge that rises sharply above it. Naturalists brought here blindfolded and then allowed a glimpse of the vegetation might consider themselves to be standing on the slopes of the North or South Downs, the more so when they see chalk turned up in molehills. Yet the nearest chalk outcrop is the Yorkshire Wolds. What is going on?

The answer is that, during the Second World War, ICI operated a fertiliser and explosives works here on behalf of the Government. Ammonia was synthesised and then combined with brought-in anhydrite to produce ammonium sulphate, leaving calcium carbonate as waste. It was this that was dumped beside the works, and turfed to make it less conspicuous to German bombers. As the chalk waste has solidified and the grassland matured, the vegetation has become surrogate, ungrazed chalk grassland. Many calcicole plants have become established (the majority already present in Northumberland but not assembled together). They include fairy flax, kidney vetch, musk thistle, traveller's-joy, perennial wall-rocket, musk mallow, rest-harrow and marjoram. The traveller's-joy and perennial wall-rocket were probably ballast plants (p. 98), although the former, so familiar on the chalk of southern England, may here be a garden escape. Of course the site lacks the southern chalk butterflies.

Lowland neutral grassland

Despite the virtual absence of old lowland meadows, there are still a few fragments of old grassland, on neutral soils, which have never (or hardly ever) been improved by artificial fertilisers or drainage. They are a feature of the southeastern coalfield area, and they have survived probably for two reasons. First, because in this former coal-mining and still industrialised area, many parcels of land were isolated from the main parts of farms by waggonways, railways, coal roads and lanes, or by settlements and industrial sites. They have therefore been managed somewhat casually, by occasional grazing. Second, there are numerous subsidence wetlands, further adding to the awkwardness of fields and making artificial drainage difficult. This is also the warmest and driest corner of Northumberland, with prevalent, heavy pelo-stagnogley soils (Chapter 5), factors that reduce leaching. An outcome has been the survival of old, casually managed, neutral pastures, in which have persisted a number of plants that were once far more widespread and abundant in permanent grassland. In other contexts the habitat has been ploughed out.

In view of the warmer, drier climate of this part of Northumberland, it is also not surprising that some of the plants that reach their northern British limits in the county, or almost so, are found in these old grasslands and are absent or scarce further north. At their northern British limits in these pastures are dyer's greenweed, saw-wort (very rare in Northumberland) and hoary ragwort. Pepper saxifrage ranges into Scotland, but with us is mainly in southeast Northumberland.

Most of these plants are present on Darras Hall recreation ground. Darras Hall is an upmarket housing development, 10 kilometres northwest of Newcastle. Sometime after 1907, when the land was purchased, an oval area of about 3 hectares of former pasture was set aside, in the middle of the housing estate, as a recreation area and has been little managed since, apart from mowing and some control of the gorse and hawthorn scrub that threatens the grassland.

On its varied soils it contains about 200 flowering plant species (A.F. Porter, pers. comm.) more than one-quarter of the county's flora, including common fleabane, which is near its northern British limit in Northumberland. Another example of the habitat is at Arcot Hall. Sadly, even these few neutral grassland relicts on the coalfield are rapidly being lost, and the habitat increasingly confined to the edges of farmland and to derelict and abandoned land, and road verges.

Although not climatically restricted, nor confined to this habitat, orchids are a feature of the damper grasslands. There are sheets of common spotted-orchid, northern marsh orchid and their hybrid swarms. They are also found abundantly on industrial sites and on new road verges.

Lowland heath

Northumberland's lowland heaths, in the sense of occurrence at low altitudes (less than 150 metres a.s.l.) and dominance by ericoid shrubs on podzolised or otherwise acidic and base-deficient mineral soils, bear little floral or faunal relationship to the southern English variety. Their vegetation is similar to that of upland heath, with which they can be contiguous, although gorse is more conspicuous than in the uplands. Where ungrazed, former lowland heaths have become substantially scrubbed up, as, for example, at Longhorsley Moor (Fig. 122). This now consists of a mosaic of heather, bracken, acidophilous grassland and gorse communities, heavily invaded by willows and birch. Most other former lowland heaths have been entirely reclaimed for agriculture, but fragments survive within woodlands and elsewhere, for example at Arcot Hall, at Shaftoe Crags, on coastal golf courses and even in a railway cutting through Shiremoor. Such heaths commonly have the densely hairy variety of heather (var. *hirsuta*), which appears to be most abundant in eastern lowland districts (although present in the west). Could the hairiness reduce water loss in a drier lowland climate?

Gorse occurs gloriously on the gravel flood plain of the College valley in the Cheviots (Plate 14a), and on formerly disturbed, but now neglected, light soils

Fig. 122 Longhorsley Moor, a rare example of lowland heath in the county.

on abandoned rural coal workings, in old quarries and on top of old plough rigs in the Cheviot foothills. As noted it is also extensive on the Whin Sill.

Arable land
A summer feature of cornfields on freely draining soils in the Tyne/North Tyne valley above and below Hexham is spectacular red sheets of common poppy, arising from a very persistent seed bank.

Saline road verges
In urban southeast Northumberland, where there are heavy applications of de-icing salt to the main roads in winter, a considerable number of salt-tolerant plants (halophytes) have been recorded on inland verges, presumably dispersed on the wheels of vehicles and in vehicle slipstreams (Matthews & Davison, 1976; Scott & Davison, 1982; Scott, 1985). It is suspected that cars returning from trips to Holy Island, where the causeway crosses salt marsh, may be important in this dispersal – many of the plants are salt-marsh species. The first observation of a maritime plant invading a roadside was of sea aster in the central reservation of the Great North Road in Gosforth, and the first published account for Britain was for Northumberland in 1976, by Matthews & Davison. The halophytes now occur in other parts of (mainly) eastern and Midland England. Heavy salt applications – up to 4 kilogrammes salt per square metre per year – produce patchily open grass swards ('salt-burn'), where, in the absence of competition, the maritime species are successful. Notable are grasses of the genus *Puccinellia*, especially reflexed saltmarsh-grass. With its short life cycle, high seed production and light seeds, it is well adapted to the open, verge habitat, and its distribution is now almost continuous along the A1 from the Scottish Border to Bedfordshire – possibly all originating from Holy Island. Lesser sea-spurrey, an annual with light seeds, has also spread widely in Northumberland, growing at 418 metres a.s.l. at Carter Bar. Species with heavier seeds have spread more slowly, for example annual sea-blite and buck's-horn plantain.

The stretch of road with the greatest number of species was at first the A1 just north of Seaton Burn, with salt-burn being greatest on the southbound carriageway. This was explained as due to salt, applied in the early morning, being thrown up as spray by the Newcastle-bound rush-hour traffic. In general, older road verges (created before 1965) were much less susceptible to salt-burn and invasion, apparently because doses in the earlier period were lighter, allowing invasion by common couch, which was tolerant enough of later increased doses to resist replacement by halophytes. The seed mixtures of more recent verges, in contrast, were susceptible to the higher salt doses then in use, removing competition to the halophytes. However, some of the salt-tolerant verge species, such as knotgrass and groundsel, are not maritime.

Most of the invasion has taken place since the mid-1960s, when heavy salt applications began. Other saline verge species are Danish scurvygrass, common scurvygrass, greater sea-spurrey, sea plantain, common saltmarsh-grass and foxtail barley – an introduced North American and Eastern Asian plant. Central reservations have early spring carpets of Danish scurvygrass, a species of well-drained habitats favoured by the use of coarse aggregate to assist road drainage.

Recent mild winters, with less salt application, have seen a loss of many of the halophytes from the verges, with common couch replacing them, although reflexed saltmarsh-grass and some others are still abundant (A.W. Davison, pers. comm.).

12

Fresh Waters

Northumberland, with Alston Moor, contains the whole of one major British river system, the Tyne, and part of another, the Tweed, although the Tweed itself forms the county and national boundary only for some 25 kilometres. While the Tweed, and also the Coquet, systems are among the more natural in Britain, the Tyne is far from natural. The North Tyne drains much of Kielder Forest, and is regulated by Kielder Water, factors that affect flow régimes, sediment loads, bed characteristics and water temperatures. The South Tyne drains the mineralised North Pennines and the effects of this on sediments were described in Chapters 6 and 11. The tidal section of the main Tyne is dredged and constrained, and until recent decades was one of the most polluted river reaches in the country, with outfalls pouring raw sewage from almost a million people straight into the river.

During the 1970s, interceptor sewers were installed along both banks of the lower Tyne, and sewage treatment works constructed at Howdon. From 2000, sewage has been further treated to secondary level. A result, together with the consequences of late twentieth century de-industrialisation, is that the river is now in a condition when salmon and sea trout are again able in very large numbers to run up the river to their spawning grounds, and common seals occasionally penetrate as far upstream as Wylam, at the tidal limit 30 kilometres from Tynemouth.

The recorded peak discharge of the River Tyne, at the gauging station at Bywell, is the highest of any British river apart from the Spey, Tay and Findhorn in the Scottish Highlands, and flows in major historic floods must have been even greater. This is despite the Tyne catchment area being much exceeded by, for example, those of the Thames, Trent and Severn. The reasons lie partly in the shape of the catchment area, with high-rainfall upland sources being equidistant and not too distant from the downstream reaches, partly in the rapid melting of the deep snow that can lie in the hills, and partly in the steep average channel gradient, conducting flood waters rapidly downstream. The huge peak discharges, combined with the relatively narrow Tyne flood plain, lead to major floods, the most damaging of which was in November 1771. This is considered to have been the biggest flood of any British river for many centuries (Archer, 1992), destroying every bridge across the Tyne other than at Corbridge, including the medieval bridge at Newcastle with its houses and shops. However, other local rivers are also prone to costly floods, including the Pont and the Wansbeck – costly owing to unwise building development on flood plains. A consequence of severe flooding is periodic rearrangement of river-bed and flood-plain habitats, especially in upland reaches where cobble gravels are shifted and redeposited over the wide beds.

Plants of the rivers and flood plains

The floras of the main rivers reflect their geology. As regards aquatic plants, the upland reaches of the Coquet and Tweed systems, in the Cheviot andesite lavas, flow over relatively base-rich alluvium, and because of this, and their unpolluted

Fig. 123 Stream water-crowfoot, showy in Cheviot burns.

condition, support notable water-crowfoot communities. Stream water-crowfoot, in particular, is extremely abundant and showy in the Coquet and its tributaries (Fig. 123).

Far from conspicuous, however, are the aquatic lichens, for which Northumberland's pure waters give it stardom. Most famous is the river jelly lichen, the county having three of the 20 or so known British localities – two in the upper Coquet system and one on the lower North Tyne. It is a totally submerged species, with a jelly-like consistency, growing on rock surfaces mainly in neutral to alkaline, fast-flowing waters.

The metallophytes of the low, alluvial terraces, flood plains and gravel beds of the North Pennine rivers were described in the previous chapter, where it was noted that the less contaminated sites are open to colonisation by a diverse, ephemeral flora, rooted in fines between the stones (Fig. 124). Its composition is influenced by a limestone component in the gravels, and on this moist, benign seed bed almost anything can turn up. Particularly showy are the various *Mimulus* species and hybrids, all garden escapes; the South Tyne has coppery monkeyflower (Plate 14c) and the yellow *M.* x *robertsii*.

The North Tyne channel gravels and river banks are neither metalliferous, nor (except very locally) calcareous, nor (unlike the South Tyne) are they replenished with montane propagules. Therefore the flora is different from, and less rich than, that of the South Tyne and its tributaries. Also, presumably because of the absence of an excessive influx of sediment derived from metal-mining activities, wide shingle beds are less characteristic of the North Tyne. Its glories are meadow-type communities on the flood plain, wherever improved fields are held back from the river banks for whatever reason. Globeflower is abundant, although oddly missing from the banks of the South Tyne. Also abundant along the North Tyne are melancholy thistle, wood and meadow crane's-bills, wood

Fig. 124 Wide shingle beds of the South Tyne, above Alston (partly metalliferous)

horsetail, giant bellflower, northern bedstraw, great burnet, wood club-rush and flat-sedge – the latter often on seasonally submerged rocks. Butterbur (the rhubarb-like leaves really were used for wrapping butter) is common in stands on well-drained alluvium along the river as it is elsewhere in Northumberland. In his *Flora*, Professor Swan raises the possibility that in most parts of the county, where only male plants occur, the plant was introduced as a medicinal herb (its roots were supposedly effective against fevers). If this is so, butterbur may be native only in the parts of Northumberland where there are also female plants – that is, largely in the valleys of the Rivers South Tyne and Tyne where female plants are common, but not that of the North Tyne. In County Durham the female plant is similarly localised, to the middle Wear. The North Tyne, and its tributary the Rede, support on their channel alluvium most of the known British population of the fugitive, ruderal plant, northern spike-rush, often in silted backwaters. Also particularly associated with the North Tyne are wood small-reed and northern hawk's-beard.

The lower North and South Tynes, the main Tyne and the Tweed are badly infested with Indian balsam (policeman's helmet) (Fig. 125). This plant, with attractive purplish-pink flowers, is a native of the western Himalayas and was introduced to Britain as a garden plant in the early nineteenth century. It has found a congenial niche on moist, fertile alluvium along rivers where, even though an annual, it swamps native perennials by its rapid and robust growth (it is that rare thing, a very competitive ruderal, and is the tallest annual in the European flora). Other unfair advantages are its frost-resistance as a seedling allowing it to germinate early in spring, copious nectar production bribing insect pollinators, mainly bumblebees (Chittka & Schürkens, 2001), and its explosively discharged large seeds, which are assumed to be dispersed by floating down-river. When it dies back in autumn, the lack of ground cover (owing to competitive exclusion by the balsam) makes river banks susceptible to erosion. Some of its populations are rather alarmingly extending back from the river banks, including into woodland shade.

Fig. 125 Indian balsam, invasive on the banks of the main rivers (Linda Reinecke).

The River Coquet is the one main river not yet colonised by Indian balsam, although small balsam, a related naturalised plant, this time from central Asia, occurs in Northumberland only on the Coquet banks. The base-rich alluvium of the upper Coquet, and other Cheviot rivers and burns, supports hairy rock-cress, maiden pink, common cudweed and shepherd's cress. *Mimulus* species – monkeyflower, blood-drop-emlets and coppery monkeyflower – are showy here too.

The Tweed, in its Northumberland section, not only has a gallery of Indian balsam on its banks, but is the centre of the county's infestation with another introduced and naturalised species, giant hogweed (Fig. 126). This is a biennial or once-flowering perennial (the largest herbaceous plant in the European flora), and was first recorded in the county in 1913. Like Indian balsam it is highly competitive, and forms dominant stands, out-competing native plants through shading and pre-emption of soil nutrients. Again the seeds are dispersed down-river. The hogweed is a native of the Caucasus and was also brought in as a garden plant. Its presence along the former flowery banks of the Tweed is a cause célèbre and has transformed the ecology, although, in flower, it is attractive at a distance. The path along the river is now through a 5-metre tall, sinister forest of triffid-like beings. The hogweed has also thoroughly invaded the river-bank woodland, as well as road verges well away from the river. Like the Indian balsam, it leaves bare ground on dieback, promoting erosion. The plant can cause severe blistering if it contacts the skin in bright sunlight, through toxic sap being excreted through hairs along the stem or pouring from the broken stem, and it is on most naturalists' list as a bad thing. A clearance programme is underway, the success, or otherwise, of which will be awaited with interest.

Fig. 126 Giant hogweed, by the Tweed at Ladykirk bridge.

Where giant hogweed, Indian balsam and another invader, Japanese knotweed, all grow together along the Tweed, the hogweed wins hands down. And in places where *Mimulus* species and dame's-violet also occur in the riverside vegetation, the Tweed banks consist of a largely alien flora. Indeed, another alien, few-flowered garlic, is also becoming somewhat over-plentiful along wooded Tweed banks. As regards native plants, however, the Tweed banks support the entire Northumberland inland population of green figwort.

Channel banks of the rivers and main burns (at the river edges of their flood plains) are a habitat for many willow species and their hybrids. Tea-leaved willow occurs particularly along the South Tyne, perhaps associated with the high proportion of limestone in that river's alluvium, whilst dark-leaved willow occurs along North, South and main Tynes – both are northern species in Britain.

Now common in the splash zone along very many burns, and in other damp habitats in the uplands, is the introduced New Zealand willowherb. It forms a low mat, with pale pink flowers, and generally occupies niches otherwise empty of flowering plants. There is a carpet of it in the rill exiting from an old mine below our Alston house. It was first recorded in Britain in 1904.

A very uncommon habitat in Northumberland is a valley-side common reed community, with the reed growing not in water (as it normally does), and where it is protected from grazing animals, but on flushed slopes. The most extensive patch is in ancient, semi-natural woodland in the valley of the Holystone Burn, in Coquetdale (Fig. 127).

Fig. 127 The valley-side common reed community, in the valley of the Holystone Burn, upper Coquetdale.

River invertebrates

The freshwater pearl mussel, a bivalve mollusc, is a rare species of the west and north of Britain. Its favoured habitat is sand and gravel beds in fast-flowing rivers, with riffles and pools. The mussel is long-lived, individuals reaching 100 years or more. Larvae (glochidia) overwinter as parasites in the gills of brown trout and salmon, and the adult is sedentary, part-embedded in the river bed. Mature individuals reach 14 centimetres in diameter and are dark, almost black, in colour; pearls are sometimes found in the shell. In Northumberland the mussel has been recorded recently only in the North Tyne catchment, and is declining, as it is widely in southern Britain, with extant populations apparently often not recruiting. Factors responsible for the decline are uncertain, but in Northumberland water quality is generally good and this may inculpate excessive siltation of the river beds owing to overgrazing in upland catchments, or as a result of bank erosion by livestock, or – in catchments with much afforestation – disturbance during ground preparation.

Also rare and declining, both nationally and locally, is a crustacean, white-clawed crayfish, the only crayfish native to Britain. The largest, and still apparently flourishing, Northumberland populations are in the Wansbeck and Aln systems. The species is generally found in more calcareous waters – it has a thick limey exoskeleton – and there are presumably sufficient Ca^{2+} and HCO_3^- ions in springs issuing from limestones in the Scremerston Coal and Limestone Groups to maintain the animal. Further south in Britain, decline has been caused by the escape of commercially farmed non-native crayfish, including the American signal crayfish, into watercourses, leading to both the spread to the native species of a fatal disease, crayfish plague, caused by the fungus *Aphanomyces astaci*, and competitive exclusion of the native crayfish. Fortunately there has been no local crayfish farming, and there have been no reports as yet of introduced species in Northumberland, although an outbreak of the disease is suspected to have caused deaths in the lower River Blyth system. The signal crayfish, however, is now in the River Derwent, in Durham. The white-clawed crayfish, itself omnivorous, is prey for otter and feral American mink, with river-bank carcasses being not uncommon. As with the pearl mussel, fragmentation of range and isolation of populations lead to increased likelihood of extinction.

The Nent, on Alston Moor, has a very low abundance and diversity of both invertebrates and fish owing to high substrate and dissolved zinc concentrations in this part of the mining area (Nuttall & Younger, 1999). Zinc is extremely toxic to fish in low pH waters, and the scarcity of invertebrate food also limits fish populations. There are, however, some brown trout in the river. A group of species that does flourish in the Nent is the zinc-tolerant, filamentous, green algae *Mougeotia* spp., which become abundant in summer partly owing to the lack of invertebrate grazers. Much of the discharge of zinc and other heavy metals into the Nent and its tributaries is in solution directly from old mine adits. The West Allen also has toxic concentrations of zinc, at least with respect to the freshwater shrimp (*Gammarus pulex*). (It is rather reassuring that *Gammarus* regularly issues from the spring-fed taps at our Alston house.)

River fishes

There is limited distributional information on freshwater species in the county, but there is no reason to suppose that in fish communities and their ecology Northumberland rivers differ from those in upland and lowland areas generally. The brook lamprey is in several Northumberland rivers (and the Derwent reservoir) and is the commonest British lamprey; unlike the two other British species (Chapter 13) it is a purely freshwater species.

The Tweed and the Tyne, apart from the century or so of the latter's disgusting industrial and sewage pollution, are famous salmon rivers, important to the local economy. Even during the pollution years a few fish made it to the upper Tyne spawning grounds, and recovery after cleansing was meteoric. The Tweed is Britain's best salmon-fishing river, and the Tyne England's. The Coquet also has good salmon runs, with few artificial barriers. Salmon are important in river food chains, the immature stages feeding on aquatic insect larvae and adventitious terrestrial insects, and in turn being preyed on by larger fish. Salmon of various ages are also taken by otter, mink, seals (penetrating up lower reaches), heron, cormorant (feeding inland), goosander, gulls (which move well up the Tweed and other rivers), eels – and mature fish, of course, by anglers. The latter have been concerned about the numbers of salmon caught offshore in drift nets near river mouths (a practice illegal off Scotland), and a buy-out of netsmen is well underway.

When the Kielder Water dam was constructed, North Tyne salmon lost long stretches of their spawning grounds in the upper river system, and, to compensate, a hatchery was provided at Kielder. Each year 160,000 or more young fish, raised from North Tyne parents, are released into the river below the dam. Recently the Kielder Burn, above the reservoir, has itself been restocked with young fish from the hatchery and these are later trapped before entering Kielder Water and transported by road around the reservoir, further to supplement stocks. On the Irthing, the waterfall at Crammel Linn blocks the upriver migration of salmon and sea trout.

The freshwater race of brown trout is ubiquitous in our rivers and quite small burns, and like salmon, the fish are important in the aquatic food chain, taking invertebrates, amphibians and small fish, and being consumed by a wide range of predators. Equally, the European eel is common in all our river systems and other water bodies, and is catholically carnivorous (poaching newly deposited salmon eggs) and catholically preyed upon, including by otters and, as a delicacy, netted, trapped or otherwise caught by humans. The Kielder Water dam, however, daunts even migrating eels, and the reservoir is therefore stocked with elvers, partly as otter food.

River birds

If any bird epitomises our rivers it is the dipper, with Northumberland, along with the Scottish Southern Uplands and the Pennines further south, having the highest population densities in the UK (Fig. 128). It is rare to walk along river banks in summer without putting up a dipper, flying upstream or downstream within its linear territory. It is found predominantly on the upland reaches of the rivers and burns, particularly in the Cheviots (perhaps because base-rich drainage from the andesite lavas increases aquatic productivity). The dipper nests on rocky river-bank outcrops or on surrogate sites under bridges, the county holding between 250 and 350 pairs. Clean, well-oxygenated, fast-flowing watercourses support its underwater, invertebrate prey, although it also takes tadpoles and small fish. Low numbers along the Nent and West Allen suggest an effect of zinc pollution on its invertebrate food, and it has been considered

Fig. 128 Dipper (copyright Allan Potts).

absent or scarce in many burns within Kielder Forest – perhaps implicating conifer-induced acidification of runoff, and reduced food supplies – but the dipper may be under-recorded here.

Even more abundant, but with a very similar distribution pattern in the county, is the common sandpiper – more likely to make its presence felt owing to its shrill piping. Unlike the largely resident dipper it is a summer visitor. The total county population is estimated to be about 400–600 pairs, and in the Cheviots some territories were found to be as little as 200 metres in length; the South Tyne is another stronghold. The common sandpiper nests on river-bed shingle, river banks and adjoining rough ground up to 400 metres from water. A third widespread river bird is the grey wagtail, with a similar distribution to the first two in the uplands, but also being found along the lowland reaches of the rivers, and in lowland tributaries. It nests in similar sites to dippers.

Another river bird is the goosander. The first record of breeding in Northumberland (and England: previously it was a Scottish breeder) was on the Coquet in 1941, and since then it has gradually increased as a breeding species in the county, with about 180 pairs. Most of the breeding pairs are along the Tyne system. On the Tweed the goosander is protected by law on the English side, but not on the Scottish side. In fact, although sawbilled ducks are adapted for grabbing fish, goosanders have not been proved to be over-detrimental to salmonid populations, taking large numbers of salmon predators including eels. Nonetheless, they have also been persecuted in Northumberland. Most commonly, goosanders nest in the hollows of river- (or lake-) bank trees. Outside of the breeding season the bird feeds on estuaries – especially that of the Tweed – ponds and reservoirs.

Very characteristic also of the upland, and some lowland, reaches of our rivers is the oystercatcher. Previously breeding only on the coast, it began to colonise South Tyne riverside gravel beds in the late 1920s and has since spread to the other rivers and then – perhaps owing to population pressure on the river shingles – to other open inland habitats, away from the rivers. This spread of inland breeding has occurred throughout much of northwestern Europe, and in northern England colonisation was from the west coast upriver and over into eastern rivers. Since the bird is a shellfish specialist, there has been speculation that some coastal food crisis caused the oystercatcher to learn an advantageous new feeding strategy, on terrestrial invertebrates such as earthworms in fields near to the rivers. All the rivers have numerous pairs of oystercatcher, and the county's population is estimated at 600–700 breeding pairs. In winter the inland populations largely move to the coasts.

In 1952–4, when Eric Ennion ran Monks' House as a field centre (Chapter 14), he carried out ecological work on the Breamish gravels and flood plain below Ingram. He had been surprised by the number of breeding pairs of linnets in the scrub, and was able to demonstrate that this bird was feeding its young not on insects (as was until then believed to be the case), but on the very abundant small seeds of ruderal plants – crucifers, legumes, Caryophyllaceae – colonising the bare gravels after a major 1948 flood. As succession advanced, the ruderal seed source was lost and the linnet population declined to normal levels (Ennion, 1960).

Bearded tit has recently bred in a patch of common reed in east Northumberland. This is the first breeding record for the county and the most northerly British record; it is characteristically a bird of East Anglian fens.

Natural lakes

We have no large natural lakes, only the small loughs scattered in the uplands (Fig. 129). Measurements by Sutcliffe (1972) showed that these vary in the chemistry of their waters and therefore in pH and productivity, and that this is reflected in their invertebrate faunas. The loughs in west Northumberland are mesotrophic, with medium concentrations of phosphorus and nitrogen, and with hard waters dominated by calcium bicarbonate derived from the local limestones. They contrast with small dystrophic lakes and ponds on non-calcareous bedrocks and amidst peaty soils, such as Coldmartin, Blackaburn and Whitfield Loughs. These are strongly acidic and poor in dissolved salts, with humic materials causing the water to resemble brown ale.

Fig. 129 Kimmer Lough, with fringing swamp of bottle sedge (left) and common reed (centre); carr in the background.

Grindon Lough (one of the western loughs) drains underground through limestone and has a markedly fluctuating water level, so is largely lacking littoral vegetation. It has the hardest water, and is noted for wintering wildfowl, with populations of bean, greylag and pink-footed geese as well as whooper swan and various ducks including wigeon. The whooper swan in particular is often also present in numbers on the other nearby loughs. Some of the dystrophic lakes, especially in the moorlands of the southwest, have breeding colonies of black-headed gull on their banks.

Reservoirs, amenity lakes and ponds

These also vary in their water chemistry. Catcleugh reservoir, for example, has low concentrations of dissolved salts and a near-neutral pH, whilst Colt Crag has moderately hard water. Catcleugh is the oldest and most mature large reservoir, with a fair list of breeding water birds including great-crested grebe, teal and tufted duck, and goosander. Linshiels Lake, a dammed amenity lake in a glacial meltwater channel in the Otterburn Training Area, was well known for its huge population of breeding black-headed gull (up to 4,000 pairs), but is now

Fig. 130 Pond at Caistron with a black-headed gull colony, one of several ponds created
following gravel working on the Coquet flood plain (John Steele).

deserted. The dam burst in 1987 (possibly weakened by military shelling),
lowering the water level and drying out the adjacent breeding area, and it is
assumed that this was one cause of the colony relocating to Caistron ponds
further down the Coquet, in gravel workings conveniently restored as a nature
reserve (Fig. 130).

At the head of Kielder Water, behind a subsidiary dam, is the smaller Bakethin
reservoir with a more constant water level, created to avoid unsightly draw-down

Fig. 131 Wallsend Swallow Pond, a subsidence pond on the coalfield (landscaped pit heap in the background).

and managed as a nature reserve. It is bordered by a pleasant landscape of birch woods and coniferous plantations, with glades and developing marginal swamp. Kielder Water itself (Plate 15a), by far the biggest reservoir, has wintering diving ducks such as goldeneye, pochard and tufted, as well as goosander, and there are passage visits by a variety of other waterfowl including whooper and mute swans and barnacle goose. Great black-backed and common gulls roost on the water. Migrating ospreys frequently linger at Kielder Water, and there is hope that, as in the Lake District, a pair will stay to breed – the fish are there in the lake. Kielder Water flooded a long stretch of the North Tyne (although with river characteristics already modified by the forest), as well as ancient, semi-natural woodland on its banks and some old meadows, and its construction was controversial at the time.

Several of the reservoirs hold groups of a few hundred wintering greylag geese, and limited greylag breeding now occurs at a number of ponds.

One of the estate amenity ponds has a breeding population of one of the rarest breeding birds in Britain, the black-necked grebe. This colony has been intensively studied by Ian Armstrong, and in recent years has numbered as many as 18 pairs, which, together with occasional pairs breeding elsewhere in the county, has meant that Northumberland has regularly contained the largest breeding population in Britain. Nesting in the county is recorded from the mid-1960s, with annual breeding from 1977. The black-necked grebe's preference is for small, shallow, eutrophic lakes with floating vegetation, a role played here by amphibious bistort, which provides cover and nesting material; the grebe's food is aquatic invertebrates and fish.

The mining of shallow coal seams, and the cover of impervious Quaternary drift, have caused the development of numerous subsidence ponds and other wetlands in southeast Northumberland (Fig. 131). The commonness, or in some cases the existence, of many aquatic, swamp, fen and marsh plants depends on these. Species include water-plantain, common spike-rush, mare's-tail, yellow iris, common reed, branched bur-reed, bulrush and various rushes. (Breton onion sellers used soft-rush from ill-drained coalfield depressions to string their onions.) Greater spearwort is present in several ponds, and uncommon Northumberland plants include lesser marshwort and trifid bur-marigold. Locally there is succession to willow or alder carr. In general, the older the ponds the more species-rich are their floras. Concern was raised in Chapter 7 about the appearance and spread of the invasive aquatic, New Zealand pigmyweed, and it is potentially a serious threat to the ecology of our ponds and lakes.

The whooper swan regularly winters at several of the coalfield ponds, and the (introduced) ruddy duck made appearances on them in the 1970s and was breeding on them by the early 1990s before spreading through Northumberland. Garganey is an occasional, and the reed bunting a common, breeder. However, greylag goose, attracted to winter corn, has caused damaging eutrophication to nearby pond roosts.

Gosforth Park lake, originally an estate amenity pond, is surrounded by reed swamp and is managed as a nature reserve by the Natural History Society of Northumbria (Fig. 132). Careful management of basin geometry, water level and the surrounding carr and dry woodland has attracted some notable birds. These include, in the reedbeds, breeding reed warbler, virtually at the species' northern limit in Britain, and water rail. Both also breed at Big Waters, a subsidence pond at Seaton Burn a few kilometres away.

Fig. 132 Gosforth Park pond, a nature reserve of the Natural History Society of Northumbria (David Noble-Rollin).

Not all subsidence ponds are in southeast Northumberland. An extensive and diverse subsidence wetland at Coanwood, in west Northumberland on an outlier of the Coal Measures, includes common reed and bottle sedge swamps, together with carr, marsh and open water. 'Natural' vegetation soon develops in artificial wetland habitats.

The existence of opencast coal working in the Druridge Bay area has provided an opportunity, on restoration, to create extensive wetland nature reserves, attractive to wintering, passage and breeding birds. Much of the credit for stimulating this activity goes to Tony Tynan, for long Honorary Secretary of the Northumberland Wildlife Trust (Chapter 15). The Trust's Hauxley Nature Reserve was the pioneering scheme, with purpose-engineered geometry, a sea-flap, and an internal bund intended to separate fresh and brackish waters. A great variety of plants has established (some with human assistance and not altogether appropriate as to geographical range), and the pond attracts wildfowl, migrating waders, gulls and terns. Breeders include greylag goose and ringed plover. The Trust's latest restoration scheme is at nearby East Chevington, where there is a newly created lake, and the largest reedbed in North East England is being established by planting. Ruffs have displayed at one of the Druridge Bay ponds, but modern breeding in Northumberland has not so far been proved.

Although five of the six certainly native British amphibians are common in Northumberland (the natterjack toad is absent), of particular interest is the great crested (or warty) newt, owing to its Europe-wide and British decline in numbers, although Britain remains a stronghold (Langton *et al.*, 2001). Its main county breeding populations are in subsidence ponds, with the high pond density in the coalfield area allowing breeding contact between subpopulations. The decline of the species in Britain is due to loss of both ponds and terrestrial habitats (used outside the breeding season, including for overwintering), and to pollution. The animal is largely, although not entirely, a lowland species, partly because its eggs are somewhat intolerant of acidic water (Fig. 133).

Fig. 133 Great crested newt, male (copyright Allan Potts).

As well as the coalfield subsidence ponds, a number of disused quarries contain ponds. On a much smaller scale, permanent pools are to be found in shell craters on the MoD's Otterburn ranges, and in some naturally clay-lined shake holes in the North Pennines. All contribute to local biodiversity (Fig. 134).

Fig. 134 Pool in shell (or bomb) crater, Otterburn Training Area.

Wetland mammals

Already by the mid-nineteenth century North East England, and especially north Northumberland, was regarded as the otter's headquarters in southern Britain: according to Mennell & Perkins (1863–4) it had retired to 'wilder, more remote and less frequented districts', and was still abundant enough here to hunt. Even in the early twentieth century, the otter was regarded as a pest in Northumberland, owing to its depredations of inland-nesting wildfowl. But further general decline of the species in southern Britain from the late 1950s (Strachan & Jefferies, 1996), caused by a combination of hunting pressure, unsympathetic river-bank engineering and flood plain management, and river pollution by organochlorine insecticides (residues of which entered the food chain), led to the otter becoming very rare in Northumberland. The position of the county at the southern edge of the range of the main Scottish population, however, offered possibilities, and it is one of the triumphs of planned conservation management that the otter is once again numerous in the county and present in all the river systems. It even utilises the Tyne at Newcastle. There is intensive monitoring of the population (O'Hara, 2002), mainly using the occurrence of otter spraint (faeces) on boulders, bridge abutments, etc. – practitioners become hooked on its fishy smell. From having been a very rare species, there may be in the order of several hundred otters now resident in Northumberland, sufficient for road deaths to be commonplace without noticeably depressing the population. Otter ledges, however, are being provided in bridge refurbishment works.

Pioneering habitat management began in the north of the county in the early 1990s, especially on the River Till, with co-operation between riparian owners, public agencies and the Northumberland Wildlife Trust, and natural colonisation from Scotland was rapid (otters move long distances along and between river corridors). The relative naturalness of the northern rivers, with an absence of significant pollution, helped. Otters require waters supporting salmonids and/or other fish, including eels, together with sufficient bank-side woody vegetation for cover and to provide holts among tree roots. Riverside trees also contribute organic matter to the aquatic food chain, and stabilise the banks, so preventing bed-sedimentation (which adversely affects fish habitats). Management for otters has therefore involved fencing off river banks from grazing livestock; either planting trees and shrubs or allowing their natural regeneration; the construction of artificial holts (normally drainage pipes ending in a wooden chamber, where possible on islands for greater security); and the excavation of flood plain lagoons or reinstatement of oxbow lakes and other backwaters as feeding habitat.

The other wetland mammal of conservation concern is the water vole, which has declined dramatically and catastrophically in Northumberland as it has across Britain (Strachan, 1998; Strachan et al., 2000). To put it simply, it was very common, and associated with all types of waterbody including ditches and reed beds, and it is now apparently rare. There was, however, a gradual national decline already underway during the twentieth century, before the recent collapse. The longer-term causes of decline have included riparian habitat degradation – loss of river-bank cover through land being cultivated up to stream margins, or river training/bank protection work. This led to fragmentation and isolation of populations, often in degraded habitats, making each subject to the laws of island biogeography: on small habitat islands, distant from each other, chance extinctions are not counterbalanced by immigration events. The recent crash is probably the result of mink predation severely exacerbating the previous pressures. American mink, escaped or released from fur-farms, has been spreading and consolidating its range, helped in Britain by the lack of competitors such as European mink (not part of our fauna) or, in England, otters. Breeding mink, probably in the first instance from local escapes, were first recorded in Northumberland on the River Blyth in 1966 (Johnston, 1974).The water vole, as the largest British vole, proved to be an ideal size of prey for mink, the juveniles and females of which are slim enough to enter vole burrows. Additionally, the mink is a catholic predator, so is still around to take water voles even when they have been reduced to a low density.

The most recent surveys indicate that the water vole has vanished from much of the county, and some of the surviving populations are well away from the main watercourses frequented by mink. Others are in urban areas of southeast Northumberland, perhaps owing to the scarcity of mink in well-populated areas. There could, however, be a bias in survey site selection in favour of the southeast. A Cumbrian survey has found a population surviving on Alston Moor, where otters may be seeing off mink, and elsewhere in the uplands the water vole may be surviving – it has been recorded in the past high on The Cheviot, in peat runnels. Otter and mink survey work over the last decade, organised by Kevin O'Hara, strongly suggests that as the otter population has increased so the mink population has declined – perhaps owing to competitive exclusion – maybe portending better times for the water vole.

13

The Coast

The seaweeds and invertebrates of the intertidal zone are beyond the scope of this book, nor does it deal with the offshore environment. Nonetheless, North Sea waters off our coast are relatively unpolluted, and this, together with the variety of sea floor and intertidal substrata and rock structure, and considerable tidal range (4.1–4.2 metres for mean spring tides), makes for very rich littoral and near-shore communities, particularly off north Northumberland. Studies have been carried out for over a century from the (now) University of Newcastle's Dove Marine Laboratory at Cullercoats, with the result that the organisms of our coast and seas are among the best known in the world. Connoisseurs of obscurity will delight in knowing that *Acrochaetium sanctae-mariae*, regarded as a filamentous red alga, is endemic to Northumberland, having been recorded nowhere else in the world. It was discovered at St Mary's Island in 1910, growing within the tissues of the brown seaweed, thong-weed (Hardy & Guiry, 2003), and has not been found since.

The North Sea is a naturally productive sea, probably owing to high sediment and therefore nutrient concentrations derived from erosion of soft rocks on its shores, and owing to its shallowness, with wave action recycling nutrients from its floor. There is also nutrient input from major rivers. Effectively the sea, as a sheltered Atlantic embayment, is a sediment trap. The resulting high marine biomass was the basis of the North Sea fishing industry, including that of the Northumberland coastal towns and villages, and sustains the populations of seabirds and seals for which our coast is famous. The birds, and grey seal, would not be here, however, without secure breeding, feeding and roosting areas: the Holy Island intertidal flats, the Farne Islands and Coquet Island, mainland cliffs and some remote beaches. Adding to the county's importance, Britain's mild winters attract birds from countries further north and east to winter on the flats, with their rich feeding: the large tidal range exposes extensive areas at low tides.

The natural history highlights of the coastline were outlined in Chapter 1, but the coast is also of geological interest. The way in which the strike of the Carboniferous sedimentary rocks intersects the coastline obliquely means that virtually the entire succession is exposed. At Collywell Bay, Seaton Sluice, an igneous dyke has cut through a coal seam and metamorphosed the coal to coke (a viewing chamber has preserved the exposure under a new sea wall).

The dunes
The Northumberland dunes are a discrete geographical unit, being largely absent from the Berwickshire and Durham coasts, and we have one of the longest, semi-continuous dune coasts in the British Isles. There are particularly extensive dune systems at Goswick, on Holy Island and at Ross Links, and otherwise they occur at the backs of bays (Druridge Bay is the longest), on spits across estuaries (at Alnmouth and Warkworth) and on some exposed coasts and

low headlands. The main spits subtend from the north, owing to southwards sediment drift.

Dunes are initiated where obstacles to wind-flow at the back of wide beaches – seaweed and/or strand-line plants – begin to trap sand. The first plant colonists, tolerant of brief submersion by seawater, are lyme-grass or sand couch, which winnow out more sand to form an embryo dune. Then marram, the main sand-binding and dune-forming grass, takes over, with potentially unlimited horizontal and vertical rhizome growth. (William Turner gave the first British description of the grass from Northumberland, as 'a kind of sea bente'.) Should another dune ridge form seawards of the first, the surface of the original ridge becomes starved of sand, causing marram to decline in vigour, and a more mature dune grassland develops. This, with increasing soil humus and moisture, and reduced marram dominance, is more species diverse. The marram-dominated dunes are 'yellow' or 'mobile dunes', owing to the bare sand among the marram (often in blow-outs), and the more mature dunes 'grey' or 'fixed dunes'. The vegetation of the latter includes abundant mosses, especially the conspicuous *Syntrichia ruraliformis*, and lichens – species of *Cladonia* and *Peltigera*, hence 'grey' (Figs 135, 136 & 137).

Most Northumberland dune systems are relatively calcareous, owing to their high shell fragment content. This may be due to the intermittently rocky shoreline and subtidal zone, substrate for marine molluscs, and/or to the enormous numbers of burrowing molluscs (for example, cockles, tellins, razor shells) of the tidal slakes, recycled by birds. The sand of the beach and the youngest dunes can have a calcium carbonate content of 7 per cent or more, and the dunes contain shell layers.

Fig. 135 Embryo dunes (foreground), Ross Links, stabilised by lyme-grass.

Fig. 136 Marram-dominated dunes, Ross Links.

Fig. 137 Bamburgh dunes, seaward of the castle (which was built on the Whin Sill) (Tim Gates: copyright reserved).

The dune vegetation that is particularly common on our coast – much more so than elsewhere in Britain (Rodwell, 2000) – is a rather rank grassland dominated by marram and false oat-grass, with abundant red fescue. It is characteristic of more or less stabilised, ungrazed or little-grazed dunes: false oat-grass is sensitive to grazing. A variant of this community, distinctive to Northumberland, contains an assemblage of dune plants whose distributions

Fig. 138 Burnet rose, a characteristic Northumberland dune plant (Geoffrey Chaytor).

scarcely overlap elsewhere. They include bloody crane's-bill (Plate 15b), purple milk-vetch, burnet rose (Fig. 138) and lesser meadow-rue. The bloody crane's-bill occurs particularly on south-facing dune slopes.

Calcareous dunes everywhere in Britain are famously flower-rich and colourful in high summer, and some of ours are no exception. The species-richness is caused by the dynamic variety of habitat, together with a lack of competitive dominance owing to both nutrient stress and, where it occurs, grazing. Particularly showy with us are common and seaside centaury (the latter at its southern east-coast limit and only occurring north of the Coquet), viper's-bugloss, lady's bedstraw, bird's-foot trefoil, common restharrow, cowslip, biting stonecrop and wild thyme. In more open vegetation, especially on south-facing dune slopes, winter annuals (flowering in spring) take advantage of seasonally moister soils. They include little mouse-ear, common whitlowgrass and early forget-me-not. Rarities with us are sea bindweed and sea-holly.

Unfortunately there has been considerable loss of species-rich dune grassland in recent decades. The cessation of grazing by cattle and sheep, and periodic reduction in rabbit populations following myxomatosis, has led to the characteristic rank grassland referred to above, reducing the variety and species-richness of dune habitats. Eutrophication from atmospheric deposition of nitrogen may also be implicated in reducing nutrient stress and favouring competitive grasses. Elsewhere it is use of the dunes as hard standing for, and feeding of, cattle which has allowed robust grasses (cock's-foot, common couch) and herbs to suppress the rich flora (Fig. 139). Absence of grazing has also resulted in succession to scrub, for example in the Bamburgh dunes – even sycamore is establishing there on both stabilised and yellow dunes. In Druridge Bay a combination of commercial sand extraction from the beach (now ceased) and coal-mining subsidence has lowered the beach, exposing the dunes to wave erosion (Fig. 140). South of Blyth, former military use, and recreational and other pressures, have caused severe deterioration of the once splendid dune system. Overall, our dunes are not what they once were. The introduction of suitably low numbers of cattle or ponies as a conservation measure to graze down the vegetation appears, however, to increase floristic diversity.

Fig. 139 Damaging use of the dunes near Cresswell as hard standing for and feeding of cattle.

Fig. 140 Sand extraction and/or subsidence has lowered the foreshore at Druridge Bay, exposing the dunes to wave erosion (David Noble-Rollin).

As to dune insects, conspicuous butterflies in summer are meadow brown, common blue and small copper, with Holy Island and the northern mainland additionally having dark green fritillary, ringlet and grayling. Also conspicuous are the patterned red and dark coloured moths, six-spot burnet (with a large population on Holy Island; Plate 15c) and cinnabar. The larvae of the latter crowd on and defoliate entire populations of ragwort plants, and there are consequently out-of-phase cycles of abundance between plant and herbivore. The larvae of garden tiger and wood tiger moths both feed on hound's-tongue.

Ubiquitous and characterful birds of the dunes are skylark and meadow pipit. The latter has dense populations in the uplands, virtually none in the agricultural lowlands, and then a band along the coast. The little tern – smallest of British breeding terns – nests in scrapes at the back of shingle or sand beaches. It has a county population of about 70 pairs, but with rather poor breeding success owing to human disturbance, blowing sand, high tides and predation.

Salt marshes
As noted in Chapter 1, salt marshes (the upper, vegetated part of intertidal flats, submerged by high tides) are rather localised. The main areas are between Holy Island and the mainland, and at the back of Budle Bay, and otherwise there are salt marshes in the spit-protected estuaries of the Aln and Coquet, together with smaller areas elsewhere. The halophytes that make up these Northumberland salt-marsh communities include sea aster, common scurvygrass, common saltmarsh-grass, spear-leaved orache, sea-purslane, saltmarsh rush, sea arrowgrass, thrift and sea plantain. In the Holy Island and Budle Bay salt marshes, sea-milkwort is particularly prominent. In general, the closed salt-marsh community contains all the plants just mentioned. Pioneer stages have various glasswort species. Our salt marshes are largely ungrazed.

Former salt marshes of the Tyne estuary have been destroyed by industrial and port development, navigation works, disposal of ballast and pollution, although simplified remnants survive or have re-established following improved water conditions. The best on the Northumberland side of the river are at Willington Gut and at Ryton Island (opposite to Ryton), but elsewhere there is at best a very narrow salt-marsh fringe, characterised especially by sea aster (Durkin, 2001).

The Tweed estuary
Most spectacular here is the large, non-breeding herd of mute swans at Berwick, consisting of birds unable to find a breeding site (north Northumberland and Scottish Borders sites are almost all occupied) or which are not yet ready to breed. Over 500 individuals gather at the estuary in summer, many to moult. This is the second largest swan gathering in Britain, with 3–4 per cent of the total population, and parties are also found some distance upriver beyond the tidal limit. Additionally, up to 800 goldeneye winter here. Other Tweed animals are at least two of the three species of lamprey that occur in the county: the lampern (or river lamprey) and the sea lamprey. Both breed in gravel beds in fresh, unpolluted water (further downstream than the brook lamprey: p. 200) and, after a filter-feeding, larval stage buried in silt or sand, migrate as adults to the sea. Here they parasitise other fish and crustaceans. Adults die after returning to rivers and spawning. Both species, together with the brook lamprey, also occur in other local rivers.

Holy Island, Budle Bay and Ross Links

Holy Island (renamed from Lindisfarne in the eleventh century), with its castle and ruined priory, is conspicuous in the coastward view from the East Coast Mainline railway and from the A1 trunk road, and is connected to the mainland at low tide by a causeway. A haunt of punt-gunning naturalist-writers such as Abel Chapman, and of ornithologists such as George Bolam and Richard Perry (Chapter 14), the slakes (sand- and mud-flats) of the sheltered intertidal strait between Holy Island and the mainland, and of Budle Bay, have for long been a bird-watching mecca. In autumn and winter enormous numbers and many species of wader and wildfowl congregate from their inland or northern breeding grounds, either to spend the winter here or before passing on further south. For many waders this is an important staging post en route from Arctic breeding grounds to African wintering quarters. Innumerable other passage migrants find resting and feeding habitats on the Island. The creation of Lindisfarne National Nature Reserve in 1964 was a recognition of both the Island's importance for birds and the need to manage conflicts between wildfowling and nature conservation. One mechanism has been the designation of sanctuary areas in the north and in Budle Bay; elsewhere wildfowling is allowed, with wigeon, mallard, teal and grey geese (especially pink-footed) being the main quarry species.

The main attraction of the slakes to wildfowl and waders, apart from the sheltered, safe environment for roosting, is the abundant invertebrate food (for example, bivalve molluscs, lugworms) in the fine sand, silt and mud substrates, rich in organic matter (Fig. 141). The more sheltered Fenham Flats and western part of Budle Bay are muddier, and the more exposed Holy Island Sands and eastern Budle Bay sandier. Additionally, below the salt marsh, are intertidal and subtidal beds of eelgrass (*Zostera* spp.): narrow-leaved eelgrass and dwarf eelgrass (also called sea-grass; not seaweeds but flowering plants), together with the green seaweed *Enteromorpha* spp. These are key food resources for the pale-bellied race of brent goose, whooper swan and wigeon (a local name for eelgrass is wigeon grass), which each have Lindisfarne populations of international importance and are the reserve's special features. The *Zostera* beds are the largest on the east coast of England.

Fig. 141 Fenham Flats (between Holy Island and the mainland). Lugworm casts indicate the invertebrate food resource (John Steele).

Another plant of the slakes is common cord-grass (*Spartina anglica*). It originated as a sterile hybrid of the native *S. maritima* and the introduced North American *S. alterniflora* in Southampton Water in the nineteenth century; this hybrid *S.x townsendii*, by chromosome doubling, gave rise to the fertile *S. anglica* (*S.x townsendii* itself is sporadic at Lindisfarne). Common cord-grass was introduced to the Northumberland coast in 1929, or possibly earlier, in an attempt to reduce coastal erosion by reducing wave action, and also as a reclamation tool owing to its effect in increasing the rate of salt-marsh accretion, but has become an aggressive competitor, through rhizome spread and dispersal by rhizome fragments and seed. It now forms monocultures, both in the normal salt marsh intertidal range and replacing some of the *Zostera* beds lower in the intertidal zone. It alters the whole aspect of the slakes and – as dense vegetation offering predator cover – is inhibiting to feeding waders. It is thought that the construction of the causeway in 1954, by reducing tidal scour and so increasing sediment accretion, has further favoured cord-grass invasion. Its spread remains a problem, and has been tackled by hand-pulling, herbicide and – to good effect – mechanical burying at the leading edge of invasion of the bare flats. *Zostera* has successfully recolonised treated areas.

Apart from the birds mentioned, Lindisfarne has internationally important numbers of bar-tailed godwit and ringed plover (with at least 1 per cent of the population wintering in western Europe and North Africa: Rehfisch *et al.*, 2003), and present in nationally important numbers are shelduck, eider, long-tailed duck, common scoter, dunlin, knot, grey plover, sanderling and redshank, all with at least 1 per cent of their British numbers. Holy Island is not noted for its breeding species, but there is a colony of black-headed gulls on the Lough, rock pipits breed on the rocky shores, eiders where it suits, shelducks in burrows in the dunes, fulmars on cliff ledges and ringed plover on high beaches. There are also tern colonies on remote beaches, with common, arctic, Sandwich and little terns. Pollen analysis, and radiocarbon dating, suggest that the Lough, in the northeast of the island, may have been created by the seventh-century monastic community, as a fish pond and/or reservoir (Walsh *et al.*, 1995).

Autumn, particularly October, is the season that grabs bird-watchers, with its southwards passage migration from Scandinavia and always the chance of a rarity. This section of east coast, standing somewhat proud, is a likely landfall for accidental drift from the Continent, as well as being on coastal migration routes, and huge numbers of passerines briefly stop over to rest and refuel. Thrushes are particularly conspicuous and occur most years in tens of thousands. Weakened migrants attract predators: merlin, peregrine, kestrel, sparrowhawk, hen harrier and short-eared owl, and the huge winter flocks, especially of dunlin, are similarly harried.

Winter, however, is even more spectacular. Brent geese (one of the black geese) are the highlight of the slakes and can number between 2,000 and 3,000. They are from the Franz Josef Land and Svalbard breeding population of the pale-bellied race of brent. Lindisfarne is the only regular British wintering ground for this population, and, when its main Baltic wintering ground freezes, Lindisfarne may accommodate a high proportion of the entire population, the world total of which is about 6,000. Wigeon numbers are normally up to 20,000, but can occasionally reach 40,000, and up to 100 whooper swans, from Icelandic breeding grounds, are one of the largest wintering flocks in England. After the eelgrass dies back the brent geese graze on protein-rich mainland cereal and pasture fields, to the obvious detriment of the crops. Greylag geese also graze on mainland fields – there are about 1,000 birds at Holy Island in most winters. The important waders were mentioned earlier, and typical numbers are:

bar-tailed godwit	up to 3,000
dunlin	6,000–7,000
knot	2,000–5,000
ringed plover	1,000, and others on passage
grey plover	1,500
sanderling	250
redshank	1,000–1,500
oystercatcher	2,000
golden plover	up to 5,000
lapwing	up to 5,000
curlew	1,000 or more

The open sea in winter has rafts of sea ducks – eiders, mostly from the Farnes, together with scaup, long-tailed duck, and common and velvet scoters – diving for molluscs, crustaceans and other invertebrates; the eiders specialise in mussels. Red-throated divers, fish-eaters, are also birds of the shallow open sea. (Conversely, fish can be bird-eaters: an angler fish was caught with a live scaup inside, and, following the same theme, Johnston recorded that a stranded humpback whale near Berwick had six cormorants in its stomach, and a seventh sticking in its throat: Perry, 1946.) The Farne Islands, to the southeast, provide something of a breakwater for the birds of the open sea.

An archaeological excavation of a settlement, Greenshiel, on Holy Island, now buried by dune sand, revealed the bones of great auk – famously extinct – in a ninth-century AD midden (Beavitt *et al.* 1987). The bird had presumably been taken for food.

The dune system on The Snook – the dune-covered spit on Holy Island – is noted for its slacks, hollows between the dunes, in many of which sand has been blown away down to the seasonal water table – in fact the slacks can be under water in winter. The damp, calcareous, sandy soils of the slack floors have low levels of nitrogen and phosphorus, preventing dominance by competitive species. This combination of factors makes for a rich flora. Notable species are bog pimpernel, marsh helleborine, coralroot orchid, early marsh orchid, curved sedge, variegated horsetail, adder's-tongue, round-leaved wintergreen, brookweed and lesser clubmoss – there is considerable similarity to the vegetation of moorland calcareous flushes (Chapter 11). It is likely that an intermediate level of grazing by rabbits best maintains floristic diversity in the slacks (Garson, 1985), although in recent years high water tables have largely precluded rabbits from them in winter, while beneficially preventing scrubbing.

A rare British plant of the seasonally inundated calcareous dune slacks with low, open vegetation, on both Holy Island and part of the mainland coast, is the liverwort, petalwort, looking rather like a very miniature lettuce. The plant disappears in the dry summer season, perennating underground. Rare mosses in Holy Island or Ross Links slacks include *Catoscopium nigritum*, *Drepanocladus lycopodioides* and *D. sendtneri*.

The Holy Island (and some mainland) dunes are infested by pirri-pirri-bur, a native of southeast Australia and New Zealand and introduced to the Tweed with the scourings from fleeces imported to the Border woollen mills (Hayward & Druce, 1919). Pirri-pirri is a Maori name, and Maoris made tea from its leaves.

It is a member of the Rosaceae, and is a creeping evergreen shrub, with a crimson-red fruiting head bearing barbed bristles. The bur presumably found its way to Holy Island either by being washed down the Tweed and drifting southwards along the coast, or by transport on human clothing, dogs or bird plumage. This is the largest British population of the plant, which is an unwelcome member of the natural sand dune community in a National Nature Reserve (Fig. 142).

Fig. 142 Pirri-pirri-bur, an unwelcome invasive member of the Holy Island dune vegetation.

Ross Links is on the mainland, between Holy Island and Budle Bay. The area of natural dunes here is very much less extensive than formerly, owing to large-scale agricultural reclamation (including dune flattening), and intensive wintering and feeding of sheep and cattle on parts of the system. Grazing, with importation of nutrients in cattle feed, has favoured pasture grasses at the expense of the former dune vegetation.

The Ross dunes are a classic example of a prograding dune system (one being built out into the sea), and of vegetation succession from embryo dunes through to fixed dunes. The sea here is shallow offshore, and an abundant sand supply has allowed successive dune ridges to be built up by the dominant east winds, each one seawards of the one before. Robertson (1955) suggested, by comparing successive maps, that the dune-covered part of the Ross peninsula had in this way grown out into the sea only since the seventeenth century, when a major storm may have shifted sand from further offshore to provide a source for blowing. (It was noted in Chapter 6 that many Northumberland dunes, in their present form and position, date only from the Little Ice Age.) Robertson counted up to 14 subparallel dune ridges at the southern end of the system, and a Second World War blockhouse is now several ridges inland. The rather flat, gently undulating, inland part of Ross Links, however, has a different origin. In part of this area the sand is not calcareous, and is probably of glacial meltwater origin, contiguous with the dunes only by chance. The other part is an old beach (possibly seventeenth century), isolated from the sea by the dune development.

The glacial sands, being originally non-calcareous, and subjected to leaching for much longer, had developed acidic, podzolic soils and a vegetation of dune heath, with heather and bell heather in drier areas and *Nardus* or *Molinia* grassland, with cross-leaved heath, in damper areas. Where there were blowouts, the less rounded shape and more heterogeneous size of the glacial sand, compared with the beach and dune sand, supported low cliffs in the blowout edges, with sand martin burrows. However, very sadly, much of the heath has been lost to agricultural intensification; some of it was ploughed.

Ross Links had a large rabbit population, once trapped for their skins, and, following reduction by clearance and myxomatosis, the population has again built up, adding to the effects of heavy cattle-grazing in reducing the interest of the farmed dunes.

A rarity of the mobile dunes at Ross is the hybrid grass, purple marram, from marram and wood small-reed. The latter is now extinct in north Northumberland.

There was a wartime gunnery range at Ross Links, and previously, in the mid-1930s, a proposal for an air-gunnery and bombing range over the whole Holy Island sand dune/tidal flat area was thwarted. The Revd J. E. Hull wrote tartly at the time, with Holy Island's heritage value in mind, 'we do not have rifle ranges in churchyards'.

The Farne Islands

These rocky islands, made of tough Whin Sill rock – the reason they have survived wave attack – are far enough away from the shore (the furthest is 7 kilometres out) to give a real sense of oceanic adventure, compounded by the breeding season din of the seabirds (Fig. 143). The islands are reached by boat from Seahouses – on the voyage it is rare not to see a gannet from the Bass Rock population flying along the coast. At high tide there are 15 islands (depending on definition) and at low tide 28: an inner group (including Inner Farne) and an outer group, plus a couple of outliers. Inner Farne, the largest, has an area of about 6.5 hectares. Their fame, apart from the St Cuthbert and later monastic associations, lies in their breeding seabirds, favoured by the absence of ground predators and of general disturbance, and breeding grey seals. Each island is a wedge-shaped piece of whin cuesta, dipping northeastwards, with a landward-facing scarp slope (sea cliff) and northeastward-facing dip slope, gently shelving into the sea. The whin has weathered in a columnar fashion, and the cliffs are riven by deep clefts.

Breeding seabirds divide into those that nest on cliff ledges and on the tops of the stacks (for example, guillemot, razorbill, kittiwake) and those that nest on or in the surface of the island tops (for example, terns, eider, puffin). The grey seals obviously haul ashore on the dip slopes. Rabbits were formerly present on several islands, were eradicated in 1968, and were later reintroduced (it is not known by whom) to Inner Farne and East and West Wideopens. They were and are a motley lot, the result of interbreeding of various domesticated breeds introduced by light-keepers. The islands have escaped myxomatosis.

The late Devensian ice sheet, flowing from northwest to southeast over the islands, scored many of the whin outcrops with conspicuous grooves, and also left a layer of till, up to 4 metres thick, on the larger islands. The resulting

Fig. 143 Brownsman Island from North Wamses, Farne Islands (Anne Wilson).

impeded drainage, together with the cool, coastal summer temperatures preserving soil moisture (enhanced by the early summer haar), has allowed the accumulation on the till of a layer of sandy maritime peat, up to 30 centimetres thick. Locally the peat rests directly on rock. It is in this peat that the puffins excavate their nesting burrows, which in some areas, together with rabbit burrows, create an unstable honeycomb.

The vegetation of Inner Farne is different from that of the other islands. Inner Farne was cultivated in medieval times (with surviving ridge and furrow) and later grazed by domestic animals. (Some other islands were also grazed from time to time.) It now has much coarse grassland, dominated by Yorkshire fog, red fescue and common sorrel, together with patches of common nettle, ragwort and competitive ruderals such as broad-leaved and curled docks. The other larger islands, in contrast, have extensive stands of sea campion (Fig. 144). This attractive plant has ramifying root systems, which retain the soil, but it suffers from puffin and gull trampling, and from plucking for nests and for display rituals. It tolerates high soil nitrogen from seabird excreta, and the high nitrogen levels, together with disturbed soils, also favour annuals such as common chickweed and Babington's orache. Grassland on Staple and some other islands is dominated by common saltmarsh-grass.

There are no trees or shrubs on the islands, apart from some elder bushes planted as shelter for the light-keepers' gardens on Inner Farne and also suited to the nitrogen-rich soils. Pollen samples from the peat (Hirons, 1971) indicate that treelessness is the natural condition of the islands, presumably owing to a combination of gales and salt spray.

Fig. 144 Sea campion, Staple Island, Farnes. It is tolerant of the high soil nitrogen levels caused by the sea-bird populations.

Breeding birds on the Farnes have been closely monitored since 1971. The numbers (pairs) of the main breeding species are approximately as follows, varying from year-to-year with the vagaries of weather and food abundance:

fulmar	220–270
cormorant	140–350
shag	900–1,900
eider	800–2,000
oystercatcher	20–35
ringed plover	4–25
black-headed gull	50–80
lesser black-backed gull	600–1,000
herring gull	150–450
kittiwake	5,000–7,000
Sandwich tern	1,800–3,500
roseate tern	up to 30, declining
common tern	110–250
arctic tern	1,000–3,500
guillemot	14,000–18,000 (=50 per cent of individuals)
razorbill	up to 216
puffin	20,000–35,000 (last estimate 1993)
rock pipit	18–36

This is about 60,000–70,000 pairs of breeding seabirds on the islands in a typical year; an enormous number. All are sustained by the high productivity of the local waters, and most have fish as their main diet, although some species take molluscs, crustaceans and other items. Sand eel is prominent in the diet of many species during the breeding season, which coincides with peak availability of the fish in these waters. Its distribution appears to be related to that of sandy bottom sediments (in which it burrows), presumably derived from glacial meltwater deposits, and there is an extensive, shallow, sandy bed just southeast of Inner Farne. However, little is known about sand eel ecology, and controls on its numbers. Prey is partitioned during the breeding season by its size, depth in the sea, and (when less abundant) distance from the islands. For example, cormorant, shag, guillemot and puffin are divers, and the puffin and guillemot can range long distances to feed (Pearson, 1968).

The seabirds and their eggs were traditionally a resource to be exploited. Effective protection began in the late nineteenth century, and since the National Trust acquired the islands in 1925 has been strict. This was a major factor in initial population increases of virtually all the birds, but the causes of continuing population increases over recent decades in some species are unclear. As regards year-on-year breeding success, sand eel abundance is probably one factor, while fluctuations in tern populations relate to June weather – in cold, wet conditions chicks perish. Levels of predation of tern eggs and chicks by the large gulls is also a factor, and shelters for tern chicks have been provided to reduce losses. Shags suffered a severe population crash owing to the 'red tide' toxin released from a dinoflagellate (*Gonyaulax*) bloom in 1968 (Coulson *et al.*, 1968) and a lesser one in 1975 (Galloway & Meek, 1978).

Apart from breeding species, the Farnes, like Holy Island, receive large numbers and many species of migrants on passage, either during long distance north–south migration or, especially in the case of thrushes, Continent-to-Britain movements.

The breeding populations partition the available habitats between them. Shags, guillemots, razorbills and kittiwakes nest on the cliff ledges and (famously the guillemots) the Pinnacle tops (Fig. 145). A small proportion of the guillemots is bridled, with a white eye-ring and a white line extending back from the eye. Razorbill numbers may be limited by their preference for ledges with overhangs, or narrow crannies, which are scarce on whin cliffs. Kittiwakes are able to make use of the narrowest cliff ledges and snags, and make a substantial contribution to the noise of the islands during the breeding season (Figs 146 & 147). Cormorants, which breed only on the Farnes in Northumberland, breed communally on the low flat islands of East Wideopens and North Wamses, amidst an indescribable smell. Terns nest on beaches and in relatively low vegetation on the dip slopes, including in sea campion. Taller vegetation, especially Yorkshire fog, leads to chick losses from wetness and chilling and is largely avoided. The arctic terns nest huggermugger, wheeling and screaming above their breeding areas and occasionally diving at and drawing blood from the heads of intruders (Figs 148 & 149). Eiders also nest on the dip slopes, mainly on Inner Farne, typically in sea campion, silverweed, common nettles or docks, and while on the nest allow very close approach (Figs 150 & 151). Appropriately, given their St Cuthbert association, they are Northumberland's most numerous breeding duck, after mallard. (The legend is that St Cuthbert, who periodically retreated to the Inner Farne, away from his duties as Prior and then Bishop of

Lindisfarne, laid down rules to protect the eiders.) The eiders remain in the Holy Island/Farnes area throughout the year. The puffins (Plate 16a) nest at the far end of burrows, which they have either excavated themselves in the peat or taken over from rabbits. While the cliff-nesting species use the same island year after year, ground-nesters – terns and puffins – switch among islands over the years. In the case of puffins this is partly a result of burrowing and vegetation destruction leading to soil erosion and loss of the habitat, necessitating a shift.

Fig. 145 Guillemots in their breeding habitat on the Pinnacles, Staple Island (David Noble-Rollin).

Fig. 147 Kittiwakes, Staple Island (Natural History Society of Northumbria).

Fig. 146 Kittiwake Gully, Staple Island: breeding shags, kittiwakes and guillemots (Anne Wilson).

Fig. 148 Arctic tern on nest, Farne Islands (David Noble-Rollin).

Fig. 149 Sandwich terns, Inner Farne (Anne Wilson).

Fig. 150 Eider duck, on nest, Inner Farne.

Fig. 151 Eider drakes (black and white) and ducks (Ian Armstrong).

The herring and lesser black-backed gulls breed on rock or in vegetation on most of the main islands, but, because they prey on the eggs and young of other species, attempts have been made to control their populations. The most effective way has proved to be to hard-boil the eggs and replace them in the nest, because if they are removed a new clutch is laid. In addition, some gull eggs are still collected for sale.

The Farnes are equally famous for their grey seals, and have a breeding colony of about 3,200, mainly on North and South Wamses and Northern Hares (Fig. 152). They are otherwise present in numbers throughout the year. (The smaller, common seal is also frequent off the Farnes, and a small colony breeds on sand banks off Holy Island.) One-third of the world's grey seal population of about 300,000 breeds in the UK (and 95 per cent of the European population), and UK grey seal numbers are increasing at about 6 per cent per year (Hilby *et al.*, 1996). Elsewhere than in Britain it is found around the northwest Atlantic, at other localities around the northeast Atlantic, and in the Baltic. Like the seabirds, the seals were traditionally a resource to be exploited – for their skins, meat and oil – and numbers were kept low on the Farnes as they were elsewhere in Britain. Twentieth-century conservation legislation, together with changing economies and attitudes, led to population increases at the main colonies, including the Farnes where there was specific protection. Here calf production increased from fewer than 100 in the early 1930s to over 2,000 in 1971, and in recent years has averaged about 1,000. There are accurate records from 1952 (Fig. 153).

Fig. 152 Grey seals, Farne Islands (Anne Wilson).

Fig. 153 Grey seal calves, Farne Islands (Natural History Society of Northumbria).

The growth in numbers of grey seals led to concern over impacts on fish stocks, especially on Tweed salmon, and over damage to nets, and official, although controversial, culls of Farne grey seal calves took place in 1958 and again from 1963, aiming to reduce the population by 25 per cent. The latter cull was halted because the National Trust decided the case was insufficiently proven, but a new cull began in 1972. It was now argued that increasing seal numbers were both damaging the fragile peat-based ecosystem and leading to unacceptable calf mortality – thought to be more than 20 per cent – owing to overcrowding in the nurseries. There was a high proportion of dead and starving calves, mainly owing to loss of contact with the mother, together with sickness owing to infection of wounds inflicted in the turmoil. While this density-dependent mortality might have maintained relatively stable numbers, it would be at the expense of the environment. Sheet erosion of the peat soil was occurring following vegetation loss, because population pressure had forced breeding females onto the fragile, vegetated peat. In the renewed culls, adults of both sexes, plus calves, were killed, and the objective was to maintain an all-age population of about 3,500, with about 1,000 breeding females. Culls continued until 1983, after which it was decided to protect the vegetated islands, particularly Staple and Brownsman, in a different way simply by preventing the seals from breeding there at all. Grey seals are sensitive to disturbance and wardens shoo them away.

On the crowded breeding islands, however, there is still high calf mortality, of up to 50 per cent or more, but such levels are probably natural, and there is no undue damage to the vegetation.

The colonial breeding nurseries are on rocky dip slopes near the sea. Bull seals establish harems of cows on defended territories, and calving in the Farnes population lasts from early November to mid-December. Cows give birth to a single pup, at first with a white coat, which is taken to sea after three weeks and then fends for itself. There is very high mortality in the first year. The young reach breeding maturity after five to seven years, and grey seals can live for 40 years. They are catholic in their prey, taking sand eels and other fish including salmon, molluscs and crustaceans.

The story of modern conservation on the Farne Islands covers two phases. First, the development of protection against commercial and hobby egg collecting, exploitation of seals, setting fire to the vegetation in puffin burrow areas and casual shooting of seabirds from pleasure steamers in the nineteenth century. (As early as 1677 a visitor, Thomas Kirk, tells how, at the Pinnacles, they threw stones at the auks and 'felled many of them into the sea': Gardner-Medwin, 1985). How the islands became a nature reserve of the National Trust in 1925 is described in Chapter 15. Second, there are the modern problems of management, partly arising *because* the islands are protected, leading to great increases in seabird and seal populations. It has become a question of maintaining an appropriate balance between populations of grey seals, rabbits, terns, puffins, large gulls and human visitors, which interact ecologically with each other, not to mention external interactions with fisheries interests. Thus:

1. Too many grey seals on vegetated islands physically destroyed the vegetation, leading to sheet erosion of the fragile peat soils, destroying puffin habitat. As noted, this problem has been solved by shooing (not shooting).
2. Too few rabbits on Inner Farne was thought to result in tall, ungrazed vegetation (especially Yorkshire fog), denying breeding habitat to terns. Their reintroduction was at first welcomed. However, it is now known that the rabbits avoid the Yorkshire fog, and they hamper attempts at revegetation of eroded areas, as well as directly causing erosion by burrowing and scraping. But visitors like them. Transplants of common saltmarsh-grass are protected by rabbit fencing, which is intrusive.
3. As noted earlier, puffins can destroy their own breeding habitat through vegetation destruction, causing sheet erosion of the peat and leading to burrow flooding and collapse. This is the most likely cause of their historic switching between islands (Hirons, 1971).
4. Too many herring and lesser black-backed gulls caused excessive predation of other breeding birds including terns, of which they are the main predators (shags, however, see gulls off). Also, gulls trample and pluck vegetation. Although gull populations are controlled, rogue individuals continue to be a problem. Black-headed gulls also prey on tern eggs.
5. Human visitors, if uncontrolled, would disturb nesting birds and increase the chances of nest predation. However, in recent decades, despite a huge increase in numbers (now more than 20,000 during the breeding season), visitor management has been successful, and visitor presence may even have reduced the natural predation of tern nests. There have been similar increases in breeding bird numbers on both visited and non-visited islands.

The continuing problems are to do with vegetation loss, mainly caused by rabbits and puffins.

Coquet Island

The island, which is managed by the RSPB as a nature reserve, lies 1.5 kilometres offshore, at the mouth of the Coquet. Landing is not permitted at any season, but round-the-island boat tours leave from Amble, and good views of the terns and puffins are had from the mooring. Coquet Island, with an area of 6.5 hectares, is at the northern tip of the Coal Measure outcrop, and consists of horizontal sandstones thinly covered by till; the sandstones form low cliffs surrounding the island, and there is a very extensive intertidal rock platform (Fig. 154). The vegetation is mainly a red fescue–Yorkshire fog grassland, which (unlike on the Farnes) is kept short by the rabbit population (there was a warren here in the eighteenth century). There are also stands of ragwort, common nettle and docks.

Fig. 154 Coquet Island (Ian Armstrong).

The main importance of the island is its tern colonies, with internationally important numbers of breeding Sandwich and roseate terns (the Sandwiches have 1,500–1,650 pairs, and the roseates at present over 50 pairs – about a third of the British breeding population), together with nationally important numbers of breeding eider (300–400 nests, 2 per cent of the British population), black-headed gull (2,200 pairs, 1.5 per cent), common tern (600–800 pairs, 5 per cent) and puffin (over 6,000 pairs, 2 per cent) – the latter using burrows in the till. For eiders this is the southernmost British east-coast breeding site. Other breeding species are the large gulls, fulmar (breeding among boulders just above high tide level), arctic tern (700 pairs) and kittiwake. The large gulls, as on the Farnes, are a threat to the breeding terns both through competition for nest space and through predation, and are controlled as a management measure. The roseate terns have been provided with shelters on nesting terraces.

The British Isles are at the northern limit of roseate tern breeding and at the southern limit for the arctic tern, so that it is rare for all three smaller terns to breed together. The roseate is the rarest breeding seabird in Britain, and Coquet Island has the largest colony.

Other coastal habitats

The approximately 17 kilometres of hard-rock cliffs on the mainland coast do not have the huge breeding seabird colonies of the islands, but kittiwake breeds in substantial numbers on the whin cliffs at Dunstanburgh and Cullernose Point, and on sandstone cliffs near Seahouses and at Needles Eye, north of Berwick. At the other end of the county it breeds in small numbers on the Magnesian Limestone cliffs at Tynemouth, and various buildings and structures on the lower Tyne have served as surrogate breeding cliffs, as far west as Newcastle Quayside, and including a tower of the Tyne Bridge itself – believed to be the furthest inland kittiwake breeding colony in Britain for this most maritime of all gulls (Fig. 155). On the Gateshead side of the Tyne a steel nesting tower has been erected for the kittiwakes, successfully replacing the formerly used Baltic Flour Mill, lately converted to an art gallery. The mainland fulmar has a similar distribution of breeding sites, although with a penchant for castles rather than commercial warehouses; it also breeds on Berwick Old Bridge, in some coastal quarries, and on crags and in quarries some distance inland. The fulmar has bred in the county from 1928. The lesser black-backed gull breeds on Newcastle rooftops and the herring gull on Berwick and North Shields ones. The rock pipit breeds along the length of the rocky coast, feeding on the shoreline.

Fig. 155 Kittiwakes nesting on window ledge, Newcastle Quayside (copyright Allan Potts).

The fern sea spleenwort occurs on a very limited number of sandstone cliffs, within reach of sea spray. It is frost-sensitive, and therefore much less abundant in Britain on North Sea than on warmer Atlantic coasts.

Wintering and passage birds of the shoreline include the Scandinavia/Arctic breeding waders, turnstone and purple sandpiper, in large numbers (Fig. 156). Although present along rocky shores in general, the purple sandpiper is especially abundant at Blyth and the turnstone at Amble, possibly because of nutrient enrichment of coastal waters from the respective town sewage outfalls causing increased invertebrate food availability. Mussels are important in the purple sandpiper diet, but the bird also turns seaweed in its search for other invertebrates. According to Bolam (1912) it followed women collecting mussels or limpets from the rocks. The turnstone is a more generalist feeder. The mudflats at Blyth have important turnstone, ringed plover and sanderling populations.

Fig. 156 Turnstone, a wintering and passage bird of the shoreline (copyright Allan Potts).

Continuing the pollution theme, prior to the installation of the Tyneside sewage treatment works in the 1970s, huge quantities of untreated sewage poured into the tidal reaches of the Tyne, and gulls, particularly herring, black-headed and common gulls, congregated to feed on sewage debris at the outfalls – to the somewhat perverse entertainment of trippers on the river launches. Kittiwakes, being fish-feeders, were predicted to be the main species benefiting from the clean-up (Fitzgerald & Coulson, 1973), and so it has proved to be.

Rather characteristic of the coastline is a somewhat unstable, steeply sloping, often grassy, clay-cliff habitat where till overlies hard-rock cliffs, or where a clay cliff at the back of the beach is high enough to block dune development. There are drifts of bluebells, and other plants of these sea banks include sea-buckthorn and wood vetch. The sea-buckthorn south of the Coquet is thought to have been planted (to stabilise sand, for amenity or as habitat), including in large quantities at the Hauxley Nature Reserve, but it is probably native at a few localities in the north, forming scrub at the mouth of Howick Burn. Where, as is commonly the case, arable fields come right down to the coast, the till cliffs are a refuge for once-common weeds such as scarlet pimpernel. Locally, base-rich springs issue from the clay cliffs and sustain flushes, supporting great willowherb, great horsetail, hemp-agrimony and grass-of-Parnassus. The flushes are prone to slumping, with cycles of habitat loss and renewal. Maritime heath, with heather and bell heather occurs locally, for example on the cliffs to the north of Berwick.

Saline lagoons are water bodies more or less connected to the sea, whose water is somewhere between fully saline and fresh. They include ponds in old quarries – brackish water-crowfoot is characteristic of these – or, like Cresswell Pond, are situated behind dunes. Cresswell Pond is the result of coal-mining subsidence, and has marginal salt marsh and an uncommon lagoonal snail *Hydrobia ventrosa*.

14

Northumbrian Naturalists

This chapter is about naturalists closely associated with Northumberland, although many of them worked in both Northumberland and Durham (for more details see Lunn, 1983). The region has produced a remarkable array of talented naturalists, particularly in the Victorian era when North East England was an important centre of innovation and wealth creation. The combination of a scientifically inquisitive culture, unknown fields to explore, opportunity through leisure and increased affluence to indulge in fashionable natural history pursuits, and formidable single-minded application and dedication, brought about notable contributions in many natural history fields. Taxonomy and systematics dominated, and catalogues of species feature largely among the publications. Men overwhelmingly outnumbered women, and, as elsewhere, churchmen played a prominent role, especially in the earlier years.

As context it will be useful to describe the history of some institutions with which many of the naturalists were associated. The Natural History Society of Northumberland, Durham and Newcastle upon Tyne was founded in 1829 and is therefore one of the more venerable surviving natural history societies in Britain. It was an offspring of the Literary and Philosophical Society of Newcastle upon Tyne (founded in 1793) and was set up in part to accept responsibility for that Society's natural history and ethnographical collections. These outgrew their first building and in 1884 were transferred to the Society's New Museum, a neoclassical building at the northern edge of the city centre. This, in 1891, was renamed the Hancock Museum in memory of the brothers John and Albany Hancock, of whom more later. The Museum remains the Society's headquarters and houses internationally important collections, especially of marine crustaceans and Carboniferous vertebrate fossils, numerous illustrations by Thomas Bewick, and one of the finest natural history libraries in the country. In 1974 the name of the Society was changed to the Natural History Society of Northumbria, vaguer if briefer. In this chapter 'Natural History Society' or 'Society' unspecified refers to this Society.

The Berwickshire Naturalists' Club, founded in 1831, was the first local field club in Britain, includes northern Northumberland in its ambit, and was the model for countless other such clubs firmly dedicated to field trips with a purpose. The Northern Naturalists' Union was established in 1924. Such unions, federations of small societies and clubs, recognised the advantages of some co-operation, for example in publication, and in 1942 the Union took over responsibility for the publication of the magazine *The Vasculum*, founded in 1915 and until then published independently by a group of local naturalists. Much of the work of the naturalists featured in this chapter was published in the Society's *Transactions*, those of the Berwickshire Naturalists' Club, or in *The Vasculum* (Fig. 157).

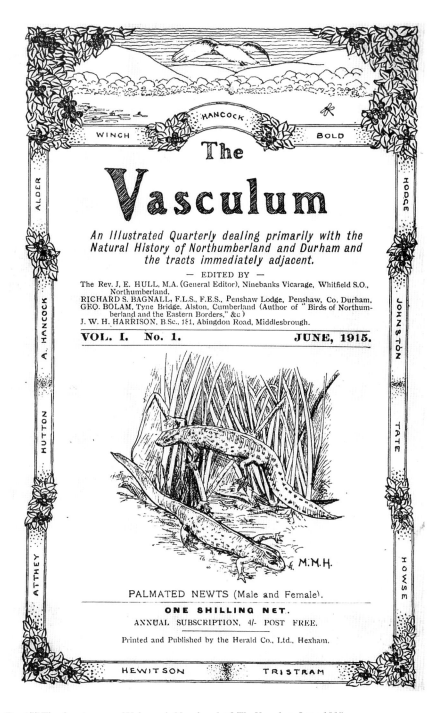

Fig. 157 The front cover of Volume 1, Number 1 of *The Vasculum*, June 1915.

Before 1800

The effective beginning of Northumberland natural history came in the sixteenth century with William Turner (ca. 1508–68). He was a native of Morpeth, and is regarded as the father of English botany by virtue especially of his *New herball*, published in parts in 1551, 1562 and 1568. This was the first attempt by an Englishman to provide, and in English (despite establishment disapproval), an illustrated account of the country's flora. Turner had graduated at Cambridge and later, in medicine, in Italy (he wrote a treatise on medicinal baths, and another on the medicinal properties of wines). He was a prominent and disputatious protestant theologian, and for a time was even an MP. The herbal, while intended as an aid to medicine, contains much local information (and it is likely that Shakespeare obtained much of his information on plants from it: Smith, 1999). Turner invented English names for many plants: ' ... one bery [herb-Paris]... is much in Northumberland, in a wodde besyde Morpeth called Cottingwood' (1548). Herb-Paris is still there, and this was the first British record for the plant. In one sense Cottingwood is where English botany began (Fig. 158). He also published in Latin, in 1544, his *Avium praecipuarum*, regarded as the first scientific book on birds and also partly based on Northumberland observations. Turner was involved in the planning of the gardens at Syon House, on the Thames, possibly the first British botanical garden.

Fig. 158 Herb Paris. The first British record for the plant was by William Turner from Morpeth (Linda Reinecke).

The next great name in local natural history is that of the Revd John Wallis (1714–93). He was born in South Tynedale, graduated at Oxford, took orders and became curate of Simonburn in lower North Tynedale. Here he became interested in botany, and later natural history in general, leading to the publication of the first authoritative account of Northumberland's natural history in 1769: *The natural history and antiquities of Northumberland* [etc.]. The book provided the first substantial foundation for the flora of the county and contained the first records of insects. He recorded some 50 species of bird, including: 'the Penguin [the name then for the great auk], a curious and uncommon bird ... taken alive a few years ago in the island of Farn ...'. As Rossiter (1999) has pointed out, that Wallis was writing shortly before major changes in land management, including intensive persecution of predators, makes his records particularly valuable.

Straddling the eighteenth and nineteenth centuries, Thomas Bewick (1753–1828) was famous as an artist-engraver on wood of birds, mammals and north-country scenes (Bain, 1979). Bewick was born on his father's farm at Cherryburn, on the banks of the Tyne near Prudhoe, and worked in Newcastle for most of his life. While his workaday engraving was on metal and glass, it is for his miniature woodcuts illustrating books on natural history, that he is internationally renowned. The *General history of quadrupeds* (mammals from around the world), contained Bewick's illustrations and text by Ralph Beilby, and was published in 1790. *Land birds* (1797) and *Water birds* (1804) did much to popularise the study of birds in this country. A visit to Bewick by John James Audubon in 1827 makes a link to the man whose work was, in a parallel way, to heighten American interest in nature. Newcastle was still a small community, with accessible countryside, and Bewick was one of the circle of Tyneside naturalists described below who took full advantage of this.

In the very first paper, in the first volume, of the Society's *Transactions*, Bewick's swan was described as a new species by Wingate (1831), and in the same volume was formally named by Selby (1831*b*) in the recently dead Bewick's honour – a happy link between the generations.

The nineteenth century

Geologists
Many of the advances in local geology were made by national figures working in the region, but among locals of national importance were Westgarth Forster (1772–1835). He was a mining engineer, based for a while at Allenheads, who published his famous *Treatise on a section of the strata from Newcastle to Cross Fell* in 1809. Thomas Sopwith (1803–79) trained in Newcastle as a cabinet-maker in the family firm and as a surveyor, and worked for North Pennine lead-mining operations successively at Alston and Allenheads. Using his woodworking skills he carved models of local geological structures and was a pioneer in structural geology. Thomas Atthey (1814–80) was born in Kenton, near Newcastle. He was sent down the pit, later (with his father) made corves, and then ran grocers' shops. His fame was in collecting and describing fossil vertebrates – fish and amphibians – from the local Coal Measures – notably from the Newsham pit heaps near Blyth. Atthey's specimens now form the core of the Hancock Museum's unique fossil amphibian collection. Another man taking advantage of the information unearthed by coal mining was Henry Witham (1779–1844). He specialised in paleobotany, and was a pioneer in thin-sectioning and microscopic examination of rocks. Sir George Airy (1801–92) was from an Alnwick farming family and became Astronomer Royal. He was the first scientist to develop the concept of what became known as isostasy: that high mountains

had deep roots and floated in denser material below. He was also instrumental in positioning the Greenwich Meridian.

Richard Howse (1821–1901) was an all-rounder who moved to the North East as a teacher, immersed himself in natural history and eventually became the first salaried curator of the Society's museum. He worked on the Permian rocks of County Durham, published a catalogue of fishes and was the first locally based geologist to write on glaciation (Howse, 1864). Another all-rounder, but working mainly overseas, was Thomas Belt (1832–78). Born in Newcastle, enthused with natural history at school, he became particularly interested in glaciation and later wrote extensively on glacial and related phenomena in Europe, Asia and the Americas. He acquired geological and mining experience in the Australian gold mines and set up as a mining consultant. This took him to Nicaragua for four years, and his *The naturalist in Nicaragua* (1874) is a classic of observation of tropical forest and savanna wildlife, freshly interpreted with Darwinian eyes. Darwin regarded it as 'the best of all natural history journals'. The book was prefaced from Nijni Novgorod (on a Russian commission) and ends 'I arrived in England [from Nicaragua] ... to find my native town [Newcastle] wealthier and dirtier than ever, with thousands of furnaces belching out smoke and poisonous gases; to find the people of England fretting about the probable exhaustion of her coal-fields in a few hundred years...'. Belt goes on to say, in so many words, a good thing too and ends with a Victorian homily about the greater importance of freedom, progress and morality.

Another local man, who wrote on both geology and history, was George Tate (1805–71), postmaster in Alnwick. One of his contributions was the geological introduction to Baker & Tate's (1868) *A new flora of Northumberland and Durham* (that G.R. Tate being George's son).

Botanists
(Clark, 1983). The towering figure early in the century was Nathaniel J. Winch (1768–1838) (Fig. 159). Born in Middlesex he moved to Newcastle as a young man. He was a Newcastle sheriff and alderman, and, after failing in business, became Secretary to the Newcastle Infirmary, and was one of the first two honorary secretaries of the Natural History Society. His main work was our first proper local *Flora* (1831a, 1837), covering fungi, lichens, mosses and liverworts as well as vascular plants. It made the North East the most thoroughly botanised area of Britain at the time, but additionally Winch pioneered the study of plant geography in Britain. As early as 1825 he related the occurrence and distribution of our flora to environmental factors, in his *Essay on the geographical distribution of plants through the counties of Northumberland, Cumberland and Durham*. The paper included lists of species reaching their northern or southern limits here, of naturalised (including ballast) species, and of rare species with different geographical distributions outside of Britain. Winch's later paper *Remarks on the distribution of the indigenous plants of Northumberland and Durham, as connected with the geological structure of these counties* (1831b) was even more influential.

Overlapping chronologically with Winch was George Johnston of Berwick-on-Tweed (1797–1855). Although he features here among the botanists – and his first substantial work was the *Flora of Berwick-upon-Tweed* (1829, 1831) – he had wide natural history interests. He was born in Berwickshire, practised medicine in Berwick and was behind the formation of the Berwickshire Naturalists' Club. His interests, however, extended to marine biology, beginning an important

Fig. 159 Nathaniel Winch, author of our first proper local *Flora* (courtesy of Royal Botanic Garden, Kew).

tradition that was to lead to local naturalists achieving great national and international eminence, and Johnston came to be regarded as the father of British marine invertebrate zoology. (There is no space to mention the other great practitioners, mainly from Tyneside, other than to note that one of them was Albany Hancock (1806–73), John's elder brother; Davis (1983, 1995) provides further information.) Johnston was also a founder, and secretary, of the Ray Society – named for the seventeenth-century naturalist John Ray, and established to undertake serious natural history publishing (Allen, 1976; Davis, 1998).

The next key event in botany was the publication by the Society in 1868 of *A new flora of Northumberland and Durham* by John G. Baker and George R. Tate.

Baker (1834–1920) was a distinguished botanist originally from Yorkshire, later Keeper of the Herbarium at Kew. Tate (1835–74) was a son of George Tate, mentioned earlier: an army surgeon, he collected plants in China. Until Swan's 1993 *Flora of Northumberland*, also published by the Society, *Baker and Tate* was *the* local flora. It was much more than a catalogue of plants and their localities, containing sections on many aspects of the environment of the two counties related to the distribution of the plants.

George C. Atkinson (1808–77) was a protégé of Bewick. Although his main interest was birds, he made a long series of meteorological observations at his successive homes in West Denton and Wylam. Later his interest turned to trees and his *Catalogue of more remarkable trees of Northumberland and Durham* was published in the Society's *Transactions* in 1873–6, as well as being published separately with photographs of some of the trees. His interest in trees had been aroused by the serious effect of atmospheric pollution, particularly from the Tyneside chemical industry, on vegetation, and the *Catalogue*, which included dead and damaged trees, was intended to focus attention on the issue. He was himself a partner in the Tyne Ironworks at Lemington, where he pioneered pollution control. Sadly, only a few years later, artists were rhapsodising about the atmospheric effects of the multicoloured smoke on Tyneside, although Atkinson's efforts contributed to later pollution control legislation (Seaton, 1990).

Ornithologists
(Meek, 1983). Prideaux John Selby (1788–1867) lived the life of a country landowner, coal-owner and magistrate at Twizell House, near Belford in north Northumberland (Jackson, 1992). He achieved international fame as an artist-ornithologist with his *Illustrations of British ornithology* issued in parts between 1821 and 1833, with accompanying text. Selby rationalised English names, so that we owe 'meadow pipit' and many others to him. Most of the plates were engraved by Selby himself (he got advice from Bewick). With his friend Sir William Jardine, of Dumfriesshire, he also published *Illustrations of ornithology* (1827 to 1843), in which they described birds from around the world, some new to science. More relevant here, however, is his *A catalogue of the birds hitherto met with in the counties of Northumberland and Durham* (1831*a*), the first systematic account. Selby was interested in many branches of natural history, including fishes and, especially, arboriculture. His *British forest trees* (1841–2), illustrated with woodcuts largely from his drawings, was based on the forest and specimen trees he planted on the Twizell estate. Twizell House, being on the Great North Road, was a handy staging post for Selby's wide circle of friends including Audubon (who gave Selby some tuition in drawing).

The second great name in Northumberland ornithology in the nineteenth century is that of John Hancock (1808–90). Born in Newcastle, he became interested in natural history as a boy, learned taxidermy and became an outstanding exponent of the craft, contributing specimens to the 1851 Great Exhibition in London. His great published contribution was his *Catalogue of the birds of Northumberland and Durham* (1874). Later in his life he developed his ideas for a new and larger natural history museum in Newcastle, to house the Society's collections, and did much to raise the necessary funds for the New Museum. Renamed the Hancock Museum after John and Albany, it still has John's mounted specimens on display.

Abel Chapman (1851–1929) was a sportsman-naturalist-writer-explorer. Born in County Durham, he entered the family brewing and wine-importing business, which involved him travelling frequently to Spain, Portugal and elsewhere. He combined business with his pleasure in wildlife, but also made numerous expeditions to Scandinavia and to Africa for big-game hunting; many of his trophies are on display in the Hancock Museum. In 1882 he became joint-lessee of the Coto Doñana, securing that area of Spain against development, and, through his friendship with Krüger in South Africa, instigated the type of National Park that conserves game: the Krüger National Park. However, Northumberland became his home. He bought an estate in the North Tyne valley, at Houxty, from where he fished and shot (on the moors and on the slakes at Holy Island) and wrote about local and overseas wildlife. Chapman was an acute and original observer, prone to acerbic comments aimed at scientific authorities.

Entomologists
(Dunn, 1983). Selby's *Fauna of Twizell* (1839) contains a list of insects taken on the estate, comprehensive by previous standards. This was partly because he perfected a method of 'sugaring' using a mixture containing honey (he was the first British naturalist to do so) to attract moths at night; he used a 'honeyed bee skep' – an empty hive smeared externally with honey. The main nineteenth-century lepidopterists, however, were Thomas J. Bold (1816–74) and John E. Robson (1833–1907). Bold was a County Durham man, but worked as a grocer's salesman in Newcastle. He was an all-round entomologist, helping to build up the Hancock Museum's insect collections. Robson, conversely, was born in Newcastle, but lived in Hartlepool (Co. Durham) where he was active in business and public life. He compiled a *Catalogue of the Lepidoptera of Northumberland, Durham and Newcastle upon Tyne*, published in the Society's *Transactions* between 1902 and 1912.

The twentieth century
Here we deal only with deceased naturalists (with one or two justified exceptions), the work of the living ones being adequately covered in the rest of the book. During the twentieth century, amateurs partly give way to professional geologists and biologists, working in the region's universities or for government agencies, although the amateur/professional distinction is a fine one with respect to some of the Victorian biologists whose work has just been described.

Geologists
Twentieth-century geologists divide into those working for the Geological Survey and those employed in universities. Among the former were Frederick M. Trotter (1897–1968). Born in Gateshead and graduating at Newcastle, he was a dispatch rider during the First World War and lost an eye from shrapnel at Vimy – ending a promising footballing career. Much of his official work was in Cumbria, including on glaciation. He was interested in North Pennine drainage evolution, and on the genesis of the semi-anthracite coals. The other main figure was R.G. Carruthers (1880–1965). From Leicestershire, he settled in the North East and was in charge of the Newcastle office of the Survey from 1921 to 1945. He is remembered particularly for his then highly controversial views on the origin of the glacial drifts – including that complex drift sequences could be emplaced during a single glacial advance (now totally accepted) and that there had been only a single glaciation in the region (not accepted).

Among academics, E.J. Garwood (1864–1949) was a Tynesider directed towards geology by Richard Howse. Although he became Professor of Geology in London, he carried out much local stratigraphical work. Remarkably, he contributed the geological accounts in all 15 volumes of the Northumberland County History, published over the period 1893 to 1940. In Newcastle, George Hickling (1883–1954) was appointed Professor of Geology in 1920. He had a particular interest in the Coal Measures. Late in his life he married Grace Watt (Hickling) about whom more below. It is not fair to claim Hickling's opposite number at Durham, Arthur Holmes (1890–1965) for this chapter, since he was a Gateshead man. A pity, because he was one of the greatest geologists of the period, famed for his work on the radiometric dating of rocks, on continental drift and as writer of the best-known introductory text. However, his student, Sir Kingsley Dunham (1910–2001), who also became Professor of Geology at Durham (where he was brought up) and then moved on to become Director of the Institute of Geological Sciences, has a place because of his outstanding contribution to understanding the mineralisation of the Northern Pennine Orefield. One of Hickling's students and later his academic colleague at Newcastle was Douglas A. Robson (1914–92), who worked particularly on the igneous rocks of the Cheviots and who is commemorated after his death through *Robson's geology of North East England* (Johnson, 1995) – the second edition of a standard account of local geology that he had himself edited. Sir Harold Jeffreys (1891–1989), a great geophysicist, was born in County Durham, studied at Newcastle, and as a young man developed an interest in ecology, contributing papers on Northumberland's vegetation.

Botanists
Professor J.W. Heslop Harrison (1881–1967) dominated the local botanical and entomological scene in the first half of the century. Born in Birtley, County Durham, a graduate of Newcastle, he was Professor of Botany and Genetics there from 1927 to 1946. He was an inspiring field naturalist, with an original and energetic turn of mind. Some of his ideas have stood the test of time and others not. He was a prickly character, somewhat academically isolated, who nonetheless evoked great loyalty among his circle. Heslop Harrison led several botanical expeditions to the Hebrides, in connection with which he stands plausibly accused by Sabbagh (1999) of planting some of his 'finds' of rarities. He strongly favoured survival through the last glaciation of some plants on local nunataks in upper Teesdale and in ice-free areas off the Hebrides, thus explaining their disjunct distributions – an idea not now generally supported. He also undertook pioneering studies on industrial melanism in moths and sawflies.

A colleague in his department was Kathleeen B. Blackburn (1892–1968). Her scientific reputation was based on microscopy, being, with Heslop Harrison, the first person to discover sex chromosomes in plants (in aspen) and, as noted in Chapter 6, was the first British scientist to apply pollen analysis to historical ecology. No doubt prompted by Heslop Harrison, she worked in the early 1930s with Arthur Raistrick (1887–1991), of the Geology Department at Newcastle until his retirement back to Yorkshire in 1956, on glaciation in the North Pennines – this was also in regard to the nunatak theory. Another Botany Department colleague was Heslop Harrison's son-in-law William A. Clark (1911–83), a Scot with a particular interest in field botany and ecology, especially in the hills and mountains. He contributed particularly to nature conservation through his part in identifying sites for SSSI status, and as nature reserves for the Northumberland Wildlife Trust. Clark is remembered for his antagonism to the Forestry Commission for its insensitive planting during its philistine years.

Evelyn M. Lobley, a nurse living in Hexham, was one of the two leading experts on the British Sphagna during her time, and for many years was a referee for the genus. She made the first records of most of the rare Sphagna in the southern part of Northumberland, including those on Muckle Moss, and was the finder of water rock-bristle (p. 99). She also recorded bryophytes more widely in the county. Bob and Jean Fitzgerald also lived in Hexham: he was a Tyneside engineer who specialised in mosses, and Jean knew the liverworts best. They both did excellent bryological work in the county and added many new records.

Still with us is George A. Swan (1917–), long retired as Professor of Organic Chemistry at Newcastle. His records go back to 1936, his first contribution to *The Vasculum* was as a research student in 1939, and his magnificent *Flora of Northumberland* (the source of so much information in this book) was published in 1993.

Ornithologists

George Bolam (1859–1934) was a friend of Abel Chapman, and, like him, a sportsman-naturalist. He practised as a land agent, and spent the later part of his life in Alston. He published two standard catalogues of the birds of Northumberland, the earlier book being full of anecdotal material (much of it about shooting birds) and folklore. He was an all-rounder, and also published on fishes, Lepidoptera and plants. Richard Perry spent much time at intervals between 1936 and 1944 on Holy Island, where he was employed as a coastguard (facilitating much bird-watching), and his *A naturalist on Lindisfarne* (1946) records his detailed observations. George W. Temperley (1875–1967) was a Newcastle man with a career in social service. He compiled no fewer than 22 annual reports on the birds of Northumberland and Durham. He was Honorary Secretary of the Society, an honorary curator of the Hancock Museum, and, with Clark, gave advice on the selection of SSSIs in the county.

Dr Eric A.R. Ennion (1900–81) was a Cambridgeshire GP who gave up his practice in 1945 to direct the country's first field study centre at Flatford Mill in Suffolk. He then bought Monks' House, on the Northumberland coast between Seahouses and Bamburgh, and, in 1951, opened it as a bird observatory and private field study centre (I spent a week there as soon as it opened as a sixth-form biology pupil.) Ennion was above all an ornithologist, although also a celebrated artist, and it was he who began the ringing of migrant birds on a large scale in the county, using a Heligoland trap and mist nets (the latter for the first time in Britain). The story of Monks' House is told in *The house on the shore* (1960).

Dr Hugh M.S. Blair was a leading British ornithologist, who rather hid his light under a bushel. A GP in South Shields, he had an extensive knowledge of the Northumberland uplands and their birds. His best known contribution was his lucid essays on the breeding habits of northern and Fennoscandian birds in the Bannerman 12 volume series *The birds of the British Isles*. Matthew Philipson was a self-taught ornithologist living in Haltwhistle, who had an intimate knowledge of the birds of western Northumberland, but was not well known. He contributed papers on the curlew and black grouse to the *Transactions of the Carlisle Natural History Society*, based on observations going back to 1910.

James Alder (1920–) is a Newcastle man who has spent a long lifetime studying dippers in Northumberland's rivers and burns, and – in the tradition of Bewick and Selby – has surpassing artistic skills, having prepared folios of bird paintings for both Queen Elizabeth II and for the late Queen Elizabeth the Queen Mother (based on the species present on their Balmoral and May estates), and ceramic bird sculptures for Royal Worcester china.

Others
T. Russell Goddard (1889–1948) was Curator of the Hancock Museum from 1923 to 1948. He produced a series of reports on the birds and grey seals of the Farne Islands, and, in 1940 introduced Grace Hickling, née Watt (1908–86) to the Islands. Grace carried on his researches there for the rest of her life. She was born and lived in Newcastle, was an intelligence officer in the Regional War Room in Newcastle, and then devoted herself full-time to natural history and to the Natural History Society. She took over a proposed book by Goddard, which became *The Farne Islands* (1951). Her main interests were the grey seals and the tern colonies. In 1951, with Ian Telfer, she undertook the first numbered tagging of grey seal calves in the world, and later wrote *Grey seals and the Farne Islands* (1962). Grace edited the *Transactions* of the Society for many years while also serving as its Honorary Secretary, jointly or solely, from 1948 until her death (Fig. 160).

Fig. 160 Grace Hickling on a Farne Island with grey seal calf (copyright Joe Payne).

The Revd Dr John E. Hull (1863–1960) was an authority on spiders, local place names and plants. He was vicar successively of Ninebanks in West Allendale and of Belford, discovering many spiders new to science or to the British Isles. Tom C. Dunn (1911–97), a protégé of Heslop Harrison and a Chester-le-Street school teacher, was the leading entomologist of recent decades, and, although firmly Durham-based, was co-author with Dr J.D. Parrack of *The moths and butterflies of Northumberland and Durham* (1986, 1992), superseding Robson's *Catalogue*.

Quite out of the ordinary was F. Alex Wills (1893–1961). He was a journalist – before that a shipyard worker – who, under the names of 'Vagabond' and 'Wayfarer' reported in local newspapers on his lengthy camping treks across Northumberland and neighbouring counties. *The ramblings of Vagabond* (1936) is a collection of his articles, and there were other books. He described, in vivid phrases and with gentle humour, the landscape, wildlife and people of the county as it was shortly before agricultural intensification and large-scale afforestation, with much emphasis on its history and legend. He particularly empathised with the still wild west, before the planting of Kielder Forest. Somewhat in parallel, Ritson Graham (1896–1983) was a Carlisle railway locomotive driver with a lifelong interest in north Cumbria and especially the wastes on the Cumbrian side of the Irthing. His *A Border naturalist* evocatively describes that area before afforestation, which he regarded as a natural history disaster. Although not evidently interested in wildlife, J. Logan Mack, in *The Border line*, also has descriptions and photographs for the same period.

Epilogue
This is an outstanding galaxy of naturalists and scientists. All of Turner, Bewick, Witham, Belt, Winch, Johnston, Selby, the Hancock brothers, Dunham (and the here-neglected invertebrate marine biologists) had national and international reputations. As to their really innovative and unique contributions, we can claim Turner's *Herbal* and *Avium* (Raven, 1947, had him 'as the true pioneer of natural history in England'); Bewick's first ever accurately illustrated handbooks to bird identification; Winch's first full county flora and his pioneering ecological papers; Atthey's fossil amphibians; Witham's palaeobotany; Johnston's first ever field club, and Ray Society, and marine biology; John Hancock's taxidermy. And we have a legacy of enthusiasm, and concern for our local flora and fauna, leading to the conservation activity described in the final chapter.

15

Conservation and a Vision for the Future

Northumbrians have played an important role in the campaigns for greater access to the countryside, for National Parks and for conservation more generally. Sir Charles Trevelyan MP (1870–1958), owner of the Wallington estate (which he gifted to the National Trust in 1941), introduced a succession of access to mountains bills in Parliament, putting the issue firmly on the agenda. His daughter, Pauline, married John G. Dower (1900–47), who spent his last years at Cambo. An architect, he became involved in countryside planning in the 1930s and passionately advocated a system of National Parks for Britain. His (uniquely) one-man Report to Parliament in 1945 laid the basis for our present system of National Parks – just as Abel Chapman had done for Africa.

Charles Trevelyan's brother, another Northumbrian, was Professor George M. Trevelyan (1876–1962), the great historian. He involved himself in, and lent his reputation to, a variety of countryside causes, notably the Youth Hostels Association and the National Trust; he purchased land at Housesteads, on Hadrian's Wall, and gifted it to the National Trust. Trevelyan in turn was the biographer of yet another Northumbrian, Sir Edward Grey (later Viscount Grey of Fallodon; 1862–1933), who served as Foreign Secretary from 1905 to 1916.

Grey had been sent down from Oxford for incorrigible idleness and was then self-educated in history, poetry (mainly Wordsworth) and ornithology. His ponds at Fallodon, created in the 1880s, pioneered the Slimbridge concept of attracting wildfowl by creating suitable habitat – a blend of zoo and wilderness, and his books gave enhanced status to bird-watching. When, much later, the Farne Islands became available for purchase Grey led the successful appeal, and the Edward Grey Institute of Field Ornithology at Oxford is part of a national memorial to him.

The Northumberland National Park

After the passage of the *National Parks and Access to the Countryside Act 1949*, a Cheviot and a Roman Wall National Park were each considered at various times, as was the inclusion in a Northumberland National Park of Kielder Forest. Even part of the Northumberland coast was a candidate, as an 'outlier'. It was finally decided to unite the Northumberland parts of both the Cheviots and the Roman Wall, while also taking in the hill country between (Woolmore, 2001). The result was a curiously shaped Northumberland National Park, somewhat resembling in silhouette a witch riding on a broomstick. Effectively it contains the uplands north of the Tyne Corridor, rather tightly drawn so as to exclude settlements and better agricultural land (so that only about 2,000 people actually live in the Park). The military's Otterburn Training Area – much smaller then than now – was included in the Park, but the greater part of Kielder Forest was left out. It was argued, probably correctly at the time, that the raw forest landscape was not of National Park quality.

In 1956 the Northumberland National Park came into being, with an area of 1,049 square kilometres and occupying about one-fifth of Northumberland. In recognition of the arguments about Kielder Forest, an abutting Border Forest Park (now Kielder Forest Park and overlapping the National Park) was simultaneously created by the Forestry Commission, with an initial emphasis on the provision of recreational facilities. In the half-century which has elapsed since then, the National Park has, with new powers under subsequent Acts, increased in strength, influence and resources, and the landscape and wildlife habitat inside the Park are immeasurably the better for its existence. In the early years much effort was devoted to resisting further afforestation. Then, in the late 1990s, the National Park became engaged in a battle with the MoD over damaging proposals to upgrade greatly the infrastructure of the Otterburn Training Area in order to accommodate new artillery weapons systems, leading to a public inquiry in 1997, reopened in 1999. The unfortunate outcome was that the Army got its infrastructure, mitigated by hugely increased investment in nature conservation and other public benefits. Much attention is now given by the National Park to sustaining and restoring conservation-friendly farming practices (about three-quarters of the farmed land of the Park is now covered by agri-environmental schemes), and to encouraging both new native woodland planting and conservation management of existing semi-natural woodland (most of the larger woods are now in management schemes). The Park's prime resource is moorland, together with its internationally important prehistoric and Roman remains. The Northumberland National Park receives fewer visitors than any of the other Parks (the Hadrian's Wall corridor is the most visited), but its remoteness, tranquillity and wilderness qualities are an important part of its attractions.

It is interesting that the Hobhouse Report on National Parks of 1947, which made recommendations to Government on their designation and management, reviewed issues to be faced in its then-proposed Roman Wall National Park. These were destruction of the Wall by whinstone quarrying, and afforestation approaching from the north. Both have been stopped. The Report also pointed out the need for a continuous footpath alongside the Wall, realised only in 2003. The landscape in parts of the National Park would, however, benefit hugely from the removal of some unsightly conifer blocks, established amidst moorland.

Areas of Outstanding Natural Beauty; Heritage Coast
The 1949 Act also provided for the designation of Areas of Outstanding Natural Beauty (AONBs), which were seen as of equivalent inherent merit to National Parks, although not necessarily of the same scale, and without the need to set up special arrangements for their planning and management. The designation of the Northumberland Coast AONB, covering the coastline from Berwick to Amble, was confirmed in 1958, and of the North Pennines AONB in 1988. The latter covers much of the North Pennine part of Northumberland, together with Alston Moor and adjacent parts of Durham, with the lead-mining heritage an important consideration. AONB status has fended off some, but not all, damaging developments. In 2003 the North Pennines AONB was awarded UNESCO-backed European Geopark status, in recognition of its world-famous geology.

In 1973 the North Northumberland Coast from the Scottish Border to Warkworth was designated by the (then) Countryside Commission as a Heritage Coast, which in 1995 was extended to include Druridge Bay. Heritage Coasts merit special protection.

The Pennine Way, Britain's first long-distance footpath (now National Trail) was approved in 1951 and officially opened in 1965. It crosses Northumberland from end to end (ignoring doubts as to whether the moorlands north of the Tyne Corridor are properly 'Pennine'), and takes in Cross Fell, Hadrian's Wall and (via a detour) The Cheviot.

English Nature

English Nature, the Government's nature conservation agency, is responsible *inter alia* for National Nature Reserves (NNRs), the system of Sites of Special Scientific Interest (SSSIs), and sites classified under the European Union's *Birds* and *Habitats Directives*. These last are respectively Special Protection Areas (SPAs) and Special Areas of Conservation (SACs). In Northumberland there are now nine National Nature Reserves. The earliest, in 1960, was Coom Rigg Moss, one of the bogs in Kielder Forest, and now part of the Kielder Mires NNR. Then came Lindisfarne, in 1964, covering the intertidal flats and dunes. The others are Derwent Gorge and Muggleswick Woods (partly in Durham), the Farne Islands, Greenlee Lough (Fig. 161), Kielderhead Moors, Muckle Moss, Newham Fen and Whitelee Moor. All feature in this book. Additionally, the extensive Moor House NNR, in upper Teesdale takes in the high ground around Cross Fell on Alston Moor. The European sites in, or partly in, Northumberland are shown in Table 6.

Table 6 E.U. protected sites.

Special Protection Areas	candidate Special Areas of Conservation
Coquet Island	Berwickshire and North Northumberland coast
Farne Islands	Border Mires, Kielder-Butterburn
Holburn Lake and Moss	Ford Moss
Lindisfarne	Harbottle Moors
North Pennine moors	Newham Fen
Northumbria coast	North Northumberland dunes
	North Pennine dales meadows
	North Pennine moors
	River Eden (includes Irthing)
	River Tweed
	Roman Wall Loughs
	Tweed estuary
	Tyne and Allen river gravels
	(In Cumbria, Moor House; Tyne and Nent gravels)

The Northumberland Wildlife Trust

In the early 1960s there was a growing feeling among naturalists that the pressures on wildlife and its habitats were too powerful to be left to the statutory system, and that a locally based voluntary sector would be better placed to campaign and lobby for policy changes. There was also an urgent need for a much more complete network of reserves to complement the NNR system, particularly as SSSI protection was then weak. The county-based naturalists' trust was an existing model, and, stimulated by the Society for the Promotion of Nature Reserves (SPNR), trusts were being set up across the country. Since in the natural history world Northumberland and Durham had always been closely knit, it was natural (no discussion even took place) that a Northumberland and Durham Naturalists' Trust should be founded, in 1962.

Fig. 161 Greenlee Lough National Nature Reserve. Its main interests are the fringing wetlands and the wintering wildfowl.

At the inaugural meeting were many of the naturalists who featured in the previous chapter. The convenor was Tony Tynan, a Yorkshireman trained as a geologist and recently appointed as Curator of the Hancock Museum (which became the headquarters of the Trust until it moved to premises at St Nicholas Hospital in Gosforth in 1993). Tynan became the first Honorary Secretary of the organisation, its mentor and guiding hand, with a wide network of contacts in the Universities of Newcastle and Durham, in the SPNR, and in the museums' and National Parks' world.

In 1971 Northumberland and Durham amicably divided, the volume of work over such a wide area being beyond the capacity of the one body, and the Northumberland Wildlife Trust came into existence. Tynan continued as its Honorary Secretary, retiring only in 2000. (Alston Moor is part of the territory of the Cumbria Wildlife Trust, although it has no reserves there.)

At first the Trust saw its main objective as being to acquire and manage nature reserves (which included geological sites), and it now has 64. (The first reserve, in 1964, was Big Waters: p. 206.) Later, like other county wildlife trusts, it expanded its activities in many directions, including the setting up of a system of Sites of Nature Conservation Importance (SNCIs), second tier sites below SSSIs, as input to the planning system. There are now about 300 of these.

In 1970, a batch of seven bogs, the first Border Mires, was leased from the Forestry Commission. The Commission was still a gung ho afforestation agency, and these internationally important sites were to be drained and afforested. Times have changed, and the Border Mires Management Committee, with the Commission as lead partner and the Trust a key player, now accepts responsibility for conservation work on a list of 58 mire sites in Kielder Forest (Plate 16b). Saving the Border Mires, mainly *Sphagnum*-dominated bogs of the type described in Chapter 8, has probably been the Trust's main direct achievement.

A European-funded project, from 1998 to 2003, has seen the restoration of a number of these candidate SAC bogs on FC land, through damming of drains, removal (in some cases to waste) of conifer crops planted on bog surfaces, and weeding of self-sown Sitka spruce. A fun conservation activity has been the mass creation of wader pools in blanket bog above the forest by blasting, using a mixture of ammonium nitrate and fuel oil. Other pools have been created by gully damming (Figs 162, 163 & 164). This has benefited birds such as dunlin whose chicks require invertebrate food. Despite all this activity, very few of the bogs are in perfect condition, owing to remaining plantation impinging on parts of their former extents.

Fig. 162 Conservation issues on the Border Mires: grips illicitly ploughed by farmer – he was forced to repair the damage by filling them in.

Fig. 163 Conservation workers damming drains on Bellcrag Flow. Plastic sheeting is now used.

Fig. 164 Creating a wader pool by blasting, Kielderhead Moors (with permission of Forestry Commission).

Some of the Trust's conservation work at Druridge Bay was described in Chapter 12. A recent acquisition, in 1999, is Whitelee Moor, at 1,508 hectares the largest wildlife trust nature reserve in England. It lies against the Scottish Border at Carter Bar, and its main interests are blanket bog and upland heather heath; it is being managed as a nature reserve/hill farm.

Other voluntary organisations
Unless we count Chillingham Park, where the feral park cattle may have been present at least from the thirteenth century, the first nature reserve in the county was the Farne Islands. Archdeacon Charles Thorp was the mid-nineteenth-century lessee of the Inner Group from the Dean and Chapter of Durham, and in 1861 became their owner. He began protective measures, employing watchers at his own expense during the bird breeding season. Conditions deteriorated again on his death, prompting the formation of a Farne Islands Association in 1881, again paying watchers. In the early 1920s it was proposed to put the Inner Group up for sale, and there were tales of a pleasure resort being developed on the Inner Farne. This led the Natural History Society to convene a meeting in 1923, with Lord Armstrong, owner of the Outer Group, in the chair. He offered to sell his islands, and, as a result of a public appeal sponsored by Viscount Grey, sufficient money was raised to buy both groups. They were handed over to the National Trust in 1925 (Fig. 165). The National Trust now also owns considerable lengths of coastal duneland in the county, as well as estates inland.

The Royal Society for the Protection of Birds (RSPB) has two reserves in Northumberland: Coquet Island and Geltsdale. The latter, on the main watershed of the North Pennines, extends into Cumbria, and is managed for its upland birds, including raptors. The Woodland Trust owns a number of woodlands, including the ancient, semi-natural woodland of Whittle Dene, in the mid-Tyne valley. The Natural History Society has managed the nature reserve at Gosforth Park, on the edge of Newcastle, since 1929.

Fig. 165 Gulls' eggs being loaded from the Farne Islands, ca. 1928. By then harvesting was on a sustainable scale (photo T. Russell Goddard, with permission of Natural History Society of Northumbria).

Other statutory bodies

From having been an organisation blind to wildlife habitat in its expansionary days, when it destroyed numerous wetland and woodland sites, Forest Enterprise (FC) is now an exemplary land manager whose nature conservation activities were described in Chapter 10.

Local authorities, apart from including nature conservation policies in development plans, manage statutory Local Nature Reserves. There is a growing number (now about a score) of these in Northumberland, including semi-natural, ancient woodland in the Wansbeck valley at Morpeth. Local authority Country Parks, although set up primarily as recreational sites in pleasant countryside, also have wildlife interest. Plessey Wood, on the River Blyth in southeast Northumberland, is again ancient, semi-natural woodland, and Tyne Riverside at Low Prudhoe includes the old ICI chalk heap.

The Environment Agency now has regard to nature conservation requirements in its general river management, and the water companies manage areas at Bakethin, the Derwent and Fontburn Reservoirs as nature reserves. Northumbrian Water Ltd, using excavated clay, has created a wetland nature reserve alongside its Howdon sewage treatment works, on previously contaminated industrial wasteland.

Other land management for nature conservation

Whereas a few years ago it was still possible to produce a more or less complete list of sites in Northumberland that were managed entirely or primarily for nature conservation, this is now, pleasingly, impossible. Many farmers, often as a result of entering competitions, have set aside parcels or more extensive areas of land for wildlife and are managing their farms as a whole in a sympathetic way. Others are not. Small-scale hobby-farmers, a growing sector, are doing likewise (I am one). More and more farms are entering into agri-environment schemes. Ladycross sandstone quarry, near Slaley, is being converted into a nature reserve. There are nature parks in urban Tyneside and elsewhere. Lowland game bird management has beneficial spin-offs for wildlife, while in the hills, especially in the Cheviots, sporting estates are reducing stocking levels in the interests of heather heath and red grouse, while creating new native woodland habitat. The College Valley Trust owns a large area of moorland on the northern flank of The Cheviot, and has created some 70 hectares of native woodland there.

The biodiversity planning process

Arising out of the Rio de Janeiro Earth Summit in 1992 and the contingent Biodiversity Convention, governments and local government are preparing and implementing Biodiversity Action Plans (BAPs). Species and habitats are prioritised and listed for their own action plans, with targets and, where possible, costs. Each of Northumberland County, Newcastle City and the National Park have prepared BAPs, and there is to be a regional biodiversity strategy for North East England. English Nature, meanwhile, has proposed regional biodiversity indicators, whose performance will be monitored as indicators of biological health. They are: *habitats*: blanket bog, upland oak wood and mixed ash wood, lowland grasslands (including Magnesian Limestone grassland), upland heathland, sand dunes, mud flats; *species*: otter, great crested newt, juniper, northern brown argus butterfly, skylark, black grouse, bloody crane's-bill. All, except Magnesian Limestone grassland and the northern brown argus, are well represented in Northumberland.

The biodiversity planning process is informed by lists of habitats and species of conservation concern, including *Red Data Books* of rare and threatened species. There are several that are national in scope, but Northumberland Wildlife Trust has compiled a *Red Data Book for Northumberland* (Kerslake, 1998, 1999).

Future Northumberland?

No one is in any doubt as to the main cause of habitat and species losses in Northumberland in the last 60 years or so. (Previously river and air pollution were significant adverse factors.) It is agricultural intensification, strongly promoted by UK Government and then European Union policies, in both the hills and the lowlands. Other developments – the loss of land to building and road construction, large-scale opencast coal working, quarrying, recreational use of duneland – have been more localised and not all have involved significant wildlife losses, while afforestation has produced gains as well as losses.

Over large tracts of the lowlands, wildlife habitat of any value is now confined to the agricultural margins: to road verges, some roadside hedges, difficult land along river and stream corridors, quarries, and the awkward outskirts of, and pockets within, villages. Otherwise simplified, immature, culturally eutrophicated ecosystems are the rule. Species-rich neutral grassland is now vanishingly scarce among the rye-grass deserts, and any vegetation more than five years old is rare, with most fields being ploughed at least as often as that. It is notable that many of the distribution maps in Swan's *Flora* show lacunae in the highly farmed areas, including for arable ruderals that once grew there. Corncockle is now extinct in the county, as is meadow brome, while corn buttercup is possibly extinct. In southeast Northumberland brownfield and abandoned land is, in general, more interesting than farmland.

In the intermediate zone, however, between arable lowlands and true uplands, a greater proportion of the old pasture and parkland landscape survives.

In the uplands, grazing levels on moorland have greatly increased, lower moorlands have been reclaimed or improved, and inbye pastures and meadows are much more intensively managed. Indeed, ancient meadows are still being lost, and botanically rich, river-side grasslands impoverished by heavy grazing. Illegal persecution of raptors continues.

A future Northumberland, richer in wildlife than now – and, despite the adverse trends, parts of it are still rich – will obviously require a redirection of agricultural policy towards environmentally friendly systems. In this context, the greatest uncertainties surround the future of hill farming, and of land management in the uplands.

Because conifer forests cover about 30 per cent of Northumberland's uplands (the wilder part of the county), they will be important in determining the county's future biodiversity. In assuming that the most natural forest management systems possible are desirable, Ratcliffe & Peterken (1995) have listed natural features that they consider appropriate to British spruce forests, and it is encouraging that many of these are being designed by the Forestry Commission into plans for the maturing Kielder Forest.

But as part of, and on top of, an environmentally sustainable agriculture and forestry, a vision for the future of Northumberland's wildlife should surely include:

- the reversion of river flood plains to more natural wetland ecosystems, both for flood control and as habitat;
- re-creation of more natural river and stream banks, by fencing against farm stock, together with riparian woodland and scrub establishment (a good start has been made under agri-environment and other conservation schemes);
- the withdrawal of intensive agriculture from the immediate coastline, allowing natural transitions from coastal to inland ecosystems to redevelop;
- careful conservation of all surviving fragments of ancient countryside amidst lowland farmland: neutral grassland, ancient semi-natural woodland;
- substantially increased native woodland planting in the lowlands and in parts of the hills – in localised clusters with high internal connectivity;
- management of hedgerow trees, many dating from enclosure times and beginning to show their age, to allow them to become veteran trees, for example by pollarding;
- the withdrawal of some farmland from agriculture altogether, in both the lowlands and the hills, to allow natural terrestrial ecosystems to redevelop;
- some very large areas of land managed entirely for nature conservation, because only on a large scale can natural processes be reintroduced and viable populations of species high in the food chain be supported;
- at Druridge Bay, the scatter of varied wetland sites to be augmented to create a superb wetland hinterland – this could include managed coastline retreat

to mitigate 'coastal squeeze' – the loss of coastal habitats between rising sea level and defended coastlines;

- any land switched to short rotation coppice or other crops for biofuels to be managed for wildlife habitat as well as for the commercial crop;
- in urban areas, greater habitat variety in urban green spaces, and introduction of sustainable drainage systems (encouraging infiltration and pond storage rather than rapid runoff);
- geological exposures in quarries and elsewhere to be preserved rather than buried or landscaped;
- important geomorphological features not to be lost under new woodland planting;
- re-establishment of some lost animals, including possibly European beaver to Kielder Forest.

Assuming a warmer future climate, owing to increased greenhouse gas concentrations, a county with larger and more interconnected areas of land managed primarily or secondarily for nature conservation will be better placed to accommodate natural shifts in habitat and species distributions.

It is important to keep places different from each other – to preserve the distinctive personalities of place. This applies not only to Northumberland as a whole, but to the different parts of it. Particularly in moorland areas, with extensive management systems, the past matters. There is a great deal of inertia in semi-natural, moorland ecosystems – the effects of former land-use decisions are propagated to the present, while ecosystems under more intensive management are quickly manipulable to meet immediate needs. Past land management systems, whether for game, for sheep, for cattle, or farming as ancillary to Border raiding or to lead mining, are reflected in the very different moorland environments within Northumberland. Current and future environmental land-management schemes should not unwittingly bring about convergence to bland uniformity.

References and Further Reading

The listed publications include both those specifically referred to in the text and others which bear less directly on the material contained in the book. The list is very far from being a comprehensive resource for all that has been written on the natural history of Northumberland.

Abel, P. D. & Green, D. W. J. (1981). Ecological and toxicological studies on the invertebrate fauna of two rivers in the North Pennine orefield. *In* **Say, P. J. & Whitton, B. A. (Eds)** *Heavy metals in Northern England: environmental and biological aspects*, pp. 109–22. Dept of Botany, University of Durham.

Allen, D. E. (1976). *The naturalist in Britain: a social history*. Allen Lane, London.

Archer, D. (1992). *Land of singing waters*. Spredden Press, Stocksfield, Northumberland.

Asher, J., Warren, M., Fox, R., Harding, P., Jeffcoate, G. & Jeffcoate, S. (2001). *The millennium atlas of butterflies in Britain and Ireland*. Oxford University Press, Oxford.

Aybes, C. & Yalden, D. W. (1995). Place-name evidence for the former distribution and status of wolves and beavers in Britain. *Mammal Review*, **25**, 201–27.

Bailey, J. & Culley, G. (1805). *General view of the agriculture of the county of Northumberland*. Third edition. Drawn up for the consideration of the Board of Agriculture. B. McMillan, London.

Bain, I. (1979). *Thomas Bewick: an illustrated record of his life and work*. The Laing Gallery, Tyne and Wear County Council Museums, Newcastle upon Tyne.

Baines, D. (1988). The effects of improvement of upland, marginal grasslands on the distribution and density of breeding wading birds (Charadriiformes) in northern England. *Biological Conservation*, **45**, 221–36.

Baker, A. J. M. & Proctor, J. (1990). The influence of cadmium, copper, lead and zinc on the distribution and evolution of metallophytes in the British Isles. *Plant Systematics and Evolution*, **173**, 91–108.

Baker, J. G. (1903). Biographical notes on the early botanists of Northumberland and Durham. *Nat. Hist. Trans. Newcastle*, **14**, 69–86.

Baker, J. G. (1868). Climatology. *In* **Baker, J. G. & Tate, G. R..** A new flora of Northumberland and Durham with sketches of its climate and physical geography. *Nat. Hist. Trans. Newcastle*, **2**, 47–67.

Baker, J. G. & Tate, G. R. (1868). A new flora of Northumberland and Durham with sketches of its climate and physical geography. *Nat. Hist. Trans. Newcastle*, **2**, 1–316.

Barber, K. E. (1981). *Peat stratigraphy and climatic change: a palaeoecological test of the theory of cyclic peat bog regeneration*. Balkema, Rotterdam.

Barber, K. E., Dumayne, L. & Stoneman, R. (1993). Climatic change and human impact during the late Holocene in northern Britain. *In* **Chambers, F. M. (Ed.)** *Climate change and human impact on* the landscape: studies in palaeoecology and environmental archaeology, pp. 225–36. Chapman & Hall, London.

Barber, K. E., Chambers, F. M., Maddy, D., Stoneman, R. & Brew, J. S. (1994). A sensitive high-resolution record of late Holocene climatic change from a raised bog in northern England. *The Holocene*, **4**, 198–205.

Barrow, G. W. S. (1966). The Anglo-Scottish Border. *Northern History*, **1**, 21–42.

Beavitt, P., O'Sullivan, D. & Young, R. (1987). Fieldwork on Lindisfarne, Northumberland, 1980–1988. *Northern Archaeology*, **8**, 1–23.

Bekker, R. M., Verweij, G. L., Bakker, J. P. & Fresco, L. F. M. (2000). Soil seed bank dynamics in hayfield succession. *J. Ecol.*, **88**, 594–607.

Belt, T. (1874). *The naturalist in Nicaragua.* John Murray, London.

Bennett, K. D. (1989). A provisional map of forest types for the British Isles 5000 years ago. *J. Quaternary Science*, **4**, 141–4.

Bilton, L. (1957). The Chillingham herd of wild cattle. *Trans. Nat. Hist. Soc. Northumb. (New Series)*, **12**, 137–60.

Bolam, G. (1912). *The birds of Northumberland and the eastern Borders.* Henry Hunter Blair, Alnwick.

Bolam, G. (1916). Jottings from the east nook of Cumberland. *Vasculum*, **2**, 37–41.

Bolam, G. (1932). A catalogue of the birds of Northumberland. *Trans. Nat. Hist. Soc. Northumb.*, **8**, 1–165.

Bowen, D. Q., Phillips, F. M., McCabe, A. M., Knutz, P. C. & Sykes, G. A. (2002). New data for the Last Glacial Maximum in Great Britain and Ireland.

Quaternary Science Reviews, **21**, 89–101.

Breakwell, K. J., Denny, M. J., Evans, S. M., Noble-Rollin, D. C. & Redfern, C. P. F. (1996). Foraging distributions of terns and puffins in coastal waters off Coquet Island (Northumberland). *Trans. Nat. Hist. Soc. Northumb.*, **57**, 13–20.

Briffa, K. & Atkinson, T. (1997). Reconstructing late-glacial and Holocene climates. *In* **Hulme, M & Barrow, E (Eds)** *Climates of the British Isles*, pp. 84–111. Routledge, London.

Bright, P. W. (1996). Status and woodland requirements of the dormouse in England. *English Nature Research Reports*, **166**, English Nature, Peterborough.

Britton, D. & Day, J. (1995). *Where to watch birds in northeast England. Northumberland, Tyne & Wear, Durham and Cleveland.* Christopher Helm, London.

Brodin, N. (2001). *A biodiversity audit for the North East.* English Nature on behalf of the North East Biodiversity Forum.

Bullock, D. (1995). The feral goat – conservation and management. *British Wildlife*, **6**, 152–9.

Butlin, R. A. (1967). Enclosure and improvement in Northumberland in the sixteenth century. *Archaeologia Aeliana (fourth series)*, **45**, 149–60.

Camden, W (1610). *Britannia.* Trans. Philemon Holland. London.

Carter, A. (1988). *Northumberland inventory of ancient woodland (provisional).* Nature Conservancy Council, Peterborough.

Chapman, A. (1907). *Bird-life of the Borders.* Second edition. Gurney & Jackson, London.

Chapman, A. (1924). *The Borders and beyond: Arctic...Cheviot...tropic.* Gurney & Jackson, London.

Chapman, S. B. (1964*a*). The

ecology of Coom Rigg Moss, Northumberland. I. Stratigraphy and present vegetation. *J. Ecol.*, **52**, 299–313.

Chapman, S. B. (1964*b*). The ecology of Coom Rigg Moss, Northumberland. II. The chemistry of peat profiles and the development of the bog system. *J. Ecol.*, **52**, 315–321.

Chapman, S. B. & Rose, R. J. (1991). Changes in the vegetation at Coom Rigg Moss National Nature Reserve within the period 1958–86. *J. Appl. Ecol.*, **28**, 140–53.

Charman, D. J. & Smith, R. S. (1992). Forestry and blanket mires of Kielder Forest, northern England: long-term effects on vegetation. In **Bragg, O. M., Hulme, P. D., Ingram, H. A. P. & Robinson, R. A. (Eds)** *Peatland ecosystems and man – an impact assessment*, pp. 226–230. British Ecological Society/International Peat Society, Dundee.

Charman, D. J., Hendon, D. & Packman, S. (1999). Multiproxy surface wetness records from replicate cores on an ombrotrophic mire: implications for Holocene palaeoclimate records. *J. Quat. Sci.*, **14**, 451–63.

Cherrill, A. J. & Lane, A. M. (1994). Bracken (*Pteridium aquilinum* (L.) Kuhn) infestation of rough grazing land in the catchment of the River Tyne, northern England. *Watsonia*, **20**, 105–14.

Chittka, L. & Schürkens, S. (2001). Successful invasion of a floral market. *Nature*, **411**, 653.

Clapham, A. R., Tutin, T. G. & Moore, D. M. (1987). *Flora of the British Isles*. Third edition. Cambridge University Press, Cambridge.

Clark, W. A. (1983). Botanists. In **Lunn, A. G. (Ed.)** *A history of naturalists in North East England*, pp. 20–35. Department of Adult Education, University of Newcastle upon Tyne.

Clifton, S. J., Ranner, D. S. & Ward, L. K. (1995). The conservation of juniper in Northumbria. *English Nature Research Report*, **152**. English Nature, Peterborough.

Clifton, S. J., Ward, L. K. & Ranner, D. S. (1997). The status of juniper *Juniperus communis* L. in North-East England. *Biological Conservation*, **79**, 67–77.

Cook, N. J. (1990). *An atlas of the butterflies of Northumberland and Durham*. Northumberland Biological Records Centre, Hancock Museum, University of Newcastle, Newcastle upon Tyne. Special Publication no. 5.

Cooke, R. (1987). Tyne and Wear inventory of ancient woodland (provisional). Nature Conservancy Council, Peterborough.

Cornish, V. (1943). *The beauties of scenery: a geographical survey*. Frederick Muller Ltd, London.

Coulson, J. C., Potts, G. R., Deans, I. R. & Fraser, S. (1968). Exceptional mortality of shags and other seabirds caused by paralytic shellfish poison. *British Birds*, **61**, 381–404.

Coult, T. (1995). The status and distribution of the grass snake (*Natrix natrix*) in Durham and Northumberland. *Vasculum*, **80**, 56–62.

Coult, T. (2001). Notes on the historical distribution of the dormouse (*Muscardinus avellanarius*) in Northumberland and Durham. *Vasculum*, **86** (2), 41–5.

Cowen, G. A., The Viscount Ridley & Tegner, H. S. (1965). Roe deer in Northumberland and Durham. *Trans. Nat. Hist. Soc. Northumb.(New Series)*, **15**, 109–20.

Crawley, M. J. (Ed.) (1997). *Plant

ecology. Second edition. Blackwell Science, Oxford.

Cuming, J. S. (1970). *Rock-head relief of south-east Northumberland and the lower Tyne valley.* Unpublished PhD thesis, University of Newcastle upon Tyne.

Dargie, T. (2000). Changes in the vegetation of Ross Links since 1955 and their relation to management. *English Nature Research Reports,* **50.** English Nature, Peterborough.

Dark, K. R. & S. P. (1996). New archaeological and palynological evidence for a sub-Roman reoccupation of Hadrian's Wall. *Archaeologia Aeliana (fifth series),* **24,** 57–72.

Dark, S. P. (1996). Palaeoecological evidence for landscape continuity and change in Britain ca A.D. 400–800. *In* **Dark, K. R. (Ed.)** *External contacts and the economy of late Roman and post-Roman Britain,* pp. 23–51. Boydell Press, Woodbridge, Suffolk.

Davies, G. & Turner, J. (1979). Pollen diagrams from Northumberland. *New Phytologist,* **82,** 783–804.

Davis, P. S. (1983). Marine biologists. In **Lunn, A. G. (Ed.)** *A history of naturalists in North East England,* pp. 45–63. Department of Adult Education, University of Newcastle upon Tyne.

Davis, P. S. (1988). History of botanical recording in Durham. *In* **Graham, G. G.** *The flora and vegetation of County Durham,* pp. 8–23. Durham Flora Committee and Durham County Conservation Trust.

Davis, P. S. (1995). George Johnston (1797–1855) of Berwick upon Tweed and the pioneers of marine biology in north-east England. *Archives of Natural History,* **22,** 349–69.

Davis, P. S. (1998). Sir William Jardine's account of the formation of the Ray Society. *Archives of Natural History,* **25,** 59–73.

Davis, P. S. & Brewer C. (Eds) (1986). *A catalogue of natural science collections in North-East England with biographical notes on the collectors.* North of England Museums Service.

Day, J. C., Hodgson, M. S. & Rossiter, B. N. (compilers & editors) (1995). *The atlas of breeding birds in Northumbria.* Northumberland and Tyneside Bird Club, Newcastle upon Tyne.

de Jong, C. B., Gill, R. M. A., van Wieren, S. E. & Burlton, F. W. E. (1995). Diet selection by roe deer *Capreolus capreolus* in Kielder Forest in relation to plant cover. *Forest Ecology and Management,* **79,** 91–7.

Dennis, R. L. H. & Eales, H. T. (1999). Probability of site occupancy in the large heath butterfly *Coenonympha tullia* determined from geographical and ecological data. *Biological Conservation,* **87,** 295–301.

Directorate of Fisheries Research (compilers) (1981). *Atlas of the seas around the British Isles.* Ministry of Agriculture, Fisheries and Food, HMS0.

Donaldson-Hudson, R. (1964). The historical evolution of the Border. *Hist. Berwicks. Nats' Club,* **36,** 219–38.

Doody, J. P. (1989). Conservation and development of the coastal dunes in Great Britain. *In* **van der Meulen, F., Jungerius, P. D. & Visser, J. H. (Eds)** *Perspectives in coastal dune management,* pp. 53–67. SPB Academic Publishing, The Hague.

Doody, J. P. (1992). The conservation of British salt-marshes. *In* **Allen, J. R. L. & Pye,**

K. (Eds) *Saltmarshes: morphodynamics, conservation and engineering significance*, pp. 80–114. Cambridge University Press, Cambridge.

Douglas, C. (1982). *Report on a survey of whin grassland in north Northumberland.* Northumberland Wildlife Trust.

Douglas, T. D. & Harrison, S. (1987). Late Devensian periglacial slope deposits in the Cheviot Hills. *In* **Boardman, J. (Ed.)** *Periglacial processes and landforms in Britain and Ireland*, pp. 237–44. Cambridge Univ. Press, Cambridge.

Dower, J. (1945). *National Parks in England and Wales.* Ministry of Town and Country Planning. Cmd 6628. HMSO, London.

Dumayne, L. (1993). Iron Age and Roman vegetation clearance in northern Britain: further evidence. *Bot. J. Scotl.*, **46**, 385–92.

Dumayne, L. & Barber, K. E. (1994). The impact of Romans on the environment of northern England: pollen data from three sites close to Hadrian's Wall. *Holocene*, **4**, 165–73.

Dumayne-Peaty, L. (1999). Continuity or discontinuity? Vegetation change in the Hadrianic-Antonine frontier zone of northern Britain at the end of the Roman occupation. *J. Biogeography*, **26**, 643–65.

Duncan, J. B. (1950). A list of the bryophytes of Northumberland. *Trans. Nat. Hist. Soc. Northumb. (New Series)*, **10**, 1–80.

Dunn, T. C. (1983). Mainly entomologists. In **Lunn, A. G. (Ed.)** *A history of naturalists in North East England*, pp. 36–44. Department of Adult Education, University of Newcastle upon Tyne.

Dunn, T. C. & Parrack, J. D. (1986).

The moths and butterflies of Northumberland and Durham. Part 2: Macrolepidoptera. *Vasculum*, suppl. **2**.

Dunn, T. C & Parrack, J. D. (1992). The moths and butterflies of Northumberland and Durham. Part 1: Microlepidoptera. *Vasculum*, suppl. **3**.

Durkin, J. L. (1997). *Vascular plants as ancient woodland indicator species for North East England.* Unpublished dissertation, Centre for Continuing Education, University of Newcastle upon Tyne.

Durkin, J. L. (2001). Salt-marshes of the River Tyne and River Wear. *Vasculum*, **86** (4), 34–41.

Durkin, J. L. (2002). The 'JA' mammal articles 1880 part 2; cetaceans, carnivores, pinnipeds and ungulates. *Vasculum*, **87** (2), 12–18.

Durkin, J. & Cooke, J. A. (1984). *A survey of* Triturus cristatus (warty, or great-crested newt) and other amphibians in Northumberland. *Vasculum*, **69**, 46–51.

Eales, H. T. (1997). *A revision of the status of the large heath butterfly* (Coenonympha tullia) *in Northumberland, part 3.* Supported by the British Ecological Society and others.

Eales, H. T. (2001a). *A survey of the insects to be found on juniper* (Juniperus communis) *L. on three sites within the Northumberland National Park: May to October 2000.* Report to Northumberland National Park.

Eales, H. T. (2001b). Notes on the occurrence of the juniper shieldbug *Elasmostethus tristriatus* (Fabricius). Heteroptera: Acanthosomidae in Northumberland and Co. Durham. V.C.s 68, 67 and 66. *Vasculum*, **86** (3), 29–32.

Edlin, H. L. (1961). The wild pines

of Kielder Forest – are they truly native? *Journal of the Forestry Commission*, **30**, 38–44.

Edwards, C. J. & Woodfall, D. L. (1979). Notes on the breeding biology of little terns in Northumberland. *Birds in Northumbria 1979*, 106–14.

EEC (1992). *Council Directive of 21 May 1992 on the conservation of natural habitats and of wild flora and fauna*. 92/43/EEC. [The Habitats Directive]

Ellis, H. A. (1999). Return of the comma *Polygonia C-album* L. (Lep.: Nymphalidae) to Northumberland; historical review and current status. *Entomologist's Records & Journal of Variation*, **111**, 227–31.

Ellis, H. A. (2001). Records of the comma *Polygonia C-album* L. in south-east Northumberland (VC67) during 2001. *Vasculum*, **86** (4), 43–4.

English Nature (1994). *Lowland heath inventory (northern counties)*. English Nature/RSPB.

Ennion, E. (1960). *The house on the shore: the story of Monks' House bird observatory*. Routledge and Kegan Paul, London.

Ferguson, R. S. (1884). Why Alston is in the Diocese of Durham, and in the County of Cumberland. *Trans. Cumb. Westd. Antiq. Archaeol. Soc. (Old Series)*, **8**, 21–8.

Fielding, M. I. (2000). *A visitors guide to the birds of Coquetdale (including Coquet Island)*. Powdene Publicity.

Fitzgerald, G. R. & Coulson, J. C. (1973). The distribution and feeding ecology of gulls on the tidal reaches of the Rivers Tyne and Wear. *Vasculum*, **58**, 29–47.

Ford, E. B. (1955). *Moths*. Collins (New Naturalist), London.

Forestry Commission (2002). *National Inventory of Woodland and Trees. England. County report for Northumberland*. Forestry Commission, Edinburgh.

Galloway, B. & Meek, E. R. (compilers) (1978, 1980, 1983). Northumberland's birds: parts [respectively] 1, 2, 3. *Trans. Nat. Hist. Soc. Northumb.*, **44**, 1–48; 49–112; 113–95.

Gardner-Medwin, D. (1985). Early bird records for Northumberland and Durham. *Trans. Nat. Hist. Soc. Northumb.*, **54**, 5–22.

Garson, P. (1985). Rabbit grazing and the dune slack flora of Holy Island, Lindisfarne National Nature Reserve. *In* Doody, P. (Ed.) *Sand dunes and their management*, pp. 205–16. Nature Conservancy Council, Peterborough.

Gibbons, D. W., Reid, J. B. & Chapman, R. A. (1993). *The new atlas of breeding birds in Britain and Ireland: 1988–91*. T & AD Poyser, London.

Gilbert, O. L. (1965). Lichens as indicators of air pollution in the Tyne valley. *In* Goodman, G. T., Edwards, R. W. & Lambert, J. M. (Eds) *Ecology and the industrial society*, pp. 35–47. Blackwell Scientific Publications, Oxford.

Gilbert, O. L. (1968). Bryophytes as indicators of air pollution in the Tyne valley. *New Phytologist*, **67**, 15–30.

Gilbert, O. L. (1980). A lichen flora of Northumberland. *Lichenologist*, **12**, 325–95.

Gilbert, O. (2000). *Lichens*. HarperCollins, London.

Goddard, T. R. (1929). *History of the Natural History Society of Northumberland, Durham and Newcastle upon Tyne 1829–1929*. Andrew Reid, Newcastle upon Tyne.

Grace, J. (1977). *Plant response to wind*. Academic Press, London.

Grace, J. (1989). Tree lines. *Phil. Trans. Roy. Soc. London (B)*, **324**, 233–45.

Grace, J. (1997). The oceanic tree-line and the limit for tree growth in Scotland. *Botanical Journal of Scotland*, **49**, 223–36.

Grace, J. & Marks, T. C. (1978). Physiological aspects of bog production at Moor House. *In* **Heal, O. W. & Perkins, D. F. (Eds)** *Production ecology of British moors and montane grasslands*, pp. 38–51. Ecological Studies, **27**. Springer-Verlag, Berlin.

Grace, J. B. (1999). The factors controlling species-density in herbaceous plant communities: an assessment. *Perspectives in plant ecology, evolution and systematics*, **2/1**, 1–28.

Graham, G. G. (1988). *The flora and vegetation of County Durham*. Durham Flora Committee and Durham County Conservation Trust.

Graham, R. (1993). *A Border naturalist: the birds and wildlife of the Bewcastle Fells and the Gilsland moors, 1930–1966*. Bookcase, Carlisle.

Gray, W. (1649). *Chorographia; or, a survey of Newcastle-upon-Tyne*. Stephen Bulkley, Newcastle upon Tyne.

Grey, E. (1907). *Fly fishing*. Fourth edition. J.M. Dent, London.

Grey, E. (1926). *Fallodon papers*. Constable & Co., London.

Grey, E. (1927). *The charm of birds*. Hodder and Stoughton, London.

Grey, J. (1841). A view of the past and present state of agriculture in Northumberland. *Journal of the Royal Agricultural Society of England*, **2**, 151–92.

Grime, J. P. (1979). *Plant strategies and vegetation processes*. John Wiley & Sons, Chichester.

Grime, J. P., Hodgson, J. G. & Hunt, R. (1988). *Comparative plant ecology: a functional approach to common British species*. Unwin Hyman, London.

Gurnell, J., Clark, M. J., Lurz, P. W. W., Shirley, M. D. F. & Rushton, S. P. (2002). Conserving red squirrels (*Sciurus vulgaris*): mapping and forecasting habitat suitability using a Geographic Information Systems approach. *Biological Conservation*, **105**, 53–64.

Gynn, E. G. & Richards, A. J. (1985). Biological Flora of the British Isles no. 161. *Acaena novae-zelandiae* T. Kirk. *J. Ecol.*, **73**, 1055–63.

Haffey, D. (1982). *A classification and evaluation of traditional hay meadows in the Northumberland National Park*. Northumberland County Council National Park and Countryside Department, Hexham.

Hall, S. J. G. (1989). Chillingham cattle: social and maintenance behaviour in an ungulate that breeds all year round. *Animal Behaviour*, **38**, 215–25.

Hall, S. J. G. & Hall, J. G. (1988). Inbreeding and population dynamics of the Chillingham cattle (*Bos taurus*). *J. Zool.*, **216**, 479–93.

Halliday, G. (1997). *A flora of Cumbria*. Centre for North-West Regional Studies, University of Lancaster.

Hancock, J. (1874). A catalogue of the birds of Northumberland and Durham. *Trans. Nat. Hist. Soc. Northumb.*, **6**, 1–174.

Harbottle, R. B. (1995). Prestwick Carr: its draining and enclosure. *Archaeologia Aeliana (fifth series)*, **23**, 1–15.

Hardy, F. G. & Guiry, M. D. (2003). *A check-list and atlas of the seaweeds of Britain and Ireland*. British Phycological Society, London.

Harris, S., Morris, P., Wray, S. & Yalden, D. (1995). *A review of British mammals: population estimates and conservation status of British* mammals other than cetaceans. Joint Nature Conservation Committee, Peterborough.

Harrison, J. W. H. (1931). Rabbits and the small copper butterfly. *Vasculum,* **17**, 68–70.

Harrison, S. (2002). Lithological variability of Quaternary slope deposits in the Cheviot Hills, UK. *Proc. Geologists' Assoc.,* **113**, 121–38.

Harvey, R. (compiler) (2002). Birds on the Fame Islands in 2001. *Trans. Nat. Hist. Soc. Northumb.,* **62**, 37–87.

Hawkey, P. (1991). The birds of the Fame Islands. *Trans. Nat. Hist. Soc. Northumb.,* **55**, 155–92.

Hayward, I. M. & Druce, G. C. (1919). *The adventive flora of Tweedside.* T. Buncle & Co., Arbroath.

Hedley, W. P. (1950). The medieval forests of Northumberland. *Archaeologia Aeliana (fourth series),* **28**. 96–104.

Hendon, D., Charman, D. J. & Kent, M. (2001). Palaeohydrological records derived from testate amoebae analysis from peatlands in northern England: within-site variability, between-site comparability and palaeoclimatic implications. *Holocene,* **11**, 127–148.

Hickling, G. (1962). *Grey seals and the Farne Islands.* Routledge and Kegan Paul, London.

Hickling, G. (1964). Fisheries and the Farne Island grey seals. *Oryx,* **7**, 172–6.

Hickling, G. (1980). The Natural History Society of Northumbria 1929–1979. *Trans. Nat. Hist. Soc. Northumb.,* **45**, 1–54.

Higham, N. (1986). *The northern counties to AD 1000* Longman, London.

Hilby, A. R. et al. (1996). *Seal stocks in Great Britain.* NERC News, Jan. 1996.

Hill, J. K., Thomas, C. D. & Huntley, B. (1999). Climate and habitat availability determine 20th century changes in a butterfly's range margins. *Proc. Roy. Soc. London (B),* **266**, 1197–1206.

Hirons, M. J. D. (1971). *The vegetation of the Farne Islands.* Unpubl. MSc thesis, University of Durham.

Hobhouse, A. (1947). *Report of the National Parks Committee (England and Wales).* Ministry of Town and Country Planning. Cmd 7121. HMSO, London.

Hollingsworth, P. M. & Swan, G. A. (1999). Genetic differentiation and hybridisation among subspecies of deergrass (*Tricophorum cespitosum* (L) Hartman) in Northumberland. *Watsonia,* **22**, 235–42.

Horton, B. P., Innes, J. B. & Shennan, I. (1999). Late Devensian and Holocene relative sea-level changes in Northumberland, England. *In* **Bridgland, D. R., Horton, B. P. & Innes, J. B. (Eds)** *The Quaternary of North-East England; field guide,* pp. 35–47. Quaternary Research Association, London.

Howse, R. (1864). On the glaciation of the counties of Northumberland and Durham. *Trans North England Inst. Mining Engineers,* **13**, 169–85.

Hudson-Edwards, K. A., Macklin, M. G., Curtis, C. D. & Vaughan, D. J. (1998). Chemical remobilisation of contaminant metals within floodplain sediments in an incising river system: implications for dating and chemical stratigraphy. *Earth Surface Processes and Landforms,* **23**, 671–84.

Hughes, P. D. M., Mauquoy, D., Barber, K. E. & Langdon, P. G. (2000). Mire-development pathways and palaeoclimate records from a full Holocene peat archive at Walton Moss, Cumbria, England. *Holocene*, **10**, 465–79.

Hull, J. E. (1920). Natural features in local place-names. *Vasculum*, **6**, 37–44.

Hull, J. E. (1936). Woodland glimpses of old Northumbria. *Vasculum*, **22**, 1–8.

Hull, J. E. (1937). Some Northumbrian plant-names. *Vasculum*, **23**, 3–8.

Huntley, J. P. (1999). Environmental evidence for Hadrian's Wall. In **Bidwell, P. (Ed.)** *Hadrian's Wall 1989–1999: a summary of recent excavations and research*, pp. 48–64. Cumb. Westd. Antiq. Archaeol. Soc. & Society of Antiquaries of Newcastle upon Tyne, Carlisle.

Ingram, H. A. P. (1982). Size and shape in raised mire ecosystems; a geophysical model. *Nature*, **297**, 300–3.

Ingram, H. A. P. (1992). Introduction to the ecohydrology of mires in the context of cultural perturbation. In **Bragg, O. M., Hulme, P. D., Ingram, H. A. P. & Robinson, R. A. (Eds)** *Peatland ecosystems and man – an impact assessment*, pp.67–93. British Ecological Society/International Peat Society, Dundee.

Ingrouille, M. J. & Smirnoff, N. (1986). *Thlaspi caerulescens* J. & C. Presl (*T. alpestre* L.) in Britain. *New Phytologist*, **102**, 219–33.

Innes, J. B. (1999). Regional vegetational history. In **Bridgland, D. R., Horton, B. P. & Innes, J. B. (Eds)** *The Quaternary of North-East England: field guide*, pp. 21–34. Quaternary Research Association, London.

Innes, J. B. & Frank, R. M. (1988). Palynological evidence for Late Flandrian coastal changes at Druridge Bay, Northumberland. *Scott. Geogr. Mag.*, **104**, 14–23.

Jackson, C. E. (1992). *Prideaux John Selby; a gentleman naturalist.* Spredden Press, Stocksfield, Northumberland.

Jarvis, R. A., Bendelow, V. C., Bradley, R. I., Carroll, D. M., Furness, R. R., Kilgour, I. N. L. & King, S. J. (1984). *Soils and their use in northern England.* Soil Survey of England and Wales: Bulletin no. 10, Harpenden.

Jeffreys, H. (1915). The Northumberland lakes. *Vasculum*, **1**, 109–13.

Jeffreys, H. (1917). The vegetation of sea sand. *Vasculum*, **3**, 1–5.

Johnson, G. A. L. (Ed.) (1995). Robson's Geology of North East England. *Trans. Nat. Hist. Soc. Northumb.*, **56**, 225–391.

Johnson, G. A. L. & Dunham, K. C. (2001). Emplacement of the Great Whin Dolerite Complex and the Little Whin Sill in relation to the structure of northern England. *Proc. Yorks. Geol. Soc.*, **53**, 177–86.

Johnston, G. (1829, 1831). *A flora of Berwick-upon-Tweed*, vols 1, 2. J. Carfrae & Son, Edinburgh and Longman, Rees, Orme, Brown & Green, London.

Johnston, S. D. (1974). Wild mink in Northumberland. *Trans. Nat. Hist. Soc. Northumb.*, **41**, 165–78.

Jones, R. L., Keen, D. H. & Robinson, J. E. (2000). Devensian Late glacial and early Holocene floral and faunal records from NE Northumberland. *Proc. Yorks. Geol. Soc.*, **53**, 97–110.

Kenward, R. E., Hodder, K. H., Rose, R. J., Walls, C. A., Parish, T., Holm, J. L., Morris, P. A., Walls, S. S. & Doyle, F. I. (1998). Comparative demography of red squirrels (*Sciurus vulgaris*) and grey squirrels (*Sciurus carolinensis*) in deciduous and conifer woodland. *J. Zool.*, **244**, 7–21.

Kenward, R. E. & Holm, J. L. (1993). On the replacement of the red squirrel in Britain: a phytotoxic explanation. *Proc. R. Soc. London, Ser. B*, **251**, 187–94.

Kerr, I. (1984). *Lindisfarne's birds.* Tyneside Bird Club, Newcastle upon Tyne.

Kerr, I. (2001*). Northumbrian birds: their history and status up to the 21st century.* Northumberland and Tyneside Bird Club, Newcastle upon Tyne.

Kerslake, L. (Ed.) (1998). Red Data Book for Northumberland. *Trans. Nat. Hist. Soc. Northumb.*, **58**, 39–322 (Joint publication with Northumberland Wildlife Trust).

Kerslake, L. (Ed.) (1999). Red Data Book for Northumberland 1999 supplement and errata. *Trans. Nat. Hist. Soc. Northumb.*, **59**, 183–92.

Key, R. (1996). Beetles and beetle recording in Cumbria. Cumbrian Wildlife. *Trans. Carlisle Nat. Hist. Soc.*, **12**, 39–50.

Körner, C. (1998). A re-assessment of high elevation treeline positions and their explanation. *Oecologia*, **115**, 445–59.

Körner, C. (1999). *Alpine plant life: functional plant ecology of high mountain ecosystems.* Springer, Berlin.

Langton, T. E. S., Beckett, C. L. & Foster, J. P. (2001). *Great crested newt: conservation handbook.* Froglife, Halesworth, Suffolk.

Lewis, F. J. (1904). Geographical distribution of vegetation in the basins of the rivers Eden, Tees, Wear, and Tyne. Part II. *Geogr. J.*, **24**, 267–85.

Lindsay, R. A. (1995). *The ecology, classification and conservation of ombrotrophic mires.* Scottish Natural Heritage, Edinburgh.

Lindsay, R. A., Charman, D. J., Everingham, F., O'Reilly, R. M., Palmer, M. A., Rowell, T. A. &

Stroud, D. A. (1988). *The Flow Country: the peatlands of Caithness and Sutherland.* Nature Conservancy Council, Peterborough.

Lindsay, R. A. & Immirzi, C. P. (1996). *An inventory of lowland raised bogs in Great Britain.* Scottish Natural Heritage Research, Survey and Monitoring Report **78**.

Little, B., Davison, M & Jardine, D. (1995). Merlins *Falco columbarius* in Kielder Forest: influences of habitat on breeding performance. *Forest Ecology and Management*, **79**, 147–52..

Lunn, A. G. (1976). *The vegetation of Northumberland: map at 1:200,000.* Department of Geography, University of Newcastle upon Tyne.

Lunn, A. G. (Ed.) (1983). *A history of naturalists in North East England.* Department of Adult Education, University of Newcastle upon Tyne.

Lunn, A. G. (1995). Quaternary. *In* **Johnson, G. A. L. (Ed.)** *Robson's Geology of North East England*, pp. 296–311. *Trans. Nat. Hist. Soc. Northumb.*, **56**.

Lurz, P. W. W., Garson, P. J. & Ogilvie, J. F. (1998). Conifer species mixtures, cone crops and red squirrel conservation. *Forestry*, **71**, 67–71.

Lurz, P. W. W., Garson, P. J. & Rushton, S. P. (1995). The ecology of squirrels in spruce dominated plantations: implications for forest management. *Forest Ecology and Management*, **79**, 79–90.

Lurz, P. W. W., Garson, P. J. & Wauters, L. (1997). Effect of temporal and spatial variation in habitat quality on red squirrel, *Sciurus vulgaris*, dispersal behaviour. *Animal Behaviour*, **54**, 427–35.

Lurz, P. W. W., Garson, P. J. & Wauters, L. (2000). Effects of temporal and spatial variations in food supply on the space and habitat use of red squirrels, *Sciurus vulgaris* L. *J. Zool.*, **251**, 167–78.

Lurz, P. W. W. & Lloyd, A. J. (2000). Body weights in grey and red squirrels: do seasonal weight increases occur in conifer woodland? *J. Zool.*, **252**, 539–43.

Mabey, R. (1996). *Flora Britannica*. Sinclair-Stevenson, London.

McDougall, P. (1975). The feral goats of Kielderhead Moor. *J. Zool.*, **176**, 215–46.

Mack, J. L. (1926). *The Border line: from the Solway Firth to the North Sea, along the marches of Scotland and England*. Revised edition. Oliver & Boyd, Edinburgh & London.

Macklin, M. (1992). Metal pollution of soils and sediments: a geographical perspective. *In* **Newson, M. (Ed.)** *Managing the human impact on the natural environment: patterns and processes*, pp. 172–95. Bellhaven Press, London.

Macklin, M. & Lewin, J. (1989). Sediment transfer and transformation of an alluvial valley floor: the River South Tyne, Northumbria, U.K. *Earth Surface Processes and Landforms*, **14**, 233–46.

Macklin, M. & Smith, R. S. (1990). Historic riparian vegetation development and alluvial metallophyte plant communities in the Tyne basin, north-east England. *In* **Thornes, JB (Ed.)** *Vegetation and erosion; processes and environments*, pp. 239–256. John Wiley & Sons, Chichester.

Macklin, M. G., Rumsby, B. T. & Heap, T. (1992). Flood alluviation and entrenchment: Holocene valley-floor development and transformation in the British uplands. *Bull. Geol. Soc. America*, **104**, 631–43.

Macklin, M. G., Rumsby, B. T.,

Heap, T. & Passmore, D. G. (1994). Thinhope Burn, Northumberland. *In* **Boardman, J. & Walden, J. (Eds)** *Cumbria: field guide*, pp. 50–7. Quaternary Research Association.

Maddison, D. (1830). *An historical and descriptive account of Prestwick Carr and its environs*. W. Orange, North Shields.

Manley, G. (1936). The climate of the northern Pennines: the coldest part of England. *Quart. J. Roy. Meteorol. Soc.*, **62**, 103–15.

Manley, G. (1946). The climate of Northumberland with notes on agriculture. *In* **Stamp, L. D.** *Northumberland. The land of Britain: the report of the Land Utilisation Survey of Britain, part 52. Northumberland*, pp. 429–39. Geographical Publications, London.

Manley, G. (1952). *Climate and the British scene*. (New Naturalist). Collins, London.

Manning, A., Birley, R. & Tipping, R. (1997). Roman impact on the environment at Hadrian's Wall: precisely dated pollen analysis from Vindolanda, northern England. *Holocene*, **7**, 175–86.

Marquiss, M., Newton, I. & Ratcliffe, D. A. (1978). The decline of the raven, *Corvus corax*, in relation to afforestation in southern Scotland and northern England. *J. Appl. Ecol.*, **15**, 129–44.

Mather, A. (1993). Afforestation in Britain. *In* **Mather, A. (Ed.)** *Afforestation: policies, planning and progress*, pp. 13–33. Belhaven Press, London & Florida.

Matthews, J. R. (1942). The germination of *Trientalis europaea*. *Journal of Botany*, London, **80**, 12–16.

Matthews, P. & Davison, A. W. (1976). Maritime species on road verges. *Watsonia*, **11**, 146–7.

Mauquoy, D. & Barber, K. (1999*a*). A replicated 3000 yr proxy-climate record from Coom Rigg Moss and Felecia Moss, the Border Mires, northern England. *J. Quat. Sci.*, **14**, 263–75.

Mauquoy, D. & Barber, K. (1999*b*). Evidence for climatic deteriorations associated with the decline of *Sphagnum imbricatum* Hornsch. ex Russ. in six ombrotrophic mires from northern England and the Scottish Borders. *Holocene*, **9**, 423–37.

McIntosh, R. (1995). The history and multi-purpose management of Kielder Forest. *Forest Ecology and Management*, **79**, 1–11.

McIntosh, R., Burlton, F. W. E. & McReddie, G. (1995). Monitoring the density of a roe deer *Capreolus capreolus* population subjected to heavy hunting pressure. *Forest Ecology and Management*, **79**, 99–106.

Meek, E. R. (1983). Ornithologists. In Lunn, A. G. (Ed.) *A history of naturalists in North East England*, pp. 64–80. Department of Adult Education, University of Newcastle upon Tyne.

Mennell, H. T. & Perkins, V. R. (1863–64). A catalogue of the mammalia of Northumberland and Durham. *Trans Tyneside Nat. Fld Club*, **6**, 111–77.

Millar, A. (1964). Notes on the climate near the upper forest limit in the Northern Pennines. *Quart. J. Forestry*, **58**, 239–46.

Mitchell, A. (1996). *Alan Mitchell's trees of Britain*. HarperCollins, London.

Moore, P. D. (1993). The origin of blanket mire, revisited. *In* Chambers, F. M. (Ed.) *Climate change and human impact on the landscape: studies in palaeoecology and environmental archaeology*, pp.

217–24. Chapman & Hall, London.

Morris, C. (Ed.) (1947). *The journeys of Celia Fiennes*. The Cresset Press, London.

Newson, M. D. (1992). Kielder Water, Kielder Forest and the North Tyne valley. *In* Whitby, M. C. (Ed.) *Land use change: the causes and* consequences, pp. 159–65. ITE Symposium **27**, HMSO, London.

Newton, I., Meek, E. R. & Little, B. (1978). Breeding ecology of the merlin in Northumberland. *British Birds*, **71**, 376–98.

Newton, I., Meek, E. R. & Little, B. (1986). Population and breeding of Northumbrian merlins. *British Birds*, **79**, 155–70.

Northumbrian River Authority (1973). *Report on survey of water resources*. NRA.

Nuttall, C. A. & Younger, P. L. (1999). Reconnaissance hydrogeochemical evaluation of an abandoned Pb-Zn orefield, Nent valley, Cumbria, UK. *Proc. Yorks. Geol. Soc.*, **52**, 395–405.

O'Hara, K. (2002). *The otter's return: Northumbrian Otters and Rivers Project Summary Report*. Northumberland Wildlife Trust.

Packham, J. R. & Willis, A. J. (1997). *Ecology of dunes, salt marsh and shingle*. Chapman & Hall, London.

Parker, A. G., Goudie, A. S., Anderson, D. E., Robinson, M. A. & Bonsall, C. (2002). A review of the mid-Holocene elm decline in the British Isles. *Progress in Physical Geography*, **26**, 1–45.

Parkinson, D. (1978). *Pollen analysis of late-glacial and post-glacial deposits at Ford Moss, Northumberland*. Unpub. BA dissertation, Department of Geography, University of Durham.

Passmore, D. G., Macklin, M. G., Stevenson, A. C., O'Brien, C. F. &

Davis, B. A. S. (1992). A Holocene alluvial sequence in the lower Tyne valley, northern Britain: a record of river response to environmental change. *Holocene*, **2**, 138–47.

Passmore, D. G. & Macklin, M. (1997). Geoarchaeology of the Tyne basin: Holocene river valley environments and the archaeological record. In: Tolan-Smith, C. (Ed.) *Landscape archaeology in Tynedale*, pp. 69–78. Tyne-Solway Ancient and Historic Landscapes Research Programme Monograph 1. Department of Archaeology, University of Newcastle upon Tyne.

Payton, R. W. (1987). Podzolic soils of the Fell Sandstone, Northumberland: their characteristics and genesis. *North of England Soils Discussion Group Proceedings* **22**, 41 pp.

Payton, R. W. & Palmer, R. C. (1989). *Soils of the Alnwick and Rothbury district (sheet 81)*. Soil Survey and Land Research Centre. Memoirs of the Soil Survey of Great Britain: England and Wales. Silsoe.

Pears, N. V. (1968). The natural altitudinal limit of forest in the Scottish Grampians. *Oikos*, **19**, 71–80.

Pearson, M. C. (1960). Muckle Moss, Northumberland. I. Historical. *J. Ecol.*, **48**, 647–66.

Pearson, M. C. (1979). Patterns of pools in peatlands (with particular reference to a valley head mire in northern England. *Acta Univ. Oul. (Finland) A*, **82**, Geol. 3:65–72.

Pearson, T. H. (1968). The feeding biology of sea-bird species breeding on the Farne Islands, Northumberland. *J. Animal Ecol.*, **37**, 521–52.

Penn, S. & Lee, H. (1980). *A survey of whin grassland flora from Walltown*

to Kirkwhelpington and including limestone grassland within the Northumberland National Park. Report to Northumberland Wildlife Trust Ltd.

Perring, F. H. & Farrell, L. (compilers) (1983). *British Red Data Books: 1. Vascular plants.* Second edition. Royal Society for Nature Conservation, Lincoln.

Perry, R. (1946). *A naturalist on Lindisfarne.* Lindsay Drummond, London.

Peterken, G. F. (1974). A method for assessing woodland flora for conservation using indicator species. *Biological Conservation*, **6**, 239–45.

Peterken, G. F. & Game, M. (1984). Historical factors affecting the number and distribution of vascular plant species in the woodland of central Lincolnshire. *J. Ecol.*, **72**, 155–82.

Petty, S. J., Lambin, X., Sherratt, T. N., Thomas, C. J., Mackinnon, J. L., Coles, C. F., Davison, M. & Little, B. (2000). Spatial synchrony in field vole *Microtus agrestis* abundance in a coniferous forest in northern England: the role of vole-eating raptors. *J. Appl. Ecol.*, **37** (suppl. 1), 136–47.

Petty, S. J., Lurz, P. W. W. & Rushton, S. P. (2003). Predation of red squirrels by northern goshawks in a conifer forest in northern England: can this limit squirrel numbers and create a conservation dilemma? *Biological Conservation*, **111**, 105–14.

Petty, S. J., Patterson, I. J., Anderson, D. I. K., Little, B. & Davison, M. (1995). Numbers, breeding performance, and diet of the sparrowhawk *Accipiter nisus* and merlin *Falco columbarius* in relation to cone crops and seed-eating finches. *Forest Ecology and Management*, **79**, 133–46.

Pigott, C. D. & Huntley, J. P. (1981). Factors controlling the distribution of *Tilia cordata* at the northern limits of its geographical range. III. Nature and causes of seed sterility. *New Phytologist*, **87**, 817–39.

Pigott, C. D. (1991). *Tilia cordata* Miller. Biological Flora of the British Isles no. 174. *J. Ecol.*, **79**, 1147–1207.

Plackett, R. (2002). Travellers 'twixt Tyne and Tweed. *Tyne and Tweed*, **56**, 2–18.

Plater, A. (2002). Holy Island (NU 136418). *In* **Huddart, D. & Glasser, N. F.** *et al. Quaternary of northern England*, pp. 532–9. Geological Conservation Review Series, **25**. JNCC, Peterborough.

Plater, A. J. & Shennan, I. (1992). Evidence of Holocene sea-level change from the Northumberland coast, eastern England. *Proc. Geologists' Assoc.*, **103**, 201–16.

Preston, C. D. & Hill, M. O. (1997). The geographical relationships of British and Irish vascular plants. *Bot. J. Linnean Soc.*, **124**, 1–120.

Preston, C. D., Pearman, D. A. & Dines, T. D. (2002). *New atlas of the British and Irish flora*. Oxford University Press, Oxford.

Radley, G. P. & Dargie, T. C. D. (1995). *Sand dune vegetation survey of Great Britain: a national inventory. Part 1 – England*. JNCC, Peterborough.

Raistrick, A & Blackburn, K. B. (1931). The late-glacial and post-glacial periods in the North Pennines. I. The glacial maximum and retreat. *Trans. Northern Naturalists' Union*, **1**, 16–29.

Raistrick, A & Blackburn, K. B. (1931). The late-glacial and post-glacial periods in the North Pennines. II. Possible glacial survivals in our flora. *Trans. Northern Naturalists' Union*, **1**, 30–36.

Ratcliffe, D. A. (1962). Breeding density in the peregrine *Falco peregrinus* and raven *Corvus corax*. *Ibis*, **104**, 13–39.

Ratcliffe, D. A. (Ed.) (1977). *A nature conservation review* (2 volumes). Cambridge University Press, Cambridge.

Ratcliffe, P. R. & Peterken, G. F. (1995). The potential for biodiversity in British upland spruce forests. *Forest Ecology and Management*, **79**, 153–60.

Raunkiaer, C. (1934). *The life forms of plants and statistical plant geography*. Clarendon Press, Oxford.

Raven, C. E. (1947). *English naturalists from Neckam to Ray*. Cambridge University Press, Cambridge.

Redpath, S. M. & Thirgood, S. J. (1999). Numerical and functional responses in generalist predators: hen harriers and peregrines on Scottish grouse moors. *J. Animal Ecol.*, **68**, 879–92.

Rehfisch, M. M., Austin, G. E., Armitage, M. J. S., Atkinson, P. W., Holloway, S. J., Musgrove, A. J. & Pollitt, M. S. (2003). Numbers of wintering waterbirds in Great Britain and the Isle of Man (1994/1995–1998/1999): II. Coastal waders (Charadrii). *Biological Conservation*, **112**, 329–41.

Richards, A. J., Lefebvre, C., Macklin, M. G., Nicholson, A. & Vekemans, X. (1989). The population genetics of *Armeria maritima* (Mill.) Willd. on the River South Tyne, UK. *New Phytologist*, **112**, 281–93.

Richards, A. J. & Porter, A. F. (1982). On the identity of a Northumberland *Epipactis*. *Watsonia*, **14**, 121–8.

Richardson, P. (compiler) (2000). *Distribution atlas of bats in Britain* *and Ireland 1980–1999*. The Bat Conservation Trust.

Robertson, D. A. (1955). *The ecology of the sand dune vegetation of Ross Links, Northumberland, with special reference to secondary succession in the blow-outs*. Unpub. PhD thesis, University of Durham.

Rodwell, J. S. (Ed.) (2000). *British plant communities, vol. 5. Maritime communities and vegetation of open habitats*. Cambridge University Press, Cambridge.

Rose, F. (1999). Indicators of ancient woodland. *British Wildlife*, **10**, 241–51.

Rossiter, A. F. (1996). The government of Hexham in the 17th century. *Hexham Historian*, **6**, 17–44.

Rossiter, B. N. (1998). Mammal and red kite bounties in Corbridge in the 17th and 18th centuries. *Vasculum*, **83**, 1–10.

Rossiter, B. N. (1999). Northumberland's birds in the 18th and early 19th centuries: the contribution of John Wallis (1714–1793). *Trans. Nat. Hist. Soc. Northumb.*, **59**, 93–136.

Rushton, S. P., Lurz, P. W. W., Fuller, R. & Garson, P. J. (1997*).* Modelling the distribution of the red and grey squirrel at the landscape scale: a combined GIS and population dynamics approach. *J. Appl. Ecol.*, **34**, 1137–54.

Rushton, S. P., Lurz, P. W. W., Gurnell, J. & Fuller, R. (2000). Modelling the spatial dynamics of parapox virus disease in red and grey squirrels: a possible cause of the decline in the red squirrel in the UK? *J. Appl. Ecol.*, **37**, 997–1012.

Ryle, G. (1969). *Forest Service: the first forty-five years of the Forestry Commission of Great Britain*. David & Charles, Newton Abbot.

Sabbagh, K. (1999). *A Rum affair: how botany's 'Piltdown Man' was unmasked*. Allen Lane, The Penguin Press, London.

Scott, N. E. (1985). The updated distribution of maritime species on British roadsides. *Watsonia*, **15**, 381–6.

Scott, N. E. & Davison, A. W. (1982). De-icing salt and the invasion of road verges by maritime plants. *Watsonia*, **14**, 41–52.

Seaton, A. V. (1990). George Clayton Atkinson and the Northumberland tree survey 1873–76. *Trans. Nat. Hist. Soc. Northumb.*, **55**, 59–83.

Selby, P. J. (1831*a*). A catalogue of birds hitherto met with in the counties of Northumberland and Durham. *Trans. Nat. Hist. Soc. Northumb.*, **1**, 244–93.

Selby, P. J. (1831*b*). Observations on the new species of swan, discovered by Mr Richard Wingate, of Newcastle upon Tyne. *Trans. Nat. Hist. Soc. Northumb.*, **1**, 17–25.

Selby, P. J. (1833). *Illustrations of British ornithology*. WH Lizars, Edinburgh.

Selby, P. J. (1839). The fauna of Twizell. *Annals of Natural History*. **3**, 361–75.

Selby, P. J. (1841–2). *A history of British forest trees indigenous and introduced*. Van Voorst, London.

Shennan, I. & Horton, B. (2002). Holocene land- and sea-level changes in Great Britain. *J. Quat. Sci.*, **17**, 511–26.

Shennan, I., Horton, B., Innes, J., Gehrels, R., Lloyd, J., McArthur, J. & Rutherford, M. (2000). Late Quaternary sea-level changes, crustal movements and coastal evolution in Northumberland, UK. *J. Quat. Sci.*, **15**, 215–37.

Simmons, I. G. & Innes, J. B. (1987). Mid-Holocene adaptations and later Mesolithic forest disturbance in northern England. *Journal of Archaeological Science*, **14**, 385–403.

Skene, K. R., Sprent, J. I., Raven, J. A. & Herdman, L. (2000). *Myrica gale* L. Biological Flora of the British Isles, no. 215. *J. Ecol.*, **88**, 1079–94.

Smith, A. A., Redpath, S. M., Campbell, S. T. & Thirgood, S. J. (2001). Meadow pipits, red grouse and the habitat characteristics of managed grouse moors. *J. Applied Ecol.*, **38**, 390–400.

Smith, L. P. (1984). *The agricultural climate of England and Wales: areal averages 1941–70*. Ministry of Agriculture, Fisheries and Food: Reference Book 435. London: HMSO.

Smith, M. (1999). William Turner (c. 1508–1568): physician, botanist and theologian. *Journal of Medical Biography*, **7**, 140–44.

Smith, R. S. (1988). Farming and the conservation of traditional meadowland in the Pennine Dales Environmentally Sensitive Area. *In* Usher, M. B. & Thompson, D. B. A. (Eds) *Ecological change in the uplands*, pp. 183–99. Special Publication **7** of the British Ecological Society.

Smith, R. S., Buckingham, H., Bullard, M. J., Shield, R. S. & Younger, A. (1996*a*). The conservation management of mesotrophic (meadow) grassland in northern England. 1. Effects of grazing, cutting date and fertilizer on the vegetation of a traditionally managed sward. *Grass & Forage Science*, **51**, 278–91.

Smith, R. S. & Charman, D. J. (1988). The vegetation of upland mires within conifer plantations in Northumberland, northern England. *J. Applied Ecol.*, **25**, 579–94.

Smith, R. S., Corkhill, P., Shiel, R. S. & Millward, D. (1996*b*). The conservation management of mesotrophic (meadow) grassland in northern England. 2. Effects of grazing, cutting date, fertilizer and seed application on the vegetation of an agriculturally improved sward. *Grass & Forage Science*, **51**, 292–305.

Smith, R. S., Lunn, A. G. & Newson, M. D. (1995). The Border Mires in Kielder Forest: a review of their ecology and conservation management. *Forest Ecology and Management*, **79**, 47–61.

Smithson, P. A. (1985). The present climate of the northern Pennines. In Boardman, J. (Ed.) *Field guide to the periglacial landforms of northern England*, pp. 1–3. Quaternary Research Association, Cambridge.

Soil Survey of England and Wales (1983). *Soils of England and Wales: sheet 1, Northern England. 1:250,000.* Harpenden.

Stapledon, R. G. (1935). *The land: now and tomorrow.* Faber & Faber, London.

Stewart, A, Pearman, D. A & Preston, C. D. (compilers and editors) (1994) *Scarce plants in Britain.* Joint Nature Conservation Committee, Peterborough.

Strachan, C., Strachan, R. & Jefferies, D. J. (2000). *Preliminary report on the changes in the water vole population of Britain as shown by the national surveys of 1989–1990 and 1996–1998.* Vincent Wildlife Trust, London.

Strachan, R. (1998). *Water vole conservation handbook.* Wildlife Conservation Research Unit, University of Oxford, Environment Agency & English Nature.

Strachan, R. & Jefferies, D. J. (1996). *Otter survey of England*

1991–94. A report on the decline and recovery of the otter in England and on its distribution, status and conservation in 1991–1994. The Vincent Wildlife Trust, London.

Stott, M., Callion, J., Kinley, I., Raven, C. & Roberts, J. (Eds) (2002). *The breeding birds of Cumbria: a tetrad atlas 1997–2001.* Cumbria Bird Club.

Strowger, J. (1998). The status and breeding biology of the dotterel *(Charadrius morinellus)* in northern England during 1972–95. *Bird Study,* **45**, 85–91.

Sutcliffe, D. W. (1972). Notes on the chemistry and fauna of water-bodies in Northumberland. *Trans. Nat. Hist. Soc. Northumb. (New Series),* **17**, 222–48.

Sutton, S. (1993). Crayfish plague in Northumberland. *Vasculum,* **78**, 4–6.

Svenning, J-C. (2002). A review of natural vegetation openness in north-western Europe. *Biological Conservation,* **104**, 133–48.

Swan, G. A. (1993). *Flora of Northumberland.* Natural History Society of Northumbria, Newcastle upon Tyne.

Swan, G. A. (1999). Identification, distribution and a new nothosubspecies of *Tricophorum cespitosum* (L) Hartman (Cyperaceae) in the British Isles and N.W. Europe. *Watsonia,* **22**, 209–33.

Swan, G. A. (2001). A supplement to the Flora of Northumberland. *Trans. Nat. Hist. Soc. Northumb.,* **61**, 71–160.

Swan, G. A. (2003). New records for the subspecies of *Tricophorum cespitosum* (deergrass) in Britain. *BSBI News,* **93**, 34–7.

Taylor, K., Rowland, A. P. & Jones, H. E. (2001). *Molinia caerulea* (L.) Moench: Biological Flora of the British Isles, no. 216. *J. Ecol.,* **89**, 126–44.

Telewski, F. W. (1995). Wind-induced physiological and developmental responses in trees. *In* **Coutts, M. P. & Grace, J. (Eds)** *Wind and trees,* pp. 237–63. Cambridge University Press, Cambridge.

Tharme, A. P., Green, R. E., Baines, D., Bainbridge, I. P. & O'Brien, M. (2001). The effect of management for red grouse shooting on the population density of breeding birds on heather-dominated moorland. *J. Applied Ecol.,* **38**, 439–57.

Thirgood, S. J., Redpath, S. M., Rothery, P. & Aebischer, N. J. (2000). Raptor predation and population limitation in red grouse. *J. Animal Ecol.,* **69**, 504–16.

Thompson, F. M. L. (1963). *English landed society in the nineteenth century.* Routledge & Kegan Paul, London.

Tipping, R. (1992). The determination of cause in the generation of major prehistoric valley fills in the Cheviot Hills, Anglo-Scottish border. *In* **Needham, S. & Macklin, M. (Eds.):** *Alluvial archaeology in Britain,* pp. 111–21. Oxbow Monograph **27**, Oxford.

Tipping, R. (1996). The Neolithic landscapes of the Cheviot Hills and hinterland: palaeoenvironmental evidence. *In* **Frodsham, P. (Ed.)** *Neolithic studies in no-man's land,* pp. 17–33. Northern Archaeology 13/14 (special edition).

Tipping, R. (1998). The chronology of late Quaternary fluvial activity in part of the Milfield basin, northeast England. *Earth Surface Processes and Landforms,* **23**, 845–56.

Tolan-Smith, M. (1997*a*). The Medieval landscape 1: approaches to the study of ancient woodland –

Horsley Wood. In **Tolan-Smith, C. (Ed.)** *Landscape archaeology in Tynedale*, pp. 43–52. Tyne-Solway Ancient and Historic Landscapes Research Pro-gramme Monograph **1**. Department of Archaeology, University of Newcastle upon Tyne.

Tolan-Smith, M. (1997*b*). The Romano-British and late prehistoric landscape: the deconstruction of a medieval landscape. In **Tolan-Smith, C. (Ed.)** *Landscape archaeology in Tynedale*, pp. 69–78. Tyne-Solway Ancient and Historic Landscapes Research Programme Monograph **1**. Department of Archaeology, University of Newcastle upon Tyne.

Topping, P. (1989). Early cultivation in Northumberland and the Borders. *Proc. Prehistoric Society*, **55**, 161–79.

Trevelyan, G. M. (1934). *The Middle Marches*. Andrew Reid, Newcastle, for the Northumberland and Newcastle Society.

Turner, J. (1978). The history of the vegetation and flora. *In* **Clapham, A. R. (Ed.)** *Upper Teesdale: the area and its natural history*, pp. 88–101. Collins, London.

Turner, J. (1979). The environment of northeast England during Roman times as shown by pollen analysis. *J. Archaeological Science*, **6**, 285–90.

Turner, J. (1984). Pollen diagrams from Cross Fell and their implications for former tree-lines. *In* **Haworth, E. Y. & Lund, J. W. G. (Eds)** *Lake sediments and environmental history*, pp.317–57. Leicester University Press, Leicester.

Turner, J. & Hodgson, J. (1981). Studies in the vegetational history of the northern Pennines. II. An atypical diagram from Pow Hill, Co. Durham. *J. Ecol.*, **69**, 171–88.

Turner, J. & Hodgson, J. (1983). Studies in the vegetational history of the northern Pennines. III. Variations in the composition of the mid-Flandrian forests. *J. Ecol.*, **71**, 95–118.

Turner, W. (1548). *The names of herbes*. *In* **Stearn, W. T., Britten, J. & Jackson, D.** (1965). *Facsimiles of Turner, W (1538), Libellus de Re Herbaria and (1548), The names of herbs*. The Ray Society, London.

Vera, F. W. M. (2000). *Grazing ecology and forest history*. CABI Publishing, Wallingford.

Visscher, P. M., Smith, D., Hall, S. J. G. & Williams, J. A. (2001). A viable herd of genetically uniform cattle. *Nature*, **409**, 303.

Waddington, C. (1996). Putting rock art to use. A model of Early Neolithic transhumance in north Northumberland. *In* **Frodsham, P. (Ed.).** *Neolithic studies in no-man's land*, pp. 147–77. Northern Archaeology 13/14 (special edition).

Wallace, H. L. & Good, J. E. G. (1995). Effects of afforestation on upland plant communities and implications for vegetation management. *Forest Ecology and Management*, **79**, 29–46.

Wallis, J. (1769). *The natural history and antiquities of Northumberland and of so much of the county of Durham as lies between the rivers Tyne and Tweed; commonly called, North Bishoprick*. 2 vols. W & W Strahan, London.

Walsh, K., O'Sullivan, D., Young, R., Crane, S. & Brown, A. G. (1995). Medieval land use, agriculture and environmental change on Lindisfarne (Holy Island), Northumbria. *In* **Butlin, R. A. & Roberts, N. (Eds)**: *Ecological relations in historical times: human impact and adaptation*, pp. 101–21.

Institute of British Geographers Special Publication **32**.

Warren, M. S., Hill, J. K., Thomas, J. A., Asher, J., Fox, R., Huntley, B., Roy, D. B., Telfer, M. G., Jeffcoate, S., Harding, P., Jeffcoate, G., Willis, S. G., Greatorex-Davies, J. N., Moss, D. & Thomas, C. D. (2001). Rapid responses of British butterflies to opposing forces of climate and habitat change. *Nature*, **414**, 65–9.

Watt, G. (1951). *The Farne Islands: their history and wildlife*. Country Life, London.

Wauters, L. A., Lurz, P. W. W. & Gurnell, J. (2000). The interspecific effects of grey squirrels (*Sciurus carolinensis*) on the space use and population dynamics of red squirrel (*Sciurus vulgaris*) in conifer plantations. *Ecological Research*, **15**, 271–84.

Wauters, L. A., Tosi, G & Gurnell, J. (2002). Interspecific competition in tree squirrels: do introduced grey squirrels (*Sciurus carolinensis*) deplete tree seeds hoarded by red squirrels (*Sciurus vulgaris*)? *Behavioural Ecology Sociobiology* **51**, 360–7.

Wheeler, B. D. & Proctor, M. C. F. (2000). Ecological gradients, subdivisions and terminology of north-west European mires. *J. Ecol.*, **88**, 187–203.

Wheeler, D. (1997). North-east England and Yorkshire. In Wheeler, D. & Mayes, J. (Eds) *Regional climates of the British Isles*, pp. 158–80. Routledge, London.

Whitehead, G. K. (1972). *The wild goats of Great Britain and Ireland*. David & Charles, Newton Abbot.

Whittingham, M. J., Percival, S. M. & Brown, A. F. (2000). Time budgets and foraging of breeding golden plover *Pluvialis apricaria*. *J. Applied Ecol.*, **37**, 632–46.

Wigginton, M. J. (Ed.) (1999). *British Red Data Books: 1. Vascular plants*. Third edition. Joint Nature Conservation Committee, Peterborough.

Williamson, M. (1996). *Biological invasions*. Chapman & Hall, London.

Willis, P. (1983). *Capability Brown in Northumberland*. Northumberland and Newcastle Society, Newcastle upon Tyne. (Reprinted from *Garden History*.)

Wills, F. A. ('The Vagabond') (1936). *The rambles of 'Vagabond'*. J. & P. Bealls, Newcastle upon Tyne.

Wilson, A. (1956). *The altitudinal range of British plants*. The North Western Naturalist, Supplement.

Wilson, C. (1858). Notes on the prior existence of the *Castor fiber* in Scotland. *Hist. Berwicks. Nats' Club*, **4**, 76–86.

Wilson, P., Orford, J. D., Knight, J., Braley, S. M. & Wintle, A. G. (2001). Late-Holocene (post-4000 years BP) coastal dune development in Northumberland, northeast England. *Holocene*, **11**, 215–29.

Winch, N. J. (1825). *An essay on the geographical distribution of plants through the counties of Northumberland, Cumberland and Durham* (Second edition). T&J Hodgson, Newcastle.

Winch, N. J. (1831a). Flora of Northumberland and Durham. *Trans. Nat. Hist. Soc. Northumb.*, **2**, 1–149.

Winch, N. J. (1831b). Remarks on the distribution of the indigenous plants of Northumberland and Durham, as connected with the geological structure of those counties. *Trans. Nat. Hist. Soc. Northumb.*, **1**, 50–7.

Winch, N. J. (1837). *Addenda to the flora of Northumberland and Durham,* pp. 151–159. T & J Hodgson, Newcastle.

Winchester, A. J. L. (2000). *The harvest of the hills: rural life in northern England and the Scottish Borders, 1400–1700.* Edinburgh University Press, Edinburgh.

Wingate, R. R. (1831). Notice of a new species of swan. *Trans. Nat. Hist. Soc. Northumb.,* **1**, 1–3.

Wishart, D. & Warburton, J. (2001). An assessment of blanket mire degradation and peatland gully development in the Cheviot Hills, Northumberland. *Scot. Geog. J.,* **117**, 185–206.

Woodward, B. B. (1866). A literary forgery: Richard of Cirencester's tractate on Britain. *Gentleman's Magazine (New Series),* **1**, 301–8, 617–24.

Woolliscroft, D. J. (1999). More thoughts on the Vallum. *Trans. Cumb. Westd. Antiq. Archaeol. Soc.,* **99**, 53–65.

Woolmore, R. (2001). *Northumberland National Park: designation history series.* Countryside Agency, unpublished document.

Yalden, D. (1999). *The history of British mammals.* Poyser, London.

17

Gazetteer

Four-figure references of the Ordnance Survey National Grid, identifying 1 kilometre squares, are normally given; the term '& adj.' indicates additional adjoining squares. For extensive areas two-figure references, identifying 10 kilometre squares, are given. The 100 kilometre grid squares NT, NU, NY and NZ cover respectively the northwest, northeast, southwest and southeast sectors of Northumberland.

Abshiels NZ 1590
Acklington NU 2201
Acomb NY 9366
Acton Burn NY 8351 & adj.
Akeld NT 9529
Akenshaw Burn NY 6189 & adj.
Allenheads NY 8645
Alllerhope Burn NT 9210 & adj.
Allerwash NY 8666
Alnmouth NU 2410
Alnwick NU 1813
Alston NY 7246
Alston Moor NY 73, NY 74
Alwinton NT 9206
Alwin valley NT 90, NT 91
Amble NU 2604
Arcot Hall NZ 2475
Ashgill NY 7540, NY 7640
Ashgill plantation NY 7739 & adj.
Ashington NZ 2787
Ayle Common NY 7150 & adj.

Bakethin reservoir NY 6391 & adj.
Bamburgh NU 1835
Barrow Burn (Alwinton) NT 9004 & adj.
Bateinghope Burn NT 6904 & adj.
Beadnell NU 2329
Beaufront Castle NY 9665

Beldon Cleugh NY 9150
Belford NU 1033
Bellcrag Flow NY 7772, NY 7872
Bellyside Crag NT 9021
Beltingham NY 7864
Berwick NU 0053
Bewcastle Fells NY 57, NY 58
Big Waters NZ 2273
Billsmoor Park NY 9496
Blackaburn Lough NY 7679
Black Needle NT 6401, NT 6402
Blanchland NY 9650
Blyth NZ 3181
Boddle Moss NY 9997
Bolton Fell Moss NY 4868 & adj.
Bradford kame NU 1631 & adj.
Braydon Crag NT 8921
Breamish valley NT 91, NU 01
Briarwood Banks NY 7861, NY 7961
Broom House farm NU 0344
Brough Law NT 9916
Brownsman Island NU 2337
Budle Bay NU 1435 & adj.
Bullman Hills NY 7037
Butt Hill channel NY 6250
Butterburn Flow NY 6775 & adj.

Bywell NZ 0461

Caistron ponds NU 0001
Cambo NZ 0285
Carham NT 7938
Carlin Tooth NT 6302
Carter Bar NT 6906
Carter Fell NT 6703 & adj.
Cash Force NY 7038
Catcleugh reservoir NT 7303 & adj.
Caw Lough NY 7669, NY 7769
Chatton NU 0528
Cherryburn NZ 0762
Cheswick NU 0346
Chew Green NT 7808
Chillingham Park NU 0725 & adj.
Chirdon NY 78
Chirdonhead NY 7181
Chollerford NY 9270
Christianbury Crag NY 5782
Close House NZ 1265
Coalcleugh NY 8085
Coanwood NY 6959
Cockle Park NZ 2091
Cold Fell NY 6055
Coldmartin Lough NU 0127
Coldstream NT 8439
College valley NT 82
Collywell Bay NZ 3476
Colt Crag Reservoir NY 9378
Coom Rigg Moss NY 6879,

General Index

Species Index

The nomenclature in this book is based on the following references:

Birds
From BOU web list, 2004, after Voous, K.H. (1977), *List of recent Holarctic bird species*, revised edition. British Ornithological Union. English names as in common usage

Butterflies
As Asher *et al.* (2001), *The millennium atlas of butterflies in Britain and Ireland*. Oxford University Press, Oxford

Flowering plants, ferns and allies
Apart from *Hieracium* and *Tricophorum*, after Stace, C. (1997), *New flora of the British Isles* (2nd edn). Cambridge Univ. Press, Cambridge

Freshwater fish
After Maitland, P.S. & Campbell, R.N. (1992), *Freshwater fishes*. New Naturalist, HarperCollins, London

Lichens
From Copppins, B.J. (2002), *Checklist of lichens of Great Britain and Ireland*. British Lichen Society, London, updated 2003; on line

Liverworts and mosses
From *Checklist of British and Irish Bryophytes* (on line) prepared by Mark Hill, built from Biological Records Centre data as used for Hill, M.O., Preston, C.D. & Smith, A.J.E. (1991-4), *Atlas of the bryophytes of Britain and Ireland*. Harley Books, Colchester, and from taxa in Blockeel, T.L. & Long, D.G. (1998), *A check-list and census catalogue of British and Irish bryophytes*, British Bryological Society, Cardiff; *Sphagnum recurvum* retained because of unknown distributions of segregates

Mammals
Nomenclature follows that for the species included in Mitchell-Jones *et al.* (1999), *The atlas of European mammals*. T&AD Poyser, London & Academic Press, London

Moths
After Waring, P. & Townsend, M. (2003), *Field guide to the moths of Great Britain and Ireland*. British Wildlife Publishing, Hook, Hampshire

Amphibia and reptiles
After Beebee, T.J.C. & Griffiths, R.A. (2000), *Amphibians and reptiles*. New Naturalist, HarperCollins, London

Seaweeds
After Hardy, F.G. & Guiry, M.D. (2003), *A check-list and atlas of the seaweeds of Britain and Ireland*. British Phycological Society, London